THE NEW YORK CITY SKETCHES

OF STEPHEN CRANE

THE
NEW YORK CITY
SKETCHES
OF
STEPHEN CRANE
and Related Pieces

Edited by

R. W. STALLMAN AND E. R. HAGEMANN

NEW YORK UNIVERSITY PRESS

1966

ACKNOWLEDGMENTS

For permission to publish here for the first time the Crane manuscripts in *The New York City Sketches of Stephen Crane and Other Pieces,* we thank Alfred A. Knopf, Inc., and Mr. William Koshland; Mr. Clifton Waller Barrett of Charlottesville, Virginia; and Mr. Roland Baughman, Head, Special Collections, Columbia University Libraries. And Mr. Lester Wells, former Rare Book Librarian, Syracuse University, for permission to publish here for the first time the Crane manuscript "A Desertion."

For constant kindnesses rendered us while we prepared the texts from original sources, we thank Mr. Harold Merklen, Research Librarian, New York Public Library; Miss Roberta Smith and Mrs. Ruth Raines, University of Connecticut Library. Also, Mr. David C. Mearns, Chief, Manuscript Division, Library of Congress.

Also, Mr. David A. Balch of Hartwood, New York, for introducing Stallman to the three gentlemen who as boys knew the young Stephen Crane at Hartwood, New York, and Twin Lakes, Pennsylvania: George E. Dimock and E. J. Dimock of Hartwood and L. B. Watson of Twin Lakes, to whom this book is dedicated.

Stallman expresses his gratitude to the American Philosophical Society and Mr. George Corner for constant grants-in-aid for research. Also, the Research Foundation of the University of Connecticut for grant-in-aid for photocopying and typing materials.

Hagemann expresses his gratitude for a 1964–1965 research grant from the University of Louisville which permitted travel, editorial conferences, and editorial assistance, a most considerate gesture to one who had so recently joined the faculty.

PREFACE

No nineteenth-century American fiction writer knew New York City's demi-world more intimately than Stephen Crane.

> Some of my best work is contained in short things which I have written for various publications, principally the New York *Press* in 1893 [1894] or thereabouts. There are some 15 or 20 short sketches of New York street life and so on which I intended to have published in book form under the title of "Midnight Sketches." That should be your first care.

Stephen wrote this to his brother William Howe from Jacksonville, Florida, a month before sailing on the unseaworthy S. S. *Commodore* to deliver a contraband cargo of guns and ammunition to General Maximo Gomez' insurrectionist army in Cuba. The implication in Crane's letter, of course, was that he might not survive the expedition; he did, even though the *Commodore* sank offshore. Crane did not get to Cuba until eighteen months later when he reported the Spanish-American War for the New York *World*.[1]

That same year, 1898, Crane saw through the press the London edition of *The Open Boat and Other Stories*, which included eight of the "Midnight Sketches." Cora Taylor, his common-law wife, placed six New York Sketches in *Last Words*, published in London two years after Crane's unhappy death in Badenweiler, Germany, 5 June 1900. Yet no Midnight or New York Sketches were printed in

1. Crane to William Howe Crane (29 November 1896) in *Stephen Crane: Letters,* edited by R. W. Stallman and Lillian Gilkes (1960). Crane's war dispatches are collected in *The War Dispatches of Stephen Crane,* edited by R. W. Stallman and E. R. Hagemann (1964).

the American edition, *The Open Boat and Other Tales of Adventure* (1898).

Section 1 of *The New York City Sketches of Stephen Crane and Other Pieces* presents the most nearly *complete* collection yet published of his writings about the City, accurately reproduced from manuscripts, from first book publication, or from first newspaper or magazine publication.[2] Section 2 is the collection of newspaper articles, also reprinted for the first time, about the Crane-Dora Clark-Charles Becker affair in New York in the fall of 1896. The Editors deleted certain articles to avoid needless repetition and, at the same time, included James L. Ford's hitherto overlooked parody of the investigative methods of Police Commissioner Frederick D. Grant. Section 3 presents Crane's best sketches of the New Jersey coast. Finally, Section 4, "Excursions," includes two articles which could not properly be included elsewhere: one describes Crane's visit to a coal mine in Scranton, Pennsylvania; the other, Crane's visit to Sing Sing, the New York State Penitentiary at Ossining.

The Crane-Clark-Becker affair titillated New Yorkers for a month or more, vying with Presidential aspirants McKinley and Bryan for attention. Crane had been interviewing Dora Clark, a woman on the town, for his *Journal* sketches of the Tenderloin.[3]

2. The Editors do not hold that Crane wrote "Veterans' Ranks/Thinner by a Year," New York *Press:* 31 May 1894. It is possible that Crane wrote the baseball story "Decoration Day Ball," published the same day in the *Press,* but its authenticity is questionable and for that reason we have preferred not to print it.

Our editorial policy throughout the book has been to amend tacitly typographical errors, for example, spelling and punctuation, where the correct version is unmistakable, in Crane's published work in newspapers and magazines; and to retain any errors in manuscripts and drafts. Thus, we have avoided undue pedantry. In a few places, the source was so defective that either a suggested reading [in brackets] or an indication of missing words [also in brackets] was necessary. We have in no way tampered with Crane's sometimes unique choice of words or rhetorical devices.

3. The Tenderloin, then the most notorious district in New York City, got its name through a New York *Sun* reporter who asked Inspector Alexander S. Williams how he liked his new assignment in the 29th precinct. Policeman Williams, who had been transferred from the 4th precinct, replied that he liked the change of posts because the 29th had better saloons and better hotels. What he implied was that the illegitimate houses in this district paid off better in graft for his police protection. What he said was that he had been living in the 4th precinct on *rump steak,* but now he'd have some *tenderloin.* That district has been named the Tenderloin ever since his remark to the *Sun* reporter. (Its

About was policeman Charles Becker of the West 30th Street Station, a 19th precinct beat cop who was getting his cut of the Tenderloin by protecting houses of prostitution and by exacting money from the streetwalkers. On the night of 16 September 1896, Becker strode out of the Grand Hotel, walked to the corner of 31st Street and Broadway, and arrested Dora Clark for soliciting and threatened to arrest Crane, who was in her company. Crane protested that she was innocent, and she was released on his testimony in a magistrate's court, thus negating Becker's charge. From that moment on, Crane knew what it meant to be an especial subect of police cognizance. He was courageous, but he was wisely out of town and in Jacksonville early in November.

Policeman Charley was destined for other things, and years later, Lieutenant Becker was convicted of participation in the murder of Herman "Beansie" Rosenthal and sentenced to the electric chair at Sing Sing. This scandal — prolonged and sensational — swept the nation and brought about investigations of police departments in cities other than New York. Becker and Rosenthal were "partners" in a gambling establishment run by Rosenthal on West 45th Street near Broadway. Then Rosenthal threatened to reveal police graft (extortion money) to District Attorney Charles S. Whitman, and in fact did publish an affidavit in the New York *World*, 14 July 1912, declaring that Lieutenant Becker had been getting his cut of the profits from the gambling house. Becker took revenge swiftly by having Rosenthal shot down by gunmen — one of them bearing the name Gyp the Blood — just outside the Hotel Metropole on West 43rd Street, east of Broadway. The gunmen were captured, convicted, and electrocuted in 1914. Becker was refused clemency by the Governor, former District Attorney Whitman, and followed his hired hoods the next year. His coffin's silver plate read: "Charles Becker/Murdered July 30, 1915/By Governor Whitman." Mrs. Becker removed that silver-plated inscription only after she was threatened with prosecution on the grounds of criminal libel.[4]

So ended the story of Policeman Charley *vs* Stephen Crane, writer, and Dora Clark, doubtful chorus girl. "She bids fair to become almost as famous as Trilby," said the Boston *Herald* on 21 September 1896. This romantic prophecy was never realized but it

---

boundaries were from 42nd to 14th Streets and from Seventh to Park and Fourth Avenues.) That was the juicy cut.

4. Drawn from Herbert Asbury's *The Gangs of New York* (1927). This Becker-Rosenthal story is retold in Jonathan Root's *The Life and Bad Times of Charlie Becker* (London, 1962).

What goes unnoticed in these book-length tales is that the Becker-

reflects what was once called the "great *Trilby* epidemic." Unfortunately for romance, the Editors, having exhumed her from utter obscurity, find her no Trilby O'Ferrall, nor Crane a Svengali. One thing, though — George du Maurier did die about this time, on 8 October, to be exact.

When Crane stepped before Magistrate Cornell in the Jefferson Market police court and protested Dora's innocence, he was not quite twenty-five; he was as famous as almost any writer in America. The gesture was indicative of the passion ruling his life: curiosity to probe a situation and report it, to experience fearlessly and report "what's what" fearlessly, honestly. Concomitantly, whether in his newspaper reporting or in his fiction and poetry, the characteristic ingredient was the note of irony and pity. He first struck off this note in his notorious report of a parade at Asbury Park, "On the New Jersey Coast," New York *Tribune*: 21 August 1892. It is said that the *Tribune* fired Crane for embarrassing it, but this is debatable. Crane here initiated a stance in prose — irony fused with pity. It reappears in *Maggie,* in "An Experiment in Misery" (an 1894 New York Sketch), in *The Black Riders* (1895), and in *The Red Badge of Courage.* Hemingway learned this combination of irony and pity from Crane — it is there on the pages of *The Sun Also Rises.*

Crane's first efforts in print were anonymous contributions to articles his mother, Mrs. Mary Helen Crane, wrote for Methodist papers, and for the *Tribune,* Detroit *Press,* and Philadelphia *Press.* She was an unusual woman of broad culture, interested in all church work, and president of the WCTU. When too busy lecturing she turned over her column to Stephen. Her oldest son, J. Townley Crane, had operated a news reporting agency since 1882 in the fashionable seaside resort of Asbury Park, New Jersey; and Stephen

---

Rosenthal case reappears in Scott Fitzgerald's *The Great Gatsby* (1925). On the empty spaces of a railroad timetable, Nick Carraway writes the names of visitors to Gatsby's parties in the summer of 1922. They include "a man named Bunsen, whom I knew at Yale." Also, Chester Becker. Fitzgerald does not say so, but Bunsen was the inventor of the Hot Seat — the Bunsen Burner. And Chester Becker has the same surname as Lieutenant Becker, who got the Hot Seat for his part in Rosenthal's death. Gatsby introduces Nick Carraway to his gangster friends in a restaurant across from the old Hotel Metropole, the scene of Rosenthal's assassination. " 'Four of them were electrocuted,' I said, remembering. 'Five, with Becker,' said gangster Wolfsheim." Thus Becker links with Bunsen in *The Great Gatsby,* and Crane's encounter with policeman Becker looks forward to Fitzgerald's cryptographic account of the Becker-Rosenthal scandal. (This note is recast here from *The Houses That James Built* by R. W. Stallman, 1961.)

gathered shore news for him and collected the names of guests at local hotels.

It is difficult, if not impossible, to ascertain with any certitude that young Stephen wrote any of these early pieces, such as "Temperance Women at the Seaside" (Ocean Grove, New Jersey), New York *Tribune*: 10 July 1889. One can but guess whether Townley or Stephen or Mary Helen wrote this notice: "A Paper on 'Press Work,' by Mrs. M. Helen Crane, of Asbury Park, brought on a lively discussion in regard to the attitude of the daily papers in publishing extended notices of prize fights and similar matters." Presumably the mother wrote this and also "Interested in Bible Lessons," *Tribune*: 18 July 1889; also, "Crowds at Ocean Grove," *Tribune*: 3 August 1889. It is difficult to imagine that either Townley of the Associated Press (later superintendent of the streets of Port Jervis, New York) or Stephen would likely have written of the wife of the Reverend Dr. B. B. Loomis: "Her mother was a devoted Christian woman, who early took the little daughter to the House of God and to the Methodist love feast." This bears the unsigned signature of Mother Crane, widow of the Reverend Jonathan Townley Crane, father of Stephen, who once in 1879 had jotted down a note: "Held the Love Feast: many present, and an unusually melting time." Nor did Stephen write "The Rise of Ocean Grove," *Tribune*: 17 August 1889.

On the other hand, "Meetings Begun at Ocean Grove" — in the *Tribune* for 2 July 1892 — was written by Crane, then twenty years old. Although unsigned, the report begins with a phrase which is characteristically his own:

> The sombre-hued gentlemen who congregate at this place in summer are arriving in solemn procession, with black valises in their hands and rebukes to frivolity in their eyes. They greet each other with quiet enthusiasm and immediately set about holding meetings. The cool, shaded Auditorium will soon begin to palpitate with the efforts of famous preachers delivering doctrines to thousands of worshippers. The tents, of which there are hundreds, are beginning to rear their white heads under the trees.

Their valises are "black," their tents are "white." These gentlemen are "sombre-hued" — this epithet is Cranesque. So is the device of contrasted colors, as well as the pointed comment on the gentlemen's eyes. And who but Stephen Crane would phrase it "quiet enthusiasm." The remainer of the dispatch is nothing but a telephone directory of names of visiting clergymen; but rather amusing is this note following the intelligence that the Gospel singers, Mr. and Mrs. A. D. Sturgis, would sing in the Auditorium that season: "A reformed convict named 'Big Frank' Carr addressed a large audience at the Bradley Beach surf meeting last Sunday night. He went considerably into the details when describing the lives and methods of 'crooks.'"

The sketch on seaside "fakirs" at Asbury Park, "Joys of Seaside Life," *Tribune*: 17 July 1892, unsigned, is again obviously by Stephen, and so are the other sketches selected here as his best work on the Jersey Coast. One of them, "The Pace of Youth," set in Asbury Park, Crane included as a Midnight Sketch in his London edition of *The Open Boat and Other Stories* in 1898.

"Big Frank" Carr was not a piece of whimsy inserted in a work that succinctly adumbrated Harold Frederic's *Theron Ware*. It was another tentative exploration into the demi-world. In *Maggie* (1893), Crane had written about the Bowery before personally exploring it, writing his first draft in the spring of 1891 in the cupola of the Delta Upsilon fraternity house while a second semester freshman at Syracuse University, a transfer from Lafayette College in Easton, Pennsylvania. He invented the plot — a Bowery version of *Madame Bovary*!

Before he departed Syracuse, he was to encounter the prostitutes housed along the railroad tracks only a few blocks from the ΔY house, and was to represent the *Tribune* as their local correspondent, although nothing appeared under his name in the paper. Here he published a literary hoax on 18 June 1891:

GREAT BUGS IN ONONDAGA./THEY SWARM IN A QUARRY AND STOP A LOCOMOTIVE./A RARE CHANCE FOR NATURAL HISTORIANS —/LIKE ELECTRIC LIGHT BUGS, BUT LARGER.

Syracuse, May 31. — Southeast of Brighton Corners, between this place and Jamesville, on the Lackawanna Railroad, are extensive limestone quarries, which have been in operation for many years, and have penetrated deeply into the rock. Through the cut thus made and into the quarries a branch track has been laid from the Lackawanna road for the hauling of the hewn stone. Night work being necessary a large part of the time an arc light has been placed high over the track of the darkest part of the cut. Several cars were loaded with stone for shipment on Friday and left on the switch pending the observance of Memorial Day. To-night in preparation for drawing the cars out the electric light was put in, and an engine with the necessary

crew left the city for the quarries. What was the surprise of all
hands upon reaching the scene of operations to find the track
beneath the electric light completely thronged with strange insects of great size, some of them lying perfectly still in bunches,
and some of them playing a sort of leap-frog game. They covered a space of not less than sixty feet along the tracks, though
toward either boundary of the occupied territory they grew
fewer, as the rays of the light began to grow dimmer. These
pickets, or skirmishers, were one and all of a most lively disposition, and ran over the ground with that lightning-like
rapidity which characterized the movements of the electric
light bugs that made their appearance all over the country
soon after the system of electric lighting became of general
adoption in cities.

The locomotive continued on its way, and as the drivers
rolled over the insects, the insects died with a crackling sound
like the successive explosions of toy torpedoes. But this was at
the beginning of the swarm; as the iron monster ploughed its
way along, the bugs became numerous and the crackling grew
to a monotonous din, as though some firecracker storehouse had
been touched off in a hundred places, until in the thick of the
swarm the engine was brought to a stop, the drivers refusing to
catch on the now slippery rails, greased by the crushed and
slaughtered bugs. An examination of the insects showed a resemblance to the electric light bug, though they are somewhat
larger than those bugs, the outer shell of the back being about
the size and shape of half a shanghai-egg shell. It was this
turtle-like armor with which the insects are equipped that made
the crackling sound as the wheels passed over them. The shell is
black and partakes of the nature of stone, having a slatey structure and being brittle. This property of the shell set the more
thoughtful people to thinking and observing, and after a time
search along the sides of the cut revealed innumerable small
holes in the rock, which seemed to have been bored into it by
some agency not that of man, and in them were traces of a
peculiar ovula, some hatched and some apparently blighted.
An erudite recluse whose abode is in the neighborhood of the
quarries had by this time appeared, for news of the strange
occurrence had spread rapidly. His opinion was that the bugs
that had blocked the track were the issue of a rare species of
lithodome — a rock-boring mollusk — crossed with some kind of
predatory insect. To secure the shipment of the freight to-night
it became necessary to let the loaded train from above in the
quarry come down the grade to the cut. Gathering momentum

all the time, its impetus when it came to the obstruction carried it by the bugs.

Five of his Sullivan County Sketches appeared in the *Tribune* in July 1892, but they, too, were unsigned. Toward the end of his freshman year at Syracuse, Crane was published in the *University Herald* in May 1891 with an article, "The King's Favor," and in December 1892 with another Sullivan County Sketch. Yet another one, "A Tent in Agony," appeared that same month in *Cosmopolitan* and marked his professional magazine debut.

The next year, *Truth,* a humor magazine, issued three New York City Sketches under his name. And *Maggie* was out in the spring of 1893 but under the name of Johnston Smith.

R.W.S.
E.R.H.

Storrs, Connecticut
Louisville, Kentucky

TABLE OF CONTENTS

ACKNOWLEDGMENTS   v
PREFACE   ix

1 NEW YORK CITY SKETCHES

Travels in New York   3
The Landlady's Daughter   8
The Art Students League Building   14
A Mournful Old Building   16
Why Did the Young Clerk Swear?   17
At Clancy's Wake   22
Some Hints for Play-Makers   25
Matinee Girls   30
A Night at the Millionaire's Club   31
An Experiment in Misery   33
An Experiment in Luxury   43
Billy Atkins Went to Omaha   51
The Gratitude of a Nation   57
An Ominous Baby   59
"Youse Wants 'Petey,' Youse Do"   62
Mr. Binks' Day Off   63
Coney Island's Failing Days   70
Stories Told by an Artist   76
In a Park Row Restaurant   83
The Silver Pageant   86
Howells Fears Realists Must Wait   88

The Men in the Storm   91
When Every One Is Panic Stricken   97
Heard on the Street Election Night   103
When Man Falls   107
The Duel That Was Not Fought   111
Sixth Avenue   117
Miss Louise Gerard — Soprano   117
A Christmas Dinner Won in Battle   119
A Lovely Jag in a Crowded Car   125
The Judgment of the Sage   129
A Great Mistake   130
A Dark-Brown Dog   132
A Tale of Mere Chance   137
Sailing Day Scenes   140
Opium's Varied Dreams   143
A Prologue   148
New York's Bicycle Speedway   149
An Appreciation by W. D. Howells   152
Evening on the Roof   153
Yellow Undersized Dog   157
In the Tenderloin: A Duel   159
The "Tenderloin" As It Really Is   162
In the "Tenderloin"   166
A Tenderloin Story: Yen-Nock Bill   170
Diamonds and Diamonds   173
A Detail   176
Stephen Crane in Minetta Lane   178
In the Broadway Cars   185
A Desertion   189
The Auction   192
A Poker Game   195
A Man by the Name of Mud   197
A Self-Made Man   200
Manacled   205
The Man from Duluth   208

2 STEPHEN CRANE, DORA CLARK, AND THE POLICE

S. Crane and Dora Clark   217
Crane Saved Her a Fine   219
Stephen Crane As Brave As His Hero   222
Adventures of a Novelist   226

No Reply from Mr. Crane 231
Stevie Crane 231
Dora Clark Makes Startling Charges 232
Novelist Crane a Hard Man to Scare 234
Novelist Crane Was True Blue 235
Crane Long Under Fire 239
Crane Risked All to Save a Woman 242
Crane Had a Gay Night 248
Mr. Crane and the Police 252
A Police Outrage on a Gallant Gentleman 254
Tried by the Police Commissioners by James L. Ford 256
Stephen Crane Not an Opium Fiend 258
A Blackguard As a Police Officer 259
Notes about Prostitutes 259
A Desertion 260
An Eloquence of Grief 261

3 ON THE NEW JERSEY COAST

Howells Discussed at Avon-by-the-Sea 267
Joys of Seaside Life 268
Summer Dwellers at Asbury Park 271
Guests Continue to Arrive 272
Selections from the Mail 273
The Pace of Youth 274
Stephen Crane at Asbury Park 283

4 EXCURSIONS

In the Depths of a Coal Mine 289
The Devil's Acre 298

1   NEW YORK CITY SKETCHES

TRAVELS IN NEW YORK/THE BROKEN-DOWN VAN.*

The gas lamps had just been lit and the two great red furniture vans with impossible landscapes on their sides rolled and plunged slowly along the street. Each was drawn by four horses, and each almost touched the roaring elevated road above. They were on the uptown track of the surface road — indeed the street was so narrow that they must be on one track or the other.

They tossed and pitched and proceeded slowly, and a horse car with a red light came up behind. The car was red, and the bullseye light was red, and the driver's hair was red. He blew his whistle shrilly and slapped the horse's lines impatiently. Then he whistled again. Then he pounded on the red dash board with his car-hook till the red light trembled. Then a car with a green light crept up behind the car with the red light; and the green driver blew his whistle and pounded on his dash board; and the conductor

----

* *Reprinted from New York* Tribune: *10 July 1892. Unsigned.*

Although unsigned, this sketch bears the unmistakable signature of Crane in such phrasings as "the red driver" on his throne, the truckman's "warlike movement," and "The great red car with the impossible landscape." The sixteen-year-old girl with vests under her arm has stepped out of the collar-and-cuff factory where — as it were — Maggie is employed. Maggie: A Girl of the Streets (1893), *a Bowery version of Flaubert's* Madame Bovary, *draws upon New York City street scenes of the kind Crane sketched in "The Broken-Down Van."*

As for Crane's unsigned writings, the Editors have identified them by internal evidence, such as above, or by manuscript drafts. If the source is a manuscript, it is obviously by Crane because it carries the signature of his handwriting.

of the red car seized his strap from his position on the rear platform and rung such a rattling tattoo on the gong over the red driver's
head that the red driver became frantic and stood up on his toes
and puffed out his cheeks as if he were playing the trombone in a
German street-band and blew his whistle till an imaginative person
could see slivers flying from it, and pounded his red dash board
till the metal was dented in and the car-hook was bent. And just
as the driver of a newly-come car with a blue light began to blow
his whistle and pound his dash board and the green conductor
began to ring his bell like a demon which drove the green driver
mad and made him rise up and blow and pound as no man ever
blew and pounded before, which made the red conductor lose the
last vestige of control of himself and caused him to bounce up and
down on his bell strap as he grasped it with both hands in a wild,
maniacal dance, which of course served to drive uncertain Reason
from her tottering throne in the red driver, who dropped his whistle and his hook and began to yell, and ki-yi, and whoop harder
than the worst personal devil encountered by the sternest of Scotch
Presbyterians ever yelled and ki-yied and whooped on the darkest
night after the good man had drunk the most hot Scotch whiskey;
just then the left-hand forward wheel on the rear van fell off and
the axle went down. The van gave a mighty lurch and then swayed
and rolled and rocked and stopped; the red driver applied his
brake with a jerk and his horses turned out to keep from being
crushed between car and van; the other drivers applied their
brakes with a jerk and their horses turned out: the two cliff-dwell-
ing men on the shelf half-way up the front of the stranded van
began to shout loudly to their brother cliff-dwellers on the forward
van; a girl, six years old, with a pail of beer crossed under the red
car horses' neck; a boy, eight years old, mounted the red car with
the sporting extras of the evening papers; a girl, ten years old, went
in front of the van horses with two pails of beer; an unclassified
boy poked his finger in the black grease in the hub of the right-hand
hind van wheel and began to print his name on the red landscape
on the van's side; a boy with a little head and big ears examined
the white rings on the martingales of the van leaders with a view of
stealing them in the confusion; a sixteen-year-old girl without any
hat and with a roll of half-finished vests under her arm crossed
the front platform of the green car. As she stepped up on to the
sidewalk a barber from a ten-cent shop said "Ah! there!" and she
answered "smarty!" with withering scorn and went down a side
street. A few drops of warm summer rain began to fall.

Well, the van was wrecked and something had got to be done.
It was on the busiest car track on Manhattan Island. The cliff-

dwellers got down in some mysterious way — probably on a rope ladder. Their brethren drove their van down a side street and came back to see what was the matter.

"The nut is off," said the captain of the wrecked van.

"Yes," said the first mate, "the nut is off."

"Hah," said the captain of the other van, "the nut is off."

"Yer right," said his first mate, "the nut is off."

The driver of the red car came up, hot and irritated. But he had regained his reason. "The nut is off," he said.

The drivers of the green and of the blue car came along. "The nut," they said in chorus, "is off."

The red, green and blue conductors came forward. They examined the situation carefully as became men occupying a higher position. Then they made this report through the chairman, the red conductor:

"The nut is gone."

"Yes," said the driver of the crippled van, who had spoken first, "yes, the damned nut is lost."

Then the driver of the other van swore, and the two assistants swore, and the three car drivers swore and the three car conductors used some polite but profane expressions. Then a strange man, an unknown man and an outsider, with his trousers held up by a trunk-strap, who stood at hand, swore harder than any of the rest. The others turned and looked at him inquiringly and savagely. The man wriggled nervously.

"You wanter to tie it up," he said at last.

"Wot yo' goin' to tie it to, you cussed fool?" asked the assistant of the head van scornfully, "a berloon?"

"Ha, ha!" laughed the others.

"Some folks make me tired," said the second van driver.

"Go and lose yourself with the nut," said the red conductor, severely.

"That's it," said the others. "Git out, 'fore we t'row you out."

The officiously profane stranger slunk away.

The crisis always produces the man.

In this crisis the man was the first van driver.

"Bill," said the first van driver, "git some candles." Bill vanished.

A car with a white light, a car with a white and red light, a car with a white light and a green bar across it, a car with a blue light and a white circle around it, another car with a red bullseye light and one with a red flat light had come up and stopped. More are coming to extend the long line. The elevated trains thundered overhead, and made the street tremble. A dozen horse-cars went down on the other track, and the drivers made derisive noises, rather than speaking derisive words at their brother van-bound drivers. Each delayed car was full of passengers, and they craned their necks and peppery old gentlemen inquired what the trouble was, and a happy individual who had been to Coney Island began to sing.

Trucks, mail-wagons and evening paper carts crowded past. A jam was imminent. A Chatham Square cab fought its way along with a man inside wearing a diamond like an arc-light. A hundred people stopped on either sidewalk; ten per cent of them whistled "Boom-de-ay." A half dozen small boys managed to just miss being killed by passing teams. Four Jews looked out of four different pawnshops. Pullers-in for three clothing stores were alert. The ten-cent barber eyed a Division-st. girl who was a millinery puller-in and who was chewing gum with an earnest, almost fierce, motion of the jaw. The ever-forward flowing tide of the growlers flowed on. The men searched under the slanting rays of the electric light for the lost nut, back past a dozen cars; scattering drops of rain continued to fall and a hand-organ came up and began an overture.

Just then Bill rose up from somewhere with four candles. The leader lit them and each van man took one and they continued the search for the nut. The humorous driver on a blue car asked them why they didn't get a fire-fly; the equally playful driver of a white car advised them of the fact that the moon would be up in the course of two or three hours. Then a gust of wind came and blew out the candles. The handorgan man played on. A dozen newsboys arrived with evening paper extras about the Presidential nomination. The passengers bought the extras and found that they contained nothing new. A man with a stock of suspenders on his arm began to look into the trade situation. He might have made a sale to the profane man with the trunkstrap but he had disappeared. The leader again asserted himself.

"Bill," he shouted, "you git a lager beer-keg." Bill was gone in an instant.

"Jim," continued the leader, in a loud voice, as if Jim were up at the sharp end of the mainmast and the leader was on the deck, "Jim, unhitch them hosses and take out the pole."

Jim started to obey orders. A policeman came and walked around the van, looked at the prostrated wheel, started to say something, concluded not to, made the handorgan man move on, and then went to the edge of the sidewalk and began talking to the Division-st. girl with the gum, to the infinite disgust of the cheap barber. The trunkstrap man came out of a restaurant with a sign of "Breakfast, 13 cents; Dinner, 15 cents," where he had been hidden and slunk into the liquor store next door with a sign of "Hot spiced rum, 6 cents; Sherry with a Big Egg in it, 5 cents." At the door he almost stepped on a small boy with a pitcher of beer so big that he had to set it down and rest every half block.

Bill was now back with the keg. "Set it right there," said the leader. "Now you, Jim, sock that pole under the axle and we'll h'ist 'er up and put the keg under."

One of the horses began kicking the front of the van. "Here, there!" shouted the leader and the horse subsided. "Six or seven o' you fellers git under that pole," commanded the leader, and he was obeyed. "Now all together!" The axle slowly rose and Bill slipped under the chime of the keg. But it was not high enough to allow the wheel to go on. "Git a paving block," commanded the leader to Bill. Just then a truck loaded with great, noisy straps of iron tried to pass. The wheels followed the car track too long, the truck struck the rear of the van and the axle went down with a crash while the keg rolled away into the gutter. Even great leaders lose their self-control sometimes; Washington swore at the Battle of Long Island; so this van leader now swore. His language was plain and scandalous. The truckman offered to lick the van man till he couldn't walk. He stopped his horses to set down to do it. But the policeman left the girl and came and made the truckman give over his warlike movement, much to the disgust of the crowd. Then he punched the suspender man in the back with the end of his club and went back to the girl. But the second delay was too much for the driver of the green car, and he turned out his horses and threw his car from the track. It pitched like a skiff in the swell of a steamer. It staggered and rocked and as it went past the van plunged into the gutter and made the crowd stand back, but the horses strained themselves and finally brought it up and at last it blundered on to its track and rolled away at a furious rate with the faces of the passengers wreathed in smiles and the conductor looking proudly back. Two other cars followed the example of the green and went lumbering past on the stones.

"Tell them fellers we'll be out of their way now in a minute," said the leader to the red conductor. Bill had arrived with the paving block. "Up with 'er, now," called the leader. The axle went up again and the keg with the stone on top of it went under. The leader seized the wheel himself and slipped it on. "Hitch on them hosses!" he commanded, and it was done. "Now, pull slow there, Bill," and Bill pulled slow. The great red car with the impossible landscape gave a preliminary rock and roll, the wheel which had made the trouble dropped down an inch or two from the keg and the van moved slowly forward. There was nothing to hold the wheel on and the leader walked close to it and watched it anxiously. But it stayed on to the corner, and around the corner, and into the side street. The red driver gave a triumphant Ki-yi and his horses plunged forward in their collars eagerly. The other drivers gave glad Ki-yis and the other horses plunged ahead. Twenty cars rolled past at a fast gait. "Now, youse fellys, move on!" said the policeman, and the crowd broke up. The cheap barber was talking to a girl with one black eye, but he retreated to his shop with the sign which promised "bay rum and a clean towel to every customer." Inside the liquor store the trunkstrap man was telling a man with his sleeves rolled up how two good men could have put their shoulders under the van and h'isted it up while a ten-year-old boy put on the wheel.

THE LANDLADY'S DAUGHTER *

i

At the foot of the street the tiny riggings of ships grew like grass. They lay black against the water which, faintly seen, appeared as impalpable as a mist. Slanting over the roofs of the southern side came a stream of copper light from the setting sun, making the higher part of the northern walls resplendent, causing each window there to blaze like a topaz, and accentuating at the same time the gentle soft shadows of the lower part and of the street.

The boarders in No. 936 were coming from their dinner in the basement. Two young clerks from a famous shoe-store lit cigarettes and taking seats upon the topmost step in front of the house, prepared to gossip in the dark way of their age. Thorpe, an old bookkeeper, took his regular evening cigar from among the lead pencils in a top pocket of his vest. He perched on the iron railing at the

---

* Published here for the first time from the holograph manuscript in the Crane Collection at Columbia University Libraries. Six sheets comprise the first draft; both drafts are untitled. This is an addition to the Crane canon.

Crane here recasts his experience of living in a New York City boardinghouse where the youth's mind — his wolfish mind — was fascinated by his landlady's daughter. He wrote this sketch during the period 1892–1894.

side of the landing. Trixell, a clerk in a Broadway flower shop, waited for a time at the head of the gloomy basement stairs. He thought that perhaps the landlady's daughter would/[1] ascend and in such case he wished to have the joy and the distinction of appearing to conduct her to her throne on the front steps. Four old ladies toiled heavily past him.

One of the shoe clerks pulled wisely at his cigarette and addressed the old book-keeper. "Say, Thorpe, Trixell seems to be making the pace for all of us, don't you think?"

Thorpe smiled. "Well he certainly does seem to be cutting some ice. Why don't some of you smooth people get a hustle on you?"

Both shoe-clerks were silent for a moment and then one said: "She's a mighty pretty girl."

"Pretty girl!" cried Thorpe. "She's the prettiest girl in town. If I was as young as you boys!"

"Well, old Holmes is older than you," said one shoe-clerk, nudging the other. "And anybody could see that you, Thorpey, me boy, could make a lobster out of Holmes."

"Holmes never had a chance. He is an old idiot. And, anyhow, you two fresh kids, what right have you got to be talking about her?"/

"None at all," they responded. "Didn't say we did, did we? We ain't hurting anybody, are we?"

"Shut up," whispered Thorpe suddenly. "Here comes Trixell."/

ii

Apparently the daughter of the house was perverse or busy for Trixell came out alone. He lit a cigarette and thrusting his hands in his pockets and throwing back his shoulders surveyed the street with composure and dignity. To an action of this kind some men can impart a majesty which radiates entirely from their minds. His glances lifted high, Trixell gazed at the meek brown houses across the way as an emperor might gaze at his passing squadrons. He said: "Baltimore won again today. That makes two straight out of the series."

But his fellow-boarders on the steps were exchanging sly glances which related apparently to another subject. Finally one of the shoe-clerks said: "You look lonesome tonight, Trix."

"Oh I don't know," he replied airily.

"What's the matter, Trix," asked Thorpe. "Lost something, haven't you?"

1. A virgule (/) indicates the end of a holograph sheet of the final draft; a sketch not completed.

"Have I?" said Trixell with irony. "What have I lost?"

"Why" — said Thorpe. "You seem to have lost — er — what's wrong, Trix? Is she sick?"

"I don't know who you mean," said Trixell cleverly. "Who do you mean?"

The shoe-clerks chuckled, "Oh, you/old rat! Maybe you don't know who he means!"

But Trixell had turned toward the door. "Ah, good evening," he said. There was a stir among the shoe-clerks. They arose and looked at the houses across the street expressing in this way their desire to have the landlady's daughter take what seat she pleased and their perfect willingness to be content with what remained. There was stiffness as well as hauteur in their poses at this time for they were of the age and class which looks upon a movement of courtesy as being almost equivalent to a proposal of marriage or at least a declaration of love. Each being willing to have the landlady's daughter care for him, each wished to appear manfully indifferent and so they pretended they had arisen quite by accident. But no one heeded them; so presently they took seat again and puffed stolidly at their cigarettes.

Evidently Trixell had arranged in his mind where the girl was to sit and he offered her the position with a bland wave of his hand. But she said: "No, thanks. I'd rather sit here." She perched side saddle fashion on one of the railings. Trixell dropped gracefully to the/top step. Thorpe coughed to celebrate some joke which he perceived and, catching a sidelong glance from a shoe-clerk, he winked gravely.

The social group being now arranged there fell upon it the singular quiet which ensues when people chase their thoughts from pole to pole and seven times around the equator in search of the effective sentence./

iii

Finally Trixell remarked: "They give transfers now on the street-car lines almost all over the city. It seems funny for them to do that in New York. I can remember when they didn't give transfers at all — not a line in New York that I know of."

There was a moment of silence. Then Thorpe told his information concerning the matter and at the end stated some kind of theory. Trixell at once objected to some part of it. He drew a heavy indictment. He talked rather too rapidly and from time to time he looked to find if the girl was heeding his eloquence.

A shoe-clerk seized this opportunity to lean backward and say confidentially to the girl: "You look tired tonight."

She pushed a lock from her temple with a gesture of fatigue. "Yes, I am. Very tired." Her foot was swinging in the way that youth proclaims its superabundant power and her cheek had upon it a flush of pink.

The shoe-clerk murmured sympathetically and having thus gone into the social whirl with success he subsided and devoted himself to his comrade./

On the steps of the next house a man in shirt sleeves was reading an evening paper while two babies tumbled on the sidewalk. In front of other houses, after dinner groups had gathered. At one corner of the block, street cars moved past endlessly like links of a chain. At the other corner, a man ground steadily at a hand-organ and the brilliant melodies from the thing were interrupted at intervals by the sudden great roar of an elevated train.

At 936, Trixell talked long. He was engaged in an essay upon the Raines law when Thorpe said: "Somebody coming here."/

iv

A young man had halted before the house and was peering up at the dim transom where some gilt numerals shone inadequately. He carried a valise and an umbrella.

The boarders of No. 936 surveyed him keenly, measuring him from his umbrella to his necktie with all the curiosity and suspicion of New Yorkers who know no shame in these matters. He evidently made an effort to have it appear that he was not aware that the steps was a fortress armed with a formidable battery of eyes.

After an ineffectual attempt to solve the riddle on the transom, he addressed a shoe-clerk. "This is 936, isn't it?"

The shoe-clerk answered in the affirmative and the young man asked: "It's a boarding-house, isn't it? Is the lady that keeps it in?" The shoe-clerk turned and glanced at the top of the steps throwing the responsibility upon the landlady's daughter.

She spoke as one having authority. "If you'll come in, please, I'll go find her."/

The young man threaded his way among the knees and outlying elbows on the steps while the boarders continued their measurements in the same silence.

In the hallway the girl lit the gas and said: "Wait here please."

"Thanks," said the young man. It entered his head to accept any room in this house which might be offered him, for the young girl seemed to him beautiful. He dwelt long in his mind upon her graceful pose as she lit the gas./

v

It is a legend that at one time the mistresses of boarding-houses welcomed their arriving prey with cordial words and smiles. It is not known that a prey of this period need expect cordial words and smiles. On the contrary, he might expect to go before a bar of judgment where he is scanned for a resemblance to men whose perfidy is engraven on the mind of the boarding-house mistress, men who lied with skill and went away leaving an empty trunk in the house and a stone heart in the breast of the landlady. These men of sin leave thorns in the path of the virtue that comes afterward. "In God we trust," is a motto often hung on boarding-house walls. Here it expresses more than usual. It expresses a limit.

The proprietress of No. 936 came slowly toward the young man. Many wrinkles about her eyes were owing to her intensity of gaze.

"Good evening," he said with a strategic smile.

"Good evening," she said.

"I've come to see if you have/any room for another boarder," he ventured still smiling.

"Well," she answered, "there's a small room on the third floor — are you in business in the city?"

"No, not now. I don't live in the city but I've come here to take a position with a cousin of mine."

She reflected. At last she said: "Well, there's only the small room on the third floor. You can look at it if you wish."

Under the influence of her preternatural composure or indifference he was beginning to believe that he resembled a thief and so at her permission to look at the room he said humbly and gratefully: "Oh thank you very much." She nodded slightly at the gas-jet in vague acknowledgment of the young man's words.

They ascended two flights and there she exhibited a small hall bed-room grim and grey like a cell. "This is six dollars a week," she observed.

He made a show of deep consideration and at last said: "Well I'll take it if you don't/mind."

As he paid her six dollars she smiled, quietly amiable, and he was made to know that he did not yet resemble a thief./

vi

Alone in his grey and grim cell at the top of the house the young man reflected on his state. Life now presented a new aspect to him and he thought upon the dim figures which peopled his changed world.

His window opened upon the gulf of the evening and from time to time a murmur of voices arose. He heard often the tones of the young girl.

He was saddened by his change of environment and he was in the mood to wonder if she would feel sorrow for him could she know his loneliness. The thought of her sympathy loomed in his mind until in proportion it was great./

vii

In the morning the young man awoke with the thought at once in his mind that he had overslept. He consulted his old silver watch however and discovered that it was not yet six o'clock. Dusky grey light entered through the unclean panes of the window. The long roar, the thunder of the city's life came from the streets. Sometimes a wagon passed the house, its wheels rattling over the cobbles with a noise like innumerable musketry volleys. Then at last a bell was rung and the tomb-like silence of the house itself was broken. Doors slammed.

As the young man entered the dining-room in the basement he paused in a slight embarrassment seeing none to direct him. Five young men and two old women with their faces turned toward their plates ate steadfastly.

He felt like retreating, but the young girl of his previous experience appeared suddenly having come from the kitchen with dishes. She smiled at him and conducted him to a seat./At the sound of the chair being drawn out from the table, the five young men and two old women looked up and seeing the new boarder gazed at him as they gazed at their plates. The young girl poured water into his glass and as she performed this office he did/not dare to let his eyes waver in fear that she would discover that the charm of her near presence affected him. Nevertheless he was enabled to watch her hand as she tipped the pitcher and he thought it a perfect hand. She asked him to make a choice between steak and bacon and eggs.

During the meal he covertly watched her. He was glad when a certain one of the five young clerks finished breakfast and left the table, for that particular clerk ogled the girl as she passed to and fro in a way that the new boarder considered exasperatingly bold and confident. It was evident that the clerk believed that the girl would descend a throne to receive one of these smiles which he performed soon after taking a mouthful of bread perhaps. And so the new boarder, reflecting upon his own nobility, rejoiced at the exit of the trickster.

He dallied with a second cup of coffee until nearly all of the boarders had vanished from the table. He tried to note each move of the young girl. Still, he thought he contrived to do this without the young girl being aware. His instinct taught him that her too sudden knowledge of his interest would somehow shame him,/for she certainly did not seem to recognize his existence in any way save as a boarder./

THE ART STUDENTS LEAGUE BUILDING *

Since the Art Student's League moved to the fine new building on West 57th St., there remains nothing but the consolation of historical value for the old structure that extends from No. 143 to No. 147 East 23rd St. This building with its common-place front is as a matter of fact one of the landmarks of American art. The old place

*Crane wrote this sketch in his "Pocket Notebook"; it is published here in its entirety for the first time. A variant version on holograph sheets is "A Mournful Old Building" (below.) Both are additions to the Crane canon. A portion of "The Art Students League Building" first appeared in R. W. Stall- man, "Stephen Crane: Some New Stories," Bulletin of the New York Public Library: September 1956.

In The Art of Authorship (1935), Edwin Valentine Mitchell mentioned the "Notebook" and thereby made known its existence for the first time. Unfortunately, it was lost almost a decade ago while being transferred from the Collamore Crane Collection to the Barrett Crane Collection. A photocopy is all that remains of it.

In October 1892, the Art Students League moved into the American Fine Arts Society building at 215 West 57th Street. Its two component societies were the National Academy of De- sign (also known as the Society of American Artists) and the Architectural League of New York. The sole occupant of this building today is the Art Students League.

Crane describes the artist's life in the old building in "Stories Told by an Artist" (below) New York Press: 28 October 1894. R. G. Vosburgh, an illustrator who did drawings for some of Crane's sketches, published an article about Crane's life there in Criterion: February 1901. The "antique rookery" is described by Corwin Knapp Linson, My Stephen Crane, ed. Edwin H. Cady (1958), and by Crane in several sketches and in The Third Violet (1897). It was in the studios of Linson, Vosburgh and Frederic Gordon during 1893–1894 that Crane completed The Red Badge of Courage.

once rang with the voices of a crowd/[1] of art students who in those days past built their ideals of art-schools upon the most approved Parisian models and it is fact generally unknown to the public that this staid puritannical old building once contained about all that was real in the Bohemian quality of New York. The exterior belies the interior in a tremendous degree. It is plastered with signs, and wears sedately the air of being what it is not./

The interior however is place of slumberous corridors rambling in puzzling turns and curves. The large studios rear their brown rafters over scenes of lonely quiet. Gradually the tinkers, the tailors, and the plumbers who have captured the ground floor are creeping toward those dim ateliers above them. One by one the/ besieged artists give up the struggle and the time is not far distant when the conquest of the tinkers, the tailors and the plumbers will be complete.

Nevertheless, as long as it stands, the old building will be to a great many artists of this country a place endeared to them by the memory of many an escapade of the old student days when the boys of the life class/used to row gaily with the boys of the "preparatory antique" in the narrow halls. Everyone was gay, joyous, and youthful in those blithe days and the very atmosphere of the old place cut the austere and decorous elements out of a man's heart and made him rejoice when he could divide his lunch of sandwiches with the model.

Who does not remember the incomparable "soap slides" of those days when/the whole class in the hour of rest, slid whooping across the floor one after another. The water and soap with which the brushes were washed used to make fine ice when splashed upon the floor and the hopes of America in art have taken many a wild career upon the slippery stretch. And who does not remember the little man who attempted the voyage when seated in a tin-wash basin and who came to grief and arose covered with soap/and deluged the studio[2] profanity.

Once when the woman's life class bought a new skeleton for the study of anatomy, they held a very swagger function in their class room and christened it "Mr. Jolton Bones" with great pomp and ceremony. Up in the boy's life class the news of the ceremony created great excitement. They were obliged to hold a rival function without delay. And the series/of great pageants, ceremonials, celebrations and fetes which followed were replete with vivid color and gorgeous action.

The Parisian custom exhaustively recounted in "Trilby" of

1. A virgule (/) indicates the end of a holograph sheet.
2. As given in the manuscript.

requiring each new member of a class to make a spread for his companions was faithfully followed. Usually it consisted of beer, crackers and brie cheese.

After the Art Student's League moved to Fifty-/Seventh St., the life class of the National Academy of Design school moved in for a time and occasionally the old building was alive with its old uproar and its old spirit. After their departure, the corridors settled down to dust and quiet. Infrequently of a night one could pass a studio door and hear the cheerful rattle of half of a dozen tongues, hear a guitar twinkling/an accompaniment to a song, see a mass of pipe smoke cloud the air. But this too vanished, and now one can only hear the commercial voices of the tinkers, the tailors and the plumbers.

In the top-most and remotest studio there is an old beam which bears this line from Emerson in half-obliterated chalk-marks: "Congratulate yourselves if you have done something strange/and entravagant and broken the monotony of a decorous age." It is a memory of the old days./

A MOURNFUL OLD BUILDING *

A mournful old building stood between two that were tall and straight and proud. In a way, it was a sad thing; symbolizing a decrepit old man whose lean shoulders are jostled by sturdy youth. The old building seemed to glance timidly upward at its two

---

* *Published here for the first time from the untitled holograph manuscript in the Columbia University Crane Collection. There are two drafts; on the second draft, which appears here, there is a note not in Crane's hand: "to be looked over."*

Crane regards a building as a metaphor of man's mournful plight, not only in this sketch but also in Maggie: A Girl of the Streets *(1893, 1896): "The shutters of the tall buildings were closed like grim lips." The saloon's door — in contrast — is an open mouth. "At the feet of the tall buildings appeared the deathly hue of the river." "A Mournful Old Building" is a variant sketch of "The Art Students League Building" (see above) and these versions are echoed in* The Third Violet: *"Occasionally one could hear the tramp of feet in the intricate corridors of the begrimed building which squatted, slumbering and old, between two exalted commercial structures, which would have had to bend afar down to perceive it. The northward march of the city's progress had happened not to overturn this aged structure, and it huddled there, lost and forgotten, while the cloud-veering towers strode on.*

neighbors, pleading for comradeship, and at times it assumed an important air derived from its environment, and said to those who viewed from the side-walks: "we three — we three buildings."

It stood there awaiting the inevitable time of downfall, when progress, to the music of tumbling walls and chimneys would come marching up the avenues. Already, from the roof one could see a host advancing, an army of enormous buildings, coming with an invincible front that extended across the city, trampling under their feet the bones of the dead, rising tall and supremely proud on the crushed memories, the annihilated hopes of generations gone. At sunset time, each threw a tremendous shadow, a gesture of menace out over the low plain of the little buildings huddling afar down.

Once this mournful old structure had been proud. It had stood with its feet unconcernedly on the grave of a past ambition and no doubt patronized the little buildings on either side.

WHY DID THE YOUNG CLERK SWEAR?/OR,/THE UNSATISFACTORY FRENCH.*

All was silent in the little gents' furnishing store. A lonely clerk with a blond mustache and a red necktie raised a languid hand to his brow and brushed back a dangling lock. He yawned and gazed gloomily at the blurred panes of the windows.

Without, the wind and rain came swirling round the brick buildings and went sweeping over the streets. A horse-car rumbled stolidly by. In the mud on the pavements, a few pedestrians struggled with excited umbrellas.

"The deuce!" remarked the clerk. "I'd give ten dollars if somebody would come in and buy something, if 'twere only cotton socks."

He awaited amid the shadows of the gray afternoon. No customers came. He heaved a long sigh and sat down on a high stool. From beneath a stack of unlaunderied shirts he drew a French novel with a picture on the cover. He yawned again, glanced lazily toward the street, and settled himself as comfortably as the gods would let him upon the high stool.

___

* *Published in* Truth: *18 March 1893; reprinted from the clipping in the* Columbia University Crane Collection. *The sketch also appeared in* Last Words (1902). *All of Crane's sketches in* Truth *are signed*

He opened the book and began to read. Soon it could have been noticed that his blond mustache took on a curl of enthusiasm, and the refractory locks on his brow showed symptoms of soft agitation.

"Silvere did not see the young girl for some days," read the clerk. "He was miserable. He seemed always to inhale that subtle perfume from her hair. At night he saw her eyes in the stars.

"His dreams were troubled. He watched the house. Eloise did not appear. One day he met Vibert. Vibert wore a black frock-coat. There were wine stains on the right breast. His collar was soiled. He had not shaved.

"Silvere burst into tears. 'I love her! I love her! I shall die!' Vibert laughed scornfully. His necktie was second-hand. Idiotic, this boy in love. Fool! Simpleton! But at last he pitied him. 'She goes to the music teacher's every morning, silly.' Silvere embraced him.

"The next day Silvere waited on the street corner. A vendor was selling chestnuts. Two gamins were fighting in an alley. A woman was scrubbing some steps. This great Paris throbbed with life.

"Eloise came. She did not perceive Silvere. She passed with a happy smile on her face. She looked fresh, fair, innocent. Silvere felt himself swooning. 'Ah, my God!'

"She crossed the street. The young man received a shock that sent the warm blood to his brain. It had been raining. There was mud. With one slender hand Eloise lifted her skirts. Silvere, leaning forward, saw her —— "

A young man in a wet mackintosh came into the little gents' furnishing store.

"Ah, beg pardon," said he to the clerk, "but, do you have an agency for a steam laundry here? I have been patronizing a Chinaman down th' avenue for some time, but he — what? No? You have none here? Well, why don't you start one, anyhow? It'd be a good thing in this neighborhood. I live just 'round the corner, and it'd be a great thing for me. I know lots of people who would — what? Oh, you don't? Oh!"

As the young man in the wet mackintosh retreated, the clerk with a blond mustache made a hungry grab at the novel. He continued to read: "Handkerchief fall in a puddle. Silvere sprang forward. He picked up the handkerchief. Their eyes met. As he returned the handkerchief, their hands touched. The young girl smiled. Silvere was in ecstasies. 'Ah, my God!'

"A baker opposite was quarreling over two sous with an old woman. A gray-haired veteran with a medal upon his breast and a butcher's boy were watching a dog-fight. The smell of dead animals came from adjacent slaughter-houses. The letters on the sign over the tinsmith's shop on the corner shone redly like great clots of blood. It was hell on roller-skates."

Here the clerk skipped some seventeen chapters descriptive of a number of intricate money transactions, the moles on the neck of a Parisian dressmaker, the process of making brandy, the milk-leg of Silvere's aunt, life in the coal-pits and scenes in the Chamber of Deputies. In these chapters the reputation of the architect of Charlemagne's palace was vindicated, and it was explained why Eloise's grandmother didn't keep her stockings pulled up.

Then he proceeded: "Eloise went to the country. The next day Silvere followed. They met in the fields. The young girl had donned the garb of the peasants. She blushed. She looked fresh, fair, innocent. Silvere felt faint with rapture. 'Ah, my God!'

"She had been running. Out of breath, she sank down in the hay. She held out her hand. 'I am glad to see you.' Silvere was enchanted at this vision. He bended toward her. Suddenly, he burst into tears. 'I love you! I love you! I love you!' he stammered.

"A row of red and white shirts hung on a line some distance away. The third shirt from the left had a button off the neck. A cat on the rear steps of a cottage near the shirts was drinking milk from a platter. The northeast portion of the platter had a crack in it.

"'Eloise!' Silvere was murmuring, hoarsely. He leaned toward her until his warm breath moved the curls on her neck. 'Eloise!' murmured Jean." [1]

"Young man," said an elderly gentleman with a dripping umbrella to the clerk with a blond mustache, "have you any night-shirts open front and back? Eh? Night-shirts open front and back, I said. D'you hear, eh? *Night-shirts open front and back!* Well, then, why didn't you say so? It would pay you to be a trifle more polite, young man. When you get as old as I am, you will find out that it pays to — what? I didn't see you adding any column of figures. In that case I'm sorry. You have no night-shirts open front and back, eh? Well, good-day."

As the elderly gentleman vanished, the clerk with a blond mustache grasped the novel like some famished animal. He read on: "A peasant stood before the two children. He wrung his hands. 'Have you seen a stray cow?' 'No,' cried the children in the same breath. The peasant wept. He wrung his hands. It was a supreme moment.

1. Misprint for Silvere.

" 'She loves me!' cried Silvere to himself, as he changed his clothes for dinner.

"It was evening. The children sat by the fireplace. Eloise wore a gown of clinging white. She looked fresh, fair, innocent. Silvere was in raptures. 'Ah, my God!'

"Old Jean the peasant saw nothing. He was mending harness. The fire crackled in the fireplace. The children loved each other. Through the open door to the kitchen came the sound of old Marie shrilly cursing the geese who wished to enter. In front of the window, two pigs were quarreling over a vegetable. Cattle were lowing in a distant field. A hay-wagon creaked slowly past. Thirty-two chickens were asleep in the branches of a tree. This subtle atmosphere had a mighty effect upon Eloise. It was beating down her self-control. She felt herself going. She was choking.

"The young girl made an effort. She stood up. 'Good-night. I must go.' Silvere took her hand. 'Eloise!' he murmured. Outside, the two pigs were fighting.

"A warm blush overspread the young girl's face. She turned wet eyes toward her lover. She looked fresh, fair, innocent. Silvere was maddened. 'Ah, my God!'

"Suddenly, the young girl began to tremble. She tried vainly to withdraw her hand. But her knee — "

"I wish to get my husband some shirts," said a shopping-woman with six bundles. The clerk with a blond mustache made a private gesture of despair and rapidly spread a score of differently patterned shirts upon the counter. "He's very particular about his shirts," said the shopping-woman. "Oh, I don't think any of these will do. Don't you keep the Invincible brand? He always wears that kind. He says they fit him better. And he's very particular about his shirts. What? You don't keep them? No? Well, how much do you think they would come at? Haven't the slightest idea? Well, I suppose I must go somewhere else, then. Um — good-day."

The clerk with the blond mustache was about to make further private gestures of despair, when the shopping-woman with six bundles turned and went out. His fingers instantly closed nervously over the book. He drew it from its hiding-place and opened it at the place where he had ceased. His hungry eyes seemed to eat the words upon the page. He continued: "struck cruelly against a chair. It seemed to awaken her. She started. She burst from the young man's arms. Outside, the two pigs were grunting amiably.

"Silvere took his candle. He went toward his room. He was in despair. 'Ah, my God!'

"He met the young girl on the stairs. He took her hand. Tears were raining down his face. 'Eloise!' he murmured.

"The young girl shivered. As Silvere put his arms about her, she faintly resisted. This embrace seemed to sap her life. She wished to die. Her thoughts flew back to the old well and the broken hay-rakes at Plassans.

"The young girl looked fresh, fair, innocent. 'Eloise!' murmured Silvere. The children exchanged a long, clinging kiss. It seemed to unite their souls.

"The young girl was swooning. Her head sank on the young man's shoulder. There was nothing in space except these warm kisses on her neck. Silvere enfolded her. 'Ah, my God!'"

"Say, young feller," said a youth with a tilted cigar to the clerk with a blond mustache, "where th'ell is Billie Carcart's joint round here? Know?"

"Next corner," said the clerk, fiercely.

"Oh, th'ell," said the youth, "yehs needn't git gay. See? When a feller asts a civil question yehs needn't git gay. See? Th'ell."

The youth stood and looked aggressive for a moment. Then he went away.

The clerk seemed almost to leap upon the book. His feverish fingers twirled the pages. When he found the place he glued his eyes to it. He read:

"Then, a great flash of lightning illumined the hallway. It threw livid hues over a row of flower-pots in the window-seat. Thunder shook the house to its foundation. From the kitchen arose the voice of old Marie in prayer.

"Eloise screamed. She wrenched herself from the young man's arms. She sprang inside her room. She locked the door. She flung herself face downward on the bed. She burst into tears. She looked fresh, fair, innocent.

"The rain, pattering upon the thatched roof, sounded, in the stillness, like the footsteps of spirits. In the sky toward Paris there shone a crimson light.

"The chickens had all fallen from the tree. They stood, sadly, in a puddle. The two pigs were asleep under the porch.

"Uptairs, in the hallway, Silvere was furious."

The clerk with a blond mustache gave, here, a wild scream of disappointment. He madly hurled the novel with the picture on the cover from him. He stood up and said "Damn!"

AT CLANCY'S WAKE.*

SCENE: *Room in the house of the lamented* CLANCY. *The curtains are pulled down. A perfume of old roses and whiskey hangs in the air. A weeping woman in black is seated at a table in the centre. A group of wide-eyed children are sobbing in a corner. Down the side of the room is a row of mourning friends of the family. Through an open door can be seen, half-hidden in shadows, the silver and black of a coffin.*

WIDOW — Oh, wirra, wirra, wirra!

CHILDREN — B-b boo-hoo-hoo!

FRIENDS (*conversing in low tones*) — Yis, Moike Clancy was a foine mahn. — Sure — None betther! — No, I don't t'ink so! — Did he? Sure, in all th' elictions! — He was th' bist in the warrud! — He licked 'im widin an inch of his loife, aisy, an' th' other wan a big shtrappin' buck of a mahn, an' him jest free of th' pneumonia! — Yis, he did! — They carried th' warrud by six hunder! — Yis, he was a foine mahn! — None betther, Gawd sav' 'im.

(*Enter* MR. SLICK, *of the "Daily Blanket," shown in by a maid-servant whose hair has become disarranged through much tear-shedding. He is attired in a suit of gray check, and wears a red rose in his buttonhole.*)

---

* Published in Truth: *3 June 1893; reprinted from a clipping in the Columbia University Crane Collection. Where the clipping first appeared is unknown. Publication in* Truth, *an illustrated humor magzine edited by James L. Ford, is not acknowledged in either W. R. Linnemann, "Stephen Crane's Contributions to* Truth," *American Literature:* May 1959, *or Ames W. Williams and Vincent Starrett,* Stephen Crane: A Bibliography (1948).

A dramatic sketch, "At Clancy's Wake" links with other similar writings, such as "A Prologue" (see below) and "Greed Rampant," and with Crane's dramas, "The Blood of the Martyr" and "Drama in Cuba." See R. W. Stallman, "Stephen Crane as Dramatist" Bulletin of the New York Public Library: October 1963, *which also published for the first time "Drama in Cuba." This Cuban War play was reprinted in R. W. Stallman and E. R. Hagemann, eds.,* The War Dispatches of Stephen Crane (1964), *the source of which was the untitled typescript in the Columbia University Crane Collection.*

MR. SLICK — Good-afternoon, Mrs. Clancy. This is a sad misfortune for you, isn't it?

WIDOW — Oh, indade, indade, young mahn, me poor heart is bruk!

MR. SLICK — Very sad, Mrs. Clancy. A great misfortune, I'm sure. Now, Mrs. Clancy, I've called to —

WIDOW — Little did I t'ink, young mahn, win they brought poor Moike in, that it was th' lasht.

MR. SLICK (with conviction) — True! True! Very true, indeed! It was a great grief to you, Mrs. Clancy. I've called this morning, Mrs. Clancy, to see if I could get from you a short obituary notice for the *Blanket* if you could —

WIDOW — An' his hid was done up in a rag, an' he was cursin' frightful. A domned Oytalian lit fall th' hod as Moike was walkin' pasht as dacint as you plaze. Win they carried 'im in, him all bloody, an' ravin' tur'ble 'bout Oytalians, me heart was near bruk, but I niver tawt — I niver tawt — I — I niver — (*Breaks forth into a long, forlorn cry. The children join in, and the chorus echoes wailfully through the rooms.*)

MR. SLICK (*as the yell, in a measure, ceases*) — Yes, indeed, a sad, sad affair. A terrible misfortune! Now, Mrs. Clancy —

WIDOW (*turning suddenly*)— Mary Ann! Where's thot lazy divil of a Mary Ann? (*As the servant appears.*) Mary Ann, bring th' bottle. Give th' gintlemin a dhrink. * * * Here's to Hiven savin' yez, young mahn! (*Drinks.*)

MR. SLICK (*drinks*) — A noble whiskey, Mrs. Clancy. Many thanks. Now, Mrs. Clancy —

WIDOW — Take anodder wan! Take anodder wan! (*Fills his glass.*)

MR. SLICK (*impatiently*)— Yes, certainly, Mrs. Clancy, certainly. (*He drinks.*) Now, could you tell me, Mrs. Clancy, where your late husband was —

WIDOW — Who — Moike? Oh, young mahn, yez can just say thot he was th' foinest mahn livin' an' breathin', an' niver a wan in th' warrud was betther. Oh, but he had th' tindther heart for 'is fambly, he did! Don't I remimber win he clipped little Patsey wid th' bottle, an' didn't he buy th' big rickin'-horse th' minit he got sober? Sure he did. Pass th' bottle, Mary Ann. (*Pours a beer glass about half-full for her guest.*)

MR. SLICK (*taking a seat*) — True, Mr. Clancy was a fine man, Mrs. Clancy — a *very* fine man. Now, I —

WIDOW (*plaintively*) — An' don't yez loike th' rum? Dhrink th' rum, mahn. It was me own Moike's fav'rite bran'. Well I remimber win he fotched it home, an' half th' demijohn gone a'ready,

an' him a'cursin up th' stairs as dhrunk as Gowd plazed. It was
a — Dhrink th' rum, young mahn, dhrink th' rum. If he cud see yez
now, Moike Clancy wud git up from 'is —

MR. SLICK (*desperately*) — Very well, very well, Mrs. Clancy!
Here's your good health! Now, can you tell me, Mrs. Clancy, when
was Mr. Clancy born?

WIDOW — Win was he borrun? Sure, divil a bit do I care win
he was borrun. He was th' good mahn to me an' his childher, an'
Gawd knows I don't care win he was borrun. Mary Ann, pass th'
bottle. Wud yez kepe th' gintlemin shtarvin' for a dhrink here in
Moike Clancy's own house? Gawd save yez!

(*When the bottle appears she pours a huge quantity out for
her guest.*)

MR. SLICK — Well, then, Mrs. Clancy, *where* was he born?

WIDOW (*staring*) — In Oirland, mahn, in Oirland! Where did
yez t'ink? (*Then, in sudden wheedling tones*) An' ain't yez goin'
to dhrink th' rum? Are yez goin' to shirk th' good whiskey what
was th' pride of Moike's loife, an' him gettin' full on it an' breakin'
th' furniter t'ree nights a week hand-runnin'? Shame on yez, an'
Gawd save yer sowl! Dhrink it oop now, there's a dear, dhrink it
oop now, an' say: "Moike Clancy, be all th' powers in th' shky Hiven
sind yez rist!"

MR. SLICK (*to himself*) — Holy smoke! (*He drinks, then regards the glass for a long time.*) * * * Well, now, Mrs. Clancy,
give me your attention for a moment, please. When did —

WIDOW — An' oh, but he was a power in th' warrud! Divil a
mahn cud vote right widout Moike Clancy at 'is elbow. An' in the
calkus, sure didn't Mulrooney git th' nominashun jes' by raison of
Moike's atthackin' th' opposashun wid th' shtove-poker Mulrooney
got it as aisy as dhirt, wid Moike rowlin' under th' tayble wid th'
other candeedate. He was a good cit'zen, was Moike — divil a
wan betther.

(MR. SLICK *spends some minutes in collecting his faculties.*)

MR. SLICK (*after he decides that he has them collected*) —
Yes, yes, Mrs. Clancy, your husband's h-highly successful pol-pol-
politic political career was w-well known to the public; but what
I want to know is — what I want to know is — what I want to know
— (*Pauses to consider.*)

WIDOW (*finally*) — Pass th' glasses, Mary Ann, yez lazy divil;
give th' gintlemin a dhrink. Here (*tendering him a glass*), take
anodder wan to Moike Clancy, an' Gawd save yez for yer koindness
to a poor widee woman!

MR. SLICK (*after solemnly regarding the glass*) — Certainly,

I-I'll take a drink. Certainly, M-Mish Clanshy. Yes, certainly, Mish Clanshy. Now, Mish Clanshy, w-w-wash was Mr. Clanshy's n-name before he married you, Mish Clanshy?

WIDOW (*astonished*) — Why, divil a bit else but Clancy!

MR. SLICK (*after reflection*) — Well, but I am mean — I mean, Mish Clanshy, I mean — what was date of birth? Did marry you 'fore then, or d-did marry you when 'e was born in N' York, Mish Clanshy?

WIDOW — Phwat th' divil —

MR. SLICK (*with dignity*) — Ansher my queshuns, pleash, Mish Clanshy. Did 'e bring chil'en withum f'm Irelan', or was you, after married in N' York, mother those chil'en 'e brought f'm Irelan'?

WIDOW — Be th' powers above, I —

MR. SLICK (*with gentle patience*) — I don't shink y' unnerstan' m' queshuns, Mish Clanshy. What I wanna fin' out is, what was 'e born in N' York for when he, before zat, came f'm Irelan'? Dash what puzzles me. I I'm completely puzzled. An' alsho, I wanna fin' out — I wanna fin' out, if poshble — zat is, if it's poshble shing, I wanna fin' out — I wanna fin' out — if poshble — I wanna — shay, who the blazesh is dead here, anyhow?

SOME HINTS FOR PLAY-MAKERS.*

We present herewith a few valuable receipts for popular dramas. It is needless to say that we have followed models which have received the sanction of tradition, and are upheld at the present day by a large and important portion of the public. We do not hesitate to claim a great excellence for our receipts, and if they withstand the ravages of time and the assaults of the press with the same fortitude that characterized their predecessors along the same lines, we have no doubt that our posterity far over the horizon of the future will turn their delighted eyes upon theatrical attractions identical with those which will here charm the senses of the enlightened public.

The plans given below are short, concise and direct; the literary essentials only are given. Play-makers using the receipts should fill in well with unimportant characters and specialty people. The dramas can be lengthened or shortened to suit the temper of the audience.

* *Reprinted from* Truth: *25 November 1893.*

i

An Irish melodrama. This play can be called "Achushla Ma-vourneen" or "Mavourneen Achushla," according to which title is preferred by the star.

CAST: HERO: HEROINE: VILLAIN.
SCENE: *The Lakes of Killarney, or, perchance, the Glen of Kildare. Mountains and lake. Foreground, canvas rocks and waterfall, grass mats; also rustic bridge, upon which is discovered the* HEROINE, *leaning against the railing and gazing down into the mirrored depths below.*

HEROINE (*reflectively*) — Ah me!
(*Enter the* VILLAIN. *He glides forward and grabs the* HEROINE *carefully.*)
VILLAIN — Ha, ha, Mary Merry weather, my pretty gazelle! At last — at last! Seek not to flee! You cannot escape me!
HEROINE — Help!
VILLAIN — At last you are in my power!
HEROINE — Help!
(*Enter* HERO.)
HERO — Not while a true son of Erin remains alive!
(*He seizes the* VILLAIN, *and, with the* VILLAIN'S *assistance, drops the* VILLAIN *over the railing of the rustic bridge into the mirrored depths below. Splash made in pan of water by club in hands of supe.*)

CURTAIN.

ii

A society play. Entitle this anything you please, so long as the one you hit upon does not refer particularly to anything connected with the drama.

CAST: THE DUCHESS; HER NIECE; A NICE MAN; *and Intriguing,* Spiteful, Contemptible, Malicious, Well-bred and Devilish Men and Women.

[ACT I]

SCENE: *Drawing-room in town house of* THE DUCHESS, *who, with* HER NIECE, *is discovered seated.*

THE DUCHESS — My dear Lucy, all men are odious pigs.
HER NIECE — But, dear ahnt —
(*Enter the Intriguing, Spiteful, Contemptible, Malicious, Well-*

bred and Devilish Men and Women, one at a time and in pairs. They retail sundry scandals about A NICE MAN. *When they retire,* HER NIECE *sheds tears on the back of a chair. There is a great and bitter woe in her eyes.*)

THE DUCHESS — My dear Lucy, all men are odious pigs.

MOURNFUL CURTAIN.

[ACT II]

SCENE: *Drawing-room in the town house of* THE DUCHESS. HER NIECE *discovered reading note.*

HER NIECE (*with sudden joy*) — Oh! then, he is really the pink of perfection, and not an odious pig, as I thought. Dottie Hightights, at the Tinsel Theatre, is his own grandmamma, and not a bad, wicked woman, as I thought.

(*Enter* A NICE MAN.)

HE — Lucy!

SHE — Albert!

QUICK CURTAIN.

iii

This is an affair with much life and go to it. It should be called "Mr. Williams, of Williamsburg," or, perhaps, "Mr. Washington, of Washington Market."

CAST: HERO; HEROINE; SISTER TO THE HERO; BROTHER TO THE HEROINE; and Various Foreign Villains.

SCENE: *The exterior of the office of the Transatlantic Cable Co., Paris. Enter* Various Foreign Villains.

A MINOR VILLAIN — Oh, but these Americans are devils — sacre bleu!

CHIEF VILLAIN (*rapidly*) — But at last we have the accursed Gringo in our clutches. This telegram, sent to the office of Bank, Note & Co., Wall Street, New York, will cause them to pay over the eight million dollars of the girl's fortune to our confederates. Then the accursed Gringo will be in our clutches.

(*Dark, tan-colored rejoicing by the Villains. Then enter the* HERO, *tranquilly, with a Colt's revolver, 44 calibre.*)

HERO — Well, you are a beautiful collection of portraits. Move, and I blow you full of holes!

CHIEF VILLAIN (*exultantly*) — Little good is your Arizona plaything now, accursed Gringo! I have but to send this despatch and —

HERO (*calmly*) — Pray don't excite yourself, my dear baron. I know that you have not the price of a cablegram.

(*Consternation among the Villains.*)

CHIEF VILLAIN — Curses on this cool American! Sapristi, he has outwitted us at every turn. He foiled us on the brick-red plains of Arizona, and he has foiled us here. We are but children in the hands of this devilish American. But for him —

(*Exit Villains biting their nails. The* HERO *returns his weapon to a handy pocket and lights a cigar. Marriage of the* HERO *to the* HEROINE, *and of the* SISTER TO THE HERO *to the* BROTHER TO THE HEROINE.)

CURTAIN.

iv

Concerning this play, we, with our large knowledge of the public pulse, declare that if you use the material given with any intelligence at all, you should score the success of your life. Use an English idiom for a title.

CAST: A STERN MAN with white whiskers; HIS NEPHEW, a meek-appearing youth from whom valorous words come strangely; DAUGHTER TO STERN MAN; Maid-servant, Dancer, Guests, Musicians, Singers, Acrobats, Jugglers, etc.

[ACT I]

SCENE: *The exterior of Brickmansion-on-the-Hudson. Picket-fence, grass mats, flowers.* STERN MAN *and* NEPHEW *discovered. Guests reclining at short distance.*

NEPHEW — Sir, your cruel and unjust treatment is driving me an exile from my home and native land. I admit that you may perhaps think yourself in the right, but as sure as my name is Percy Armistead, you will one day live to regret this hour.

STERN MAN (*in an asphalt voice*) — No more of this idle talk, sir! Get you gone, and never more darken my doors! Sooner than marry my daughter to you, I would see her, in her youth and beauty, laid in the grave. Your luggage will presently be at the door. In the meantime, that my guests may not lack entertainment, I have procured Lestelle Twofete, the celebrated and lovely dancer from the Pallacio di Blaze, who will now render us her new and beautiful dance, entitled "Butterflies in the Dark."

(*Dance; stage lights lowered; rainbow effects.*)

STERN MAN — Bravo, my dear Lestelle, bravo! What, sir (*turning fiercely upon* NEPHEW) — are you not yet gone?

NEPHEW (*gulping back evidence of strong emotion*) — I go in one moment, cruel uncle; but before leaving my native shore forever, I cannot refrain from singing that original ballad entitled, "In the Wrong Room, or, When She Turned Up the Gas, He Jumped from an Eighth-story Window."

(*Song by* NEPHEW.)

ONE OF THE GUESTS — How sad to see the departure of this young man! It makes me quite doleful.

ANOTHER GUEST — Yes, indeed. Pray let us have some merriment to dispel the mournfulness of this occasion.

(*They produce musical instruments from various convenient places, and line up across the stage.*)

(*Grand chorus; obligato solo on valise, checked for Paterson, N.J., by* NEPHEW.)

CURTAIN.

[ACT II]

SCENE: *Drawing-room.* DAUGHTER TO STERN MAN *discovered musing. Maid-servant dusting chairs.*

DAUGHTER — Ah me! how long it seems since Percy left us! The hours drag by on leaden wings. Well (*sighs*), I must try to make the time, until his return, go as quickly as possible.

(*Song and Dance by* DAUGHTER.)

MAID-SERVANT — Sure it's the light feet yez have got, Miss Amy! That dance reminds me of the song I just heard four men singing out in the front yard.

DAUGHTER — Pray call them in, dear Jane. (*Aside to audience.*) Anything to keep my mind from dwelling upon poor Percy's absence.

(*Exit* MAID-SERVANT. *Enter Quartet. They sing.*)

(*Later the* MAID-SERVANT *re-enters with Musicians, Jugglers, Tumblers, etc., whom she has found in the front yard, and brings in to make her young mistress forget her grief. Grand entertainment. Enter* STERN MAN.)

STERN MAN — Ah, my dear Amy! having a little amusement? (*Shows telegram.*) Here's a despatch from Percy saying that he has forgiven me, and will return in eighteen months.

DAUGHTER — Oh, how glad that makes me! Come, we will sing our old duet that we have not sung since dear Percy left.

(*Duet; involuntary chorus by Jugglers, Acrobats, etc.*)

STERN MAN — And, now, cannot our friends here afford us some entertainment to while away the time until Percy's return?

(*A man comes to the front and sings a topical song. At its conclusion enter* NEPHEW.)

DAUGHTER — Dear Percy, how I have longed for this moment!

NEPHEW — Dearest Amy, in honor of this occasion I will give a recitation — my own composition.

(*Recitation — "The Escape from Paterson." Red lights; rolling-mill thunder.*)

STERN MAN — And now let us sing that good old song entitled, "O'Shaughnessy Fanned Him with an Axe"; your old favorite, my dear boy.

(*Song, with grand chorus by Acrobats, Jugglers, etc.*)

CURTAIN.

MATINEE GIRLS *

Here are some matinee girls. To read of them, you would think they provided every theatre in New York but really I don't think them a very familiar type. I often wonder too if they are so ridiculous as we are told to believe. My curiosity over-came me so far once that I listened to the conversation of two of them. As a matter of fact, it was much more rational than that of the man at my elbow who was talking of himself. I have wondered if they were an exception. I believe they were not and for the following formidable reason.

After you get a fact fixed into the public mind, it has ceased to be true in many cases. The public began to be told long ago that it worshipped actors, men of paint and cloth, who were so human that in reality after the play they were likely to sup on welsh rabbits and beer. Just as the public came to believe it, it ceased to be. Today, a man, or a matinee girl too, sees actor and beer and welsh rabbit all together and has not an idea that a man six feet can live on bunches of violets.

---

* *Reprinted from* Bulletin of the New York Public Library: *September 1960. Drawn from Crane's "Pocket Notebook," this sketch has kinship with "In a Park Row Restaurant" (see below), which Crane also wrote in his "Notebook" and subsequently published in the New York* Press: *28 October 1894. This is an addition to the Crane canon.*

A NIGHT AT THE MILLIONAIRE'S CLUB.*

A dozen of the members were enjoying themselves in the library. Their eyes were for the most part fixed in concrete stares at the ceiling where the decorations cost seventy-four dollars per square inch. An ecstatic murmur came from the remote corners of the apartment where each chair occupied two thousand dollars worth of floor. William C. Whitney was neatly arranged in a prominent seat to impart a suggestion of brains to the general effect. A clock had been chiming at intervals of ten minutes during the evening, and at each time of striking, Mr. Depew had made a joke, per agreement.

The last one, however, had smashed a seven-thousand dollar vase over by the window and Mr. Depew was hesitating. He had some doubt whether, after all, his jokes were worth that much commercially. His fellow members continued to ecstatically admire their isolation from the grimy vandals of the world. The soft breathing of the happy company made a sound like the murmur of pines in a summer wind. In the distance, a steward could be seen charging up seven thousand dollars to Mr. Depew's account; all, otherwise, was joy and perfect peace.

At this juncture, a seventeen-cent lackey upholstered in a three hundred dollar suit of clothes, made his appearance. He skated gracefully over the polished floor on snowshoes. Halting in the centre of the room, he made seven low bows and sang a little ode to Plutus. Then he made a swift gesture, a ceremonial declaration that he was lower than the mud on the gaiters of the least wealthy of those before him, and spoke: "Sirs, there is a deputation of visitors in the hall who give their names as Ralph Waldo Emerson, Nathaniel Hawthorne, George Washington and Alexander Hamilton. They beg the favor of an audience."

A slumbering member in a large arm chair aroused and said: "Who?" And this pertinent interrogation was followed by others in various tones of astonishment and annoyance. "What's their names?" "Who did you say?" "What the devil do they want here?"

---

* Published in Truth: 21 April 1894; reprinted from a clipping in the Columbia University Crane Collection, which bears in Crane's hand the identification of the magazine: "Truth. New York."

The lackey made seven more bows and sang another little ode. Then he spoke very distinctly: "Sirs, persons giving their names as Ralph Waldo Emerson, Nathaniel Hawthorne, George Washington and Alexander Hamilton desire the favor of an audience. They — "

But he was interrupted. "Don't know 'em!" "Who the deuce are these people anyhow!" "By Jove, here's a go! Want to see us, deuce take me!" "Well, I'm — "

It was at this point that Erroll Van Dyck Strathmore suddenly displayed those qualities which made his friends ever afterward look upon him as a man who would rise supreme at a crisis. He asked one question, but it was terse, sharp, and skillful, a master-piece of a man with presence of mind:

"Where are they from?"

"Sir," said the lackey, "they said they were from America!"

Strathmore paused but a moment to formulate his second searching question. His friends looked at him with admiration and awe. "Do they look like respectable people?"

The lackey arched his eyebrows. "Well — I don't know, sir." He was very discreet.

This reply created great consternation among the members. There was a wild scramble for places of safety. There were hurried commands given to the lackey. "Don't bring 'em in here!" "Throw 'em out!" "Kill 'em!" But over all the uproar could be heard the voice of the imperturbably Strathmore. He was calmly giving orders to the servant.

"You will tell them that as we know no one in America, it is not possible that we have had the honor of their acquaintance, but that nevertheless it is our pleasure to indulge them a little, as it is possible that they are respectable people. However, they must not construe this into permission to come again. You will say to them that if they will repair quietly to any convenient place, wash their hands and procure rubber bibs, they may return and look at the remains of a cigarette which I carelessly threw upon the door-step. Tell the steward to provide each man with a recipe for Mr. Jones-Jones Smith-Jones' terrapin stew and a gallery ticket for the Kilanyi living pictures, then bid them go in safety. Afterward, you will sponge off the front steps and give the door-mat to one of those down-town clubs. You may go."

As the servant skated forth on his errand, Mr. Whitney fell in a death-like swoon, unnoticed, as the company thronged about the adroit, the brave Erroll Van Dyck Strathmore. "Bravo, old man, you saved us!" "What skill, what diplomacy!" "Egad, but you have courage!"

Suddenly the clock noted the time of ten minutes after twelve.

Mr. Depew sprang to his feet. A broad smile illuminated his face.

"Say, fellows, the other day —" But he was surrounded by slumbering figures. His smile changed then to a glare of bitter disappointment. In a burst of rage he hurled a champagne bottle at the clock and broke it to smithereens. Its cost was $4,675. He strode over to the ex-secretary. When Mr. Whitney had become aroused, the following conversation ensued:

"Say, Willie, what are we doing here?"

"I don't know, Chauncey!"

"Well, let's float, then!"

"Float it is, Chauncey!"

On the sidewalk they turned to regard each other.

"An antidote, Willie?"

"Well, I should say, Chauncey!"

They started on a hard run down the avenue.

AN EXPERIMENT IN MISERY/AN EVENING, A NIGHT AND A MORN-/ING WITH THOSE CAST OUT./THE TRAMP LIVES LIKE A KING/BUT HIS ROYALTY, TO THE NOVITIATE, HAS DRAWBACKS OF SMELLS AND BUGS./LODGED WITH AN AS-SASSIN/A WONDERFULLY VIVID PICTURE OF A STRANGE PHASE OF NEW YORK LIFE,/WRITTEN FOR "THE PRESS" BY/THE AUTHOR OF "MAGGIE." *

Two men stood regarding a tramp.

"I wonder how he feels," said one, reflectively. "I suppose he is homeless, friendless, and has, at the most, only a few cents in his pocket. And if this is so, I wonder how he feels."

---

* *Reprinted from New York* Press: *22 April 1894.*

This autobiographical sketch has as its mise en scène *the City Hall Park, located a few blocks from the Bowery. Crane is the young man who encounters another outcast to share his poverty. Together they go in search of a cheap boardinghouse where cots are seven cents for the night. This meeting with the seedy outcast and the flophouse business comprise the whole sketch, but what gives it importance is Crane's tone and style: irony combined with pity. It is the same as in* Maggie.

The other being the elder, spoke with an air of authoritative wisdom. "You can tell nothing of it unless you are in that condition yourself. It is idle to speculate about it from this distance."

"I suppose so," said the younger man, and then he added as from an inspiration: "I think I'll try it. Rags and tatters, you know, a couple of dimes, and hungry, too, if possible. Perhaps I could discover his point of view or something near it."

"Well, you might," said the other, and from those words begins this veracious narrative of an experiment in misery.

The youth went to the studio of an artist friend, who, from his store, rigged him out in an aged suit and a brown derby hat that had been made long years before. And then the youth went forth to try to eat as the tramp may eat, and sleep as the wanderers sleep.[1] It was late at night, and a fine rain was swirling softly down, covering the pavements with a bluish luster. He began a weary trudge toward the downtown places, where beds can be hired for coppers. By the time he had reached City Hall Park he was so completely plastered with yells of "bum" and "hobo," and with various unholy epithets that small boys had applied to him at intervals that he was in a state of profound dejection, and looked searchingly for an outcast of high degree that the two might share miseries. But the lights threw a quivering glare over rows and circles of deserted benches that glistened damply, showing patches of wet sod behind them. It seemed that their usual freights of sorry humanity had fled on this night to better things. There were only squads of well dressed Brooklyn people, who swarmed toward the Bridge.

[HE FINDS HIS FIELD.]

The young man loitered about for a time, and then went shuffling off down Park row. In the sudden descent in style of the dress of the crowd he felt relief. He began to see others whose tatters matched his tatters. In Chatham square there were aimless men strewn in front of saloons and lodging houses. He aligned himself with these men, and turned slowly to occupy himself with the pageantry of the street.

The mists of the cold and damp night made an intensely blue haze, through which the gaslights in the windows of stores and saloons shone with a golden radiance. The street cars rumbled softly, as if going upon carpet stretched in the aisle made by the pillars of the elevated road. Two interminable processions of

1. This opening passage and the concluding one have not appeared in any reprinted text of "An Experiment in Misery" since 1894, except in R. W. Stallman, ed., *Stephen Crane: An Omnibus* (1952, 1954).

people went along the wet pavements, spattered with black mud that made each shoe leave a scar-like impression. The high buildings lurked a-back, shrouded in shadows. Down a side street there were mystic curtains of purple and black, on which lamps dully glittered like embroidered flowers.

A saloon stood with a voracious air on a corner. A sign leaning against the front of the doorpost announced: "Free hot soup to-night." The swing doors snapping to and fro like ravenous lips, made gratified smacks, as if the saloon were gorging itself with plump men.

Caught by the delectable sign, the young man allowed himself to be swallowed. A bartender placed a schooner of dark and portentous beer on the bar. Its monumental form up-reared until the froth a-top was above the crown of the young man's brown derby.

[HE FINDS HIS SUPPER.]

"Soup over there, gents," said the bartender, affably. A little yellow man in rags and the youth grasped their schooners and went with speed toward a lunch counter, where a man with oily but imposing whiskers ladled genially from a kettle until he had furnished his two mendicants with a soup that was steaming hot and in which there were little floating suggestions of chicken. The young man, sipping his broth, felt the cordiality expressed by the warmth of the mixture, and he beamed at the man with oily but imposing whiskers, who was presiding like a priest behind an altar. "Have some more, gents?" he inquired of the two sorry figures before him. The little yellow man accepted with a swift gesture, but the youth shook his head and went out, following a man whose wondrous seediness promised that he would have a knowledge of cheap lodging houses.

On the sidewalk he accosted the seedy man. "Say, do you know a cheap place t' sleep?"

The other hesitated for a time, gazing sideways. Finally he nodded in the direction of up the street. "I sleep up there," he said, "when I've got th' price."

"How much?"

"Ten cents."

The young man shook his head dolefully. "That's too rich for me."

[ENTER THE ASSASSIN.]

At that moment there approached the two a reeling man in strange garments. His head was a fuddle of bushy hair and whiskers from which his eyes peered with a guilty slant. In a close scrutiny it was possible to distinguish the cruel lines of a mouth, which looked as if its lips had just closed with satisfaction over some tender and piteous morsel. He appeared like an assassin steeped in crime performed awkwardly.

But at this time his voice was tuned to the coaxing key of an affectionate puppy. He looked at the men with wheedling eyes and began to sing a little melody for charity.

"Say, gents, can't yeh give a poor feller a couple of cents t' git a bed. Now, yeh know how a respecter'ble gentlem'n feels when he's down on his luck an' I — "

The seedy man, staring with imperturbable countenance at a train which clattered overhead, interrupted in an expressionless voice: "Ah, go t' h — !"

But the youth spoke to the prayerful assassin in tones of astonishment and inquiry. "Say, you must be crazy! Why don't yeh strike somebody that looks as if they had money?"

The assassin, tottering about on his uncertain legs, and at intervals brushing imaginary cobwebs from before his nose, entered into a long explanation of the psychology of the situation. It was so profound that it was unintelligible.

When he had exhausted the subject the young man said to him: "Let's see th' five cents."

The assassin wore an expression of drunken woe at this sentence, filled with suspicion of him. With a deeply pained air he began to fumble in his clothing, his red hands trembling. Presently he announced in a voice of bitter grief, as if he had been betrayed: "There's on'y four."

[HE FINDS HIS BED.]

"Four," said the young man thoughtfully. "Well, look-a-here, I'm a stranger here, an' if ye'll steer me to your cheap joint I'll find the other three."

The assassin's countenance became instantly radiant with joy. His whiskers quivered with the wealth of his alleged emotions. He seized the young man's hand in a transport of delight and friendliness.

"B'gawd," he cried, "if ye'll do that, b'gawd, I'd say yeh was a damned good feller, I would, an' I'd remember yeh all m' life, I would, b'gawd, an' if I ever got a chance I'd return th' compliment" — he spoke with drunken dignity — "b'gawd, I'd treat yeh white, I would, an' I'd allus remember yeh — "

The young man drew back, looking at the assassin coldly.

"Oh, that's all right," he said. "You show me th' joint — that's all you've got t' do."

The assassin, gesticulating gratitude, led the young man along a dark street. Finally he stopped before a little dusty door. He raised his hand impressively. "Look-a-here," he said, and there was a thrill of deep and ancient wisdom upon his face, "I've brought yeh here, an' that's my part, ain't it? If th' place don't suit yeh yeh needn't git mad at me, need yeh? There won't be no bad feelin', will there?"

"No," said the young man.

The assassin waved his arm tragically and led the march up the steep stairway. On the way the young man furnished the assassin with three pennies. At the top a man with benevolent spectacles looked at them through a hole in the board. He collected their money, wrote some names on a register, and speedily was leading the two men along a gloom shrouded corridor.

[A PLACE OF SMELLS.]

Shortly after the beginning of this journey the young man felt his liver turn white, for from the dark and secret places of the building there suddenly came to his nostrils strange and unspeakable odors that assailed him like malignant diseases with wings. They seemed to be from human bodies closely packed in dens; the exhalations from a hundred pairs of reeking lips; the fumes from a thousand bygone debauches; the expression of a thousand present miseries.

A man, naked save for a little snuff colored undershirt, was parading sleepily along the corridor. He rubbed his eyes, and, giving vent to a prodigious yawn, demanded to be told the time.

"Half past one."

The man yawned again. He opened a door, and for a moment his form was outlined against a black, opaque interior. To this door came the three men, and as it was again opened the unholy odors rushed out like released fiends, so that the young man was obliged to struggle as against an overpowering wind.

It was some time before the youth's eyes were good in the intense gloom within, but the man with benevolent spectacles led him skillfully, pausing but a moment to deposit the limp assassin upon a cot. He took the youth to a cot that lay tranquilly by the window, and, showing him a tall locker for clothes that stood near the head with the ominous air of a tombstone, left him.

[TO THE POLITE, HORRORS.]

The youth sat on his cot and peered about him. There was a gas jet in a distant part of the room that burned a small flickering orange hued flame. It caused vast masses of tumbled shadows in all parts of the place, save where, immediately about it, there was a little gray haze. As the young man's eyes became used to the darkness he could see upon the cots that thickly littered the floor the forms of men sprawled out, lying in deathlike silence or heaving and snoring with tremendous effort, like stabbed fish.

The youth locked his derby and his shoes in the mummy case near him and then lay down with his old and familiar coat around his shoulders. A blanket he handled gingerly, drawing it over part of the coat. The cot was leather covered and cold as melting snow. The youth was obliged to shiver for some time on this affair, which was like a slab. Presently, however, his chill gave him peace, and during this period of leisure from it he turned his head to stare at his friend, the assassin, whom he could dimly discern where he lay sprawled on a cot in the abandon of a man filled with drink. He was snoring with incredible vigor. His wet hair and beard dimly glistened and his inflamed nose shone with subdued luster like a red light in a fog.

Within reach of the youth's hand was one who lay with yellow breast and shoulders bare to the cold drafts. One arm hung over the side of the cot and the fingers lay full length upon the wet cement floor of the room. Beneath the inky brows could be seen the eyes of the man exposed by the partly opened lids. To the youth it seemed that he and this corpse-like being were exchanging a prolonged stare and that the other threatened with his eyes. He drew back, watching this neighbor from the shadows of his blanket edge. The man did not move once through the night, but lay in this stillness as of death, like a body stretched out, expectant of the surgeon's knife.

[MEN LAY LIKE THE DEAD.]

And all through the room could be seen the tawny hues of naked flesh, limbs thrust into the darkness, projecting beyond the cots; upreared knees; arms hanging, long and thin, over the cot edges. For the most part they were statuesque, carven, dead. With the curious lockers standing all about like tombstones there was a strange effect of a graveyard, where bodies were merely flung.

Yet occasionally could be seen limbs wildly tossing in fantastic nightmare gestures, accompanied by guttural cries, grunts, oaths. And there was one fellow off in a gloomy corner, who in his dreams was oppressed by some frightful calamity, for of a sudden he began to utter long wails that went almost like yells from a hound, echoing wailfully and weird through this chill place of tombstones, where men lay like the dead.

The sound, in its high piercing beginnings that dwindled to final melancholy moans, expressed a red and grim tragedy of the unfathomable possibilities of the man's dreams. But to the youth these were not merely the shrieks of a vision pierced man. They were an utterance of the meaning of the room and its occupants. It was to him the protest of the wretch who feels the touch of the imperturbably granite wheels and who then cries with an impersonal eloquence, with a strength not from him, giving voice to the wail of a whole section, a class, a people. This, weaving into the young man's brain and mingling with his views of these vast and somber shadows that like mighty black fingers curled around the naked bodies, made the young man so that he did not sleep, but lay carving biographies for these men from his meager experience. At times the fellow in the corner howled in a writhing agony of his imaginations.

[THEN MORNING CAME.]

Finally a long lance point of gray light shot through the dusty panes of the window. Without, the young man could see roofs drearily white in the dawning. The point of light yellowed and grew brighter, until the golden rays of the morning sun came in bravely and strong. They touched with radiant color the form of a small, fat man, who snored in stuttering fashion. His round and shiny bald head glowed suddenly with the valor of a decoration. He sat up, blinked at the sun, swore fretfully and pulled his blanket over the ornamental splendors of his head.

The youth contentedly watched this rout of the mystic shadows before the bright spears of the sun and presently he slumbered. When he awoke he heard the voice of the assassin raised in valiant curses. Putting up his head he perceived his comrade seated on the side of the cot engaged in scratching his neck with long finger nails that rasped like files.

"Hully Jee dis is a new breed. They've got can openers on their feet," he continued in a violent tirade.

The young man hastily unlocked his closet and took out his clothes. As he sat on the side of the cot, lacing his shoes, he glanced about and saw that daylight had made the room comparatively commonplace and uninteresting. The men, whose faces seemed stolid, serene or absent, were engaged in dressing, while a great crackle of bantering conversation arose.

A few were parading in unconcerned nakedness. Here and there were men of brawn, whose skins shone clear and ruddy. They took splendid poses, standing massively, like chiefs. When they had dressed in their ungainly garments there was an extraordinary change. They then showed bumps and deficiencies of all kinds.

There were others who exhibited many deformities. Shoulders were slanting, bumped, pulled this way and pulled that way. And notable among these latter men was the little fat man who had refused to allow his head to be glorified. His pudgy form, builded like a pear, bustled to and fro, while he swore in fishwife fashion. It appeared that some article of his apparel had vanished.

The young man, attired speedily, went to his friend, the assassin. At first the latter looked dazed at the sight of the youth. This face seemed to be appealing to him through the cloud wastes of his memory. He scratched his neck and reflected. At last he grinned, a broad smile gradually spreading until his countenance was a round illumination. "Hello, Willie," he cried, cheerily.

"Hello," said the young man. "Are yeh ready t' fly?"

"Sure." The assassin tied his shoe carefully with some twine and came ambling.

When he reached the street the young man experienced no sudden relief from unholy atmospheres. He had forgotten all about them, and had been breathing naturally and with no sensation of discomfort or distress.

He was thinking of these things as he walked along the street, when he was suddenly startled by feeling the assassin's hand, trembling with excitement, clutching his arm, and when the assassin spoke, his voice went into quavers from a supreme agitation.

"I'll be hully, bloomin' blowed, if there wasn't a feller with a nightshirt on up there in that joint!"

The youth was bewildered for a moment, but presently he turned to smile indulgently at the assassin's humor.

"Oh, you're a d — liar," he merely said.

Whereupon the assassin began to gesture extravagantly and take oath by strange gods. He frantically placed himself at the mercy of remarkable fates if his tale were not true. "Yes, he did! I cross m' heart thousan' times!" he protested, and at the time his eyes were large with amazement, his mouth wrinkled in unnatural glee. "Yessir! A nightshirt! A hully white nightshirt!"

"You lie!"

"Nosir! I hope ter die b'fore I kin git anudder ball if there wasn't a jay wid a hully, bloomin' white nightshirt!"

His face was filled with the infinite wonder of it. "A hully white nightshirt," he continually repeated.

The young man saw the dark entrance to a basement restaurant. There was a sign which read, "No mystery about our hash," and there were other age stained and world battered legends which told him that the place was within his means. He stopped before it and spoke to the assassin. "I guess I'll git somethin' t' eat."

[BREAKFAST.]

At this the assassin, for some reason, appeared to be quite embarrassed. He gazed at the seductive front of the eating place for a moment. Then he started slowly up the street. "Well, goodby, Willie," he said, bravely.

For an instant the youth studied the departing figure. Then he called out, "Hol' on a minnet." As they came together he spoke in a certain fierce way, as if he feared that the other could think him to be weak. "Look-a-here, if yeh wanta git some breakfas' I'll lend yeh three cents t' do it with. But say, look-a-here, you've gota git out an' hustle. I ain't goin' t' support yeh, or I'll go broke b'fore night. I ain't no millionaire."

"I take me oath, Willie," said the assassin, earnestly, "th' on'y thing I really needs is a ball. Me t'roat feels like a fryin' pan. But as I can't git a ball, why, th' next bes' thing is breakfast, an' if yeh do that fer me, b'gawd, I'd say yeh was th' whitest lad I ever see."

They spent a few moments in dexterous exchanges of phrases, in which they each protested that the other was, as the assassin had originally said, a "respecter'ble gentlem'n." And they concluded with mutual assurances that they were the souls of intelligence and virtue. Then they went into the restaurant.

There was a long counter, dimly lighted from hidden sources. Two or three men in soiled white aprons rushed here and there.

[A RETROSPECT.]

The youth bought a bowl of coffee for two cents and a roll for one cent. The assassin purchased the same. The bowls were webbed with brown seams, and the tin spoons wore an air of having emerged from the first pyramid. Upon them were black, moss like encrustations of age, and they were bent and scarred from the attacks of long forgotten teeth. But over their repast the wanderers waxed warm and mellow. The assassin grew affable as the hot mixture went soothingly down his parched throat, and the young men felt courage flow in his veins.

Memories began to throng in on the assassin, and he brought forth long tales, intricate, incoherent, delivered with a chattering swiftness as from an old woman. " — great job out'n Orange. Boss keep yeh hustlin', though, all time. I was there three days, and then I went an' ask'im t' lend me a dollar. 'G-g-go ter the devil,' he ses, an' I lose me job."

— "South no good. Damn niggers work for twenty-five an' thirty cents a day. Run white man out. Good grub, though. Easy livin'."

— "Yas; useter work little in Toledo, raftin' logs. Make two or three dollars er day in the spring. Lived high. Cold as ice, though, in the winter" —

"I was raised in northern N'York. O-o-o-oh, yeh jest oughto live there. No beer ner whisky, though, way off in the woods. But all th' good hot grub yeh can eat. B'gawd, I hung around there long as I could till th' ol' man fired me. 'Git t'hell outa here, yeh wuthless skunk, git t'hell outa here an' go die,' he ses. 'You're a fine father,' I ses, 'you are,' an' I quit 'im."

As they were passing from the dim eating place they encountered an old man who was trying to steal forth with a tiny package of food, but a tall man with an indomitable mustache stood dragon fashion, barring the way of escape. They heard the old man raise a plaintive protest. "Ah, you always want to know what I take out, and you never see that I usually bring a package in here from my place of business."

[THE LIFE OF A KING.]

As the wanderers trudged slowly along Park row, the assassin began to expand and grow blithe. "B'gawd, we've been livin' like kings," he said, smacking appreciative lips.

"Look out or we'll have t' pay fer it t' night," said the youth, with gloomy warning.

But the assassin refused to turn his gaze toward the future. He went with a limping step, into which he injected a suggestion of lamblike gambols. His mouth was wreathed in a red grin.

In the City Hall Park the two wanderers sat down in the little circle of benches sanctified by traditions of their class. They huddled in their old garments, slumbrously conscious of the march of the hours which for them had no meaning.

The people of the street hurrying hither and thither made a blend of black figures, changing, yet frieze like. They walked in their good clothes as upon important missions, giving no gaze to the two wanderers seated upon the benches. They expressed to the young man his infinite distance from all that he valued. Social position, comfort, the pleasures of living, were unconquerable kingdoms. He felt a sudden awe.

And in the background a multitude of buildings, of pitiless hues and sternly high, were to him emblematic of a nation forcing its regal head into the clouds, throwing no downward glances; in the sublimity of its aspirations ignoring the wretches who may flounder at its feet. The roar of the city in his ear was to him the confusion of strange tongues, babbling heedlessly; it was the clink of coin, the voice of the city's hopes which were to him no hopes.

He confessed himself an outcast, and his eyes from under the lowered rim of his hat began to glance guiltily, wearing the criminal expression that comes with certain convictions.

"Well," said the friend, "did you discover his point of view?"

"I don't know that I did," replied the young man; "but at any rate I think mine own has undergone a considerable alteration."

AN EXPERIMENT/IN LUXURY/THE EXPERIENCES OF A YOUTH WHO/SOUGHT OUT CROESUS./IN THE GLITTER OF WEALTH./A FUZZY ACROBATIC KITTEN WHICH HELD/GREAT RICHNESS AT BAY./ LIFE OF THE WOMAN OF GOLD/ARE THERE, AFTER ALL, BURRS UNDER/EACH FINE CLOAK AND BENEFITS/IN ALL BEGGARS' GARB? *

"If you accept this invitation you will have an opportunity to make another social study," said the old friend.

The youth laughed. "If they caught me making a study of them they'd attempt a murder. I would be pursued down Fifth avenue by the entire family."

"Well," persisted the old friend who could only see one thing at a time, "it would be very interesting. I have been told all my life

---

* *Reprinted from New York* Press: *29 April 1894.*

The demi-world of "An Experiment in Misery" (see above) and of Maggie *stands in contrast to the society world of millionaires in "A Night at the Millionaire's Club" (see above) and "An Experiment in Luxury." Crane's own life was anything but an experiment in luxury.*

that millionaires have no fun, and I know that the poor are always
assured that the millionaire is a very unhappy person. They are
informed that miseries swarm around all wealth, that all crowned
heads are heavy with care, and — "

"But still — " began the youth.

"And, in the irritating, brutalizing, enslaving environment of
their poverty, they are expected to solace themselves with these
assurances," continued the old friend. He extended his gloved palm
and began to tap it impressively with a finger of his other hand.
His legs were spread apart in a fashion peculiar to his oratory. "I
believe that it is mostly false. It is true that wealth does not release a man from many things from which he would gladly purchase release. Consequences cannot be bribed. I suppose that every
man believes steadfastly that he has a private tragedy which makes
him yearn for other existences. But it is impossible for me to believe
that these things equalize themselves; that there are burrs under
all rich cloaks and benefits in all ragged jackets, and the preaching
of it seems wicked to me. There are those who have opportunities;
there are those who are robbed of — "

"But look here," said the young man; "what has this got to do
with my paying Jack a visit?"

"It has got a lot to do with it," said the old friend sharply. "As
I said, there are those who have opportunities; there are those who
are robbed — "

"Well, I won't have you say Jack ever robbed anybody of anything, because he's as honest a fellow as ever lived," interrupted the
youth, with warmth. "I have known him for years, and he is a
perfectly square fellow. He doesn't know about these infernal
things. He isn't criminal because you say he is benefited by a condition which other men created."

"I didn't say he was," retorted the old friend. "Nobody is
responsible for anything. I wish to Heaven somebody was, and
then we could all jump on him. Look here, my boy, our modern
civilization is — "

"Oh, the deuce!" said the young man.

The old friend then stood very erect and stern. "I can see by
your frequent interruptions that you have not yet achieved sufficient pain in life. I hope one day to see you materially changed.
You are yet — "

"There he is now," said the youth, suddenly. He indicated a
young man who was passing. He went hurriedly toward him, pausing once to gesture adieu to his old friend.

❋   ❋   ❋

The house was broad and brown and stolid like the face of a peasant. It had an inanity of expression, an absolute lack of artistic strength that was in itself powerful because it symbolized something. It stood, a homely pile of stone, rugged, grimly self reliant, asserting its quality as a fine thing when in reality the beholder usually wondered why so much money had been spent to obtain a complete negation. Then from another point of view it was important and mighty because it stood as a fetich, formidable because of traditions of worship.

[AT THE PORTALS OF LUXURY.]

When the great door was opened the youth imagined that the footman who held a hand on the knob looked at him with a quick, strange stare. There was nothing definite in it; it was all vague and elusive, but a suspicion was certainly denoted in some way. The youth felt that he, one of the outer barbarians, had been detected to be a barbarian by the guardian of the portal, he of the refined nose, he of the exquisite sense, he who must be more atrociously aristocratic than any that he serves. And the youth, detesting himself for it, found that he would rejoice to take a frightful revenge upon this lackey who, with a glance of his eyes, had called him a name. He would have liked to have been for a time a dreadful social perfection whose hand, waved lazily, would cause hordes of the idolatrous imperfect to be smitten in the eyes. And in the tumult of his imagination he did not think it strange that he should plan in his vision to come around to this house and with the power of his new social majesty, reduce this footman to ashes.

He had entered with an easy feeling of independence, but after this incident the splendor of the interior filled him with awe. He was a wanderer in a fairy land, and who felt that his presence marred certain effects. He was an invader with a shamed face, a man who had come to steal certain colors, forms, impressions that were not his. He had a dim thought that some one might come to tell him to begone.

His friend, unconscious of this swift drama of thought, was already upon the broad staircase. "Come on," he called. When the youth's foot struck from a thick rug and clanged upon the tiled floor he was almost frightened.

There was cool abundance of gloom. High up stained glass caught the sunlight, and made it into marvelous hues that in places touched the dark walls. A broad bar of yellow gilded the leaves of lurking plants. A softened crimson glowed upon the head and shoulders of a bronze swordsman, who perpetually strained in a terrific lunge, his blade thrust at random into the shadow, piercing there an unknown something.

An immense fire place was at one end, and its furnishings gleamed until it resembled a curious door of a palace, and on the threshold, where one would have to pass, a fire burned redly. From some remote place came the sound of a bird twittering busily. And from behind heavy portieres came a subdued noise of the chatter of three, twenty or a hundred women.

He could not relieve himself of this feeling of awe until he had reached his friend's room. There they lounged carelessly and smoked pipes. It was an amazingly comfortable room. It expressed to the visitor that he could do supremely as he chose, for it said plainly that in it the owner did supremely as he chose. The youth wondered if there had not been some domestic skirmishing to achieve so much beautiful disorder. There were various articles left about defiantly, as if the owner openly flaunted the feminine ideas of precision. The disarray of a table that stood prominently defined the entire room. A set of foils, a set of boxing gloves, a lot of illustrated papers, an inkstand and a hat lay entangled upon it. Here was surely a young man, who, when his menacing mother, sisters or servants knocked, would open a slit in the door like a Chinaman in an opium joint, and tell them to leave him to his beloved devices. And yet, withal, the effect was good, because the disorder was not necessary, and because there are some things that when flung down, look to have been flung by an artist. A baby can create an effect with a guitar. It would require genius to deal with the piled up dishes in a Cherry street sink.

["THE WORLD OF CHANCE."]

The youth's friend lay back upon the broad seat that followed the curve of the window and smoked in blissful laziness. Without one could see the windowless wall of a house overgrown with a green, luxuriant vine. There was a glimpse of a side street. Below were the stables. At intervals a little fox terrier ran into the court and barked tremendously.

The youth, also blissfully indolent, kept up his part of the conversation on the recent college days, but continually he was beset by a stream of sub-conscious reflection. He was beginning to see a vast wonder in it that they two lay sleepily chatting with no more apparent responsibility than rabbits, when certainly there were men, equally fine perhaps, who were being blackened and mashed in the churning life of the lower places. And all this had merely happened; the great secret hand had guided them here and had guided others there. The eternal mystery of social condition exasperated him at this time. He wondered if incomprehensible justice were the sister of open wrong.

And, above all, why was he impressed, awed, overcome by a mass of materials, a collection of the trophies of wealth, when he knew that to him their dominant meaning was that they represented a lavish expenditure? For what reason did his nature so deeply respect all this? Perhaps his ancestors had been peasants bowing heads to the heel of appalling pomp of princes or rows of little men who stood to watch a king kill a flower with his cane. There was one side of him that said there were finer things in life, but the other side did homage.

[THE GLORY OF GOLD.]

Presently he began to feel that he was a better man than many — entitled to a great pride. He stretched his legs like a man in a garden, and he thought that he belonged to the garden. Hues and forms had smothered certain of his comprehensions. There had been times in his life when little voices called to him continually from the darkness; he heard them now as an idle, half-smothered babble on the horizon edge. It was necessary that it should be so, too. There was the horizon, he said, and, of course, there should be a babble of pain on it. Thus it was written; it was a law, he thought. And, anyway, perhaps it was not so bad as those who babbled tried to tell.

In this way and with this suddenness he arrived at a stage. He was become a philosopher, a type of the wise man who can eat but three meals a day, conduct a large business and understand the purposes of infinite power. He felt valuable. He was sage and important.

There were influences, knowledges that made him aware that he was idle and foolish in his new state, but he inwardly reveled like a barbarian in his environment. It was delicious to feel so high and mighty, to feel that the unattainable could be purchased like a penny bun. For a time, at any rate, there was no impossible. He indulged in monarchical reflections.

[PARENTAL PORTRAITS.]

As they were dressing for dinner his friend spoke to him in this wise: "Be sure not to get off anything that resembles an original thought before my mother. I want her to like you, and I know that when any one says a thing cleverly before her he ruins himself with her forever. Confine your talk to orthodox expressions. Be dreary and unspeakably commonplace in the true sense of the word. Be damnable."

"It will be easy for me to do as you say," remarked the youth.

"As far as the old man goes," continued the other, "he's a blooming good fellow. He may appear like a sort of a crank if he happens to be in that mood, but he's all right when you come to know him. And besides he doesn't dare do that sort of thing with me, because I've got nerve enough to bully him. Oh, the old man is all right."

On their way down the youth lost the delightful mood that he had enjoyed in his friend's rooms. He dropped it like a hat on the stairs. The splendor of color and form swarmed upon him again. He bowed before the strength of this interior; it said a word to him which he believed he should despise, but instead he crouched. In the distance shone his enemy, the footman.

"There will be no people here to-night, so you may see the usual evening row between my sister Mary and me, but don't be alarmed or uncomfortable, because it is quite an ordinary matter," said his friend, as they were about to enter a little drawing room that was well apart from the grander rooms.

[THE JOYS OF A MILLIONAIRE.]

The head of the family, the famous millionaire, sat on a low stool before the fire. He was deeply absorbed in the gambols of a kitten who was plainly trying to stand on her head that she might use all four paws in grappling with an evening paper with which her playmate was poking her ribs. The old man chuckled in complete glee. There was never such a case of abstraction, of want of care. The map of millions was in a far land where mechanics and bricklayers go, a mystic land of little, universal emotions, and he had been guided to it by the quaint gestures of a kitten's furry paws.

His wife, who stood near, was apparently not at all a dweller in thought lands. She was existing very much in the present. Evidently she had been wishing to consult with her husband on some tremendous domestic question, and she was in a state of rampant irritation, because he refused to acknowledge at this moment that she or any such thing as a tremendous domestic question was in existence. At intervals she made savage attempts to gain his attention.

As the youth saw her she was in a pose of absolute despair. And her eyes expressed that she appreciated all the tragedy of it. Ah, they said, hers was a life of terrible burden, of appalling responsibility; her pathway was beset with unsolved problems, her horizon was lined with tangled difficulties, while her husband — the man of millions, continued to play with the kitten. Her expression was an admission of heroism.

[THE GOLD WOMAN.]

The youth saw that here at any rate was one denial of his oratorical old friend's statement. In the face of this woman there was no sign that life was sometimes a joy. It was impossible that there could be any pleasure in living for her. Her features were as lined and creased with care and worriment as those of an apple woman. It was as if the passing of each social obligation, of each binding form of her life, had left its footprints, scarring her face.

Somewhere in her expression there was terrible pride, that kind of pride which, mistaking the form for the real thing, worships itself because of its devotion to the form.

In the lines of the mouth and the set of the chin could be seen the might of a grim old fighter. They denoted all the power of machination of a general, veteran of a hundred battles. The little scars at the corners of her eyes made a wondrously fierce effect, baleful, determined, without regard somehow to ruck of pain. Here was a savage, a barbarian, a spear woman of the Philistines, who fought battles to excel in what are thought to be the refined and worthy things in life; here was a type of Zulu chieftainess who scuffled and scrambled for place before the white altars of social excellence. And woe to the socially weaker who should try to barricade themselves against that dragon.

It was certain that she never rested in the shade of the trees. One could imagine the endless churning of that mind. And plans and other plans coming forth continuously, defeating a rival here, reducing a family there, bludgeoning a man here, a maid there. Woe and wild eyes followed like obedient sheep upon her trail.

Too, the youth thought he could see that here was the true abode of conservatism — in the mothers, in those whose ears displayed their diamonds instead of their diamonds displaying their ears, in the ancient and honorable controllers who sat in remote corners and pulled wires and respected themselves with a magnitude of respect that heaven seldom allows on earth. There lived tradition and superstition. They were perhaps ignorant of that which they worshipped, and, not comprehending it at all, it naturally followed that the fervor of their devotion could set the sky ablaze.

As he watched, he saw, that the mesmeric power of a kitten's waving paws was good. He rejoiced in the spectacle of the little fuzzy cat trying to stand on its head, and by this simple antic defeating some intention of a great domestic Napoleon.

[THE BUSINESS OF BEING BEAUTIFUL.]

The three girls of the family were having a musical altercation over by the window. Then and later the youth thought them adorable. They were wonderful to him in their charming gowns. They had time and opportunity to create effects, to be beautiful. And it would have been a wonder to him if he had not found them charming, since making themselves so could but be their principal occupation.

Beauty requires certain justices, certain fair conditions. When in a field no man can say: "Here should spring up a flower; here one should not." With incomprehensible machinery and system, nature sends them forth in places both strange and proper, so that, somehow, as we see them each one is a surprise to us. But at times, at places, one can say: "Here no flower can flourish." The youth wondered then why he had been sometimes surprised at seeing women fade, shrivel, their bosoms flatten, their shoulders crook forward, in the heavy swelter and wrench of their toil. It must be difficult, he thought, for a woman to remain serene and uncomplaining when she contemplated the wonder and the strangeness of it.

The lights shed marvelous hues of softened rose upon the table. In the encircling shadows the butler moved with a mournful, deeply solemn air. Upon the table there was color of pleasure, of festivity, but this servant in the background went to and fro like a slow religious procession.

The youth felt considerable alarm when he found himself involved in conversation with his hostess. In the course of this talk he discovered the great truth that when one submits himself to a thoroughly conventional conversation he runs risks of being most amazingly stupid. He was glad that no one cared to overhear it.

The millionaire, deprived of his kitten, sat back in his chair and laughed at the replies of his son to the attacks of one of the girls. In the rather good wit of his offspring he took an intense delight, but he laughed more particularly at the words of the son.

[CROESUS DINES.]

Indicated in this light chatter about the dinner table there was an existence that was not at all what the youth had been taught to see. Theologians had for a long time told the poor man that riches did not bring happiness, and they had solemnly repeated this phrase until it had come to mean that misery was commensurate with dollars, that each wealthy man was inwardly a miserable wretch. And when a wail of despair of rage had come from the night of the slums they had stuffed this epigram down the throat of he who cried out and told him that he was a lucky fellow. They did this because they feared.

The youth, studying this family group, could not see that they had great license to be pale and haggard. They were no doubt fairly good, being not strongly induced toward the bypaths. Various worlds turned open doors toward them. Wealth in a certain sense is liberty. If they were fairly virtuous he could not see why they should be so persistently pitied.

And no doubt they would dispense their dollars like little seeds upon the soil of the world if it were not for the fact that since the days of the ancient great political economist, the more exalted forms of virtue have grown to be utterly impracticable.

BILLY ATKINS/WENT TO OMAHA/THE TALE OF A GREAT YEARNING IN/THE HEART OF A HOBO./ THROUGH FIRE AND WATER/NOTHING STOPPED HIM, ALTHOUGH ALL/HANDS WERE AGAINST HIM./A JOURNEY OF SACRIFICES/AND THE REWARD AT ITS END HAD ITS/DRAWBACKS, TOO— A CLEVER STUDY/OF TRAMP CHARACTER.*

Billie Atkins is a traveler. He has seen the cold blue gleam of the northern lakes, the tangled green thickets of Florida and the white peaks of the Rockies. All this has he seen and much more, for he has been a tramp for sixteen years.

One winter evening when the "sitting room" of a lodging house just off the Bowery was thronged with loungers Billie came

---

* *Reprinted from New York Press: 20 May 1894.*

Billy Atkins tells his story in a lodging house just off the Bowery, and Crane heard it there — the same house described in "An Experiment in Misery" (see above). He wrote the piece before he went West in 1895 for the Bacheller Syndicate.

Another Eastern-Western tale is "A Man and Some Others," written after Crane's sojourn in Mexico. A former Bowery saloon bouncer dies in a gunfight with José and a band of "greasers." Another Western tale, "A Freight Car Incident," links with "Billy Atkins."

in, mellow with drink and in the eloquent stage. He chose to charm them with a description of a journey from Denver to Omaha. They all listened with appreciation, for when Billie is quite drunk he tells a tale with indescribable gestures and humorous emotions that makes one feel that, after all, the buffets of fate are rather more comic than otherwise.

It seems that when Billie was in Denver last winter it suddenly occurred to him that he wished to be in Omaha. He did not deem it necessary to explain his fancy: he merely announced that he happened to be in Denver last winter and that then it occurred to him that he wished to be in Omaha. Apparently these ideas come to his class like bolts of compelling lightning. After that swift thought of Omaha it was impossible for Denver to contain him; he must away. When the night express on the Union Pacific pulled out Billie "made a great sneak" behind some freight cars and climbed onto the "blind" end of the baggage car.

It was a very dark night and Billie congratulated himself that he had not been discovered. He huddled to a little heap on the car platform and thought, with a woman's longing, of Omaha.

However, it was not long before an icy stream of water struck Billie a startling blow in the face, and as he raised his eyes he saw in the red glare from the engine a very jocular fireman crouching on the coal and holding the nozzle of a small hose in his hand. And at frequent intervals during the night this jocular fireman would climb up on the coal and play the hose on Billie. The drenched tramp changed his position and curled himself up into a little ball and swore graphically, all to no purpose. The fireman persisted with his hose and when he thought that Billie was getting too comfortable he came back to the rear of the tender and doused him with a pailful of very cold water.

But Billie stuck to his position. For one reason the express went too fast for him to get safely off, and for another reason he wished to go to Omaha.

The train rushed out of the shadow of the mountains and into the cold gray of dawn on the prairies. The biting chill of the morning made Billie shake in his wet clothes. He adjusted himself on the edge of the rocking car platform where he could catch the first rays of the sun. And it was this change of position that got him into certain difficulties. At about 8 o'clock the express went roaring through a little village. Billie, sunning himself on the edge of the steps, espied three old farmers seated on the porch of the village store. They grinned at him and waved their arms.

"I taut they was jest givin' me er jolly," said Billie, "so I waved me hand at 'em an' gives 'em er laugh, an' th' train went on. But it turned out they wasn't motionin' t' me at all, but was all th' while givin' er tip t' th' brakey that I was on th' blind. An' 'fore I knew it th' brakey came over th' top, or aroun' th' side, or somehow, an' I was a-gittin' kicked in th' neck.

"'Gitoffahere! gitoffahere!'

"I was dead escared b'cause th' train was goin' hell bentin'.

"'Oh, please, mister,' I sez, 'I can't git off — th' train's goin' too fast.'

"But he kept on kickin' me fer a while til finally he got tired an' stopped th' train b'cause I could a-never got off th' way she was runnin'. By this time th' passengers in all th' cars got onto it that they was puttin' er bum off th' blind, an' when I got down off th' step, I see every winder in th' train was fuller heads, an' they gimme er great laugh until I had t' turn me back an' walk off."

As it happened, the nearest station to where Billie then found himself was eighteen miles distant. He dried his clothes as best he could and then swore along the tracks for a mile or two. But it was weary business — tramping along in the vast vacancy of the plains. Billie got tired and lay down to wait for a freight train. After a time one came and as the long string of boxcars thundered past him, he made another "great sneak" and a carefully calculated run and grab. He got safely on the little step and then he began to do what he called "ridin' th' ladder." That is to say, he clung to the little iron ladder that is fastened to the end of each car. He remained hanging there while the long train crept slowly over the plains.

He did not dare to show himself above the top of the car for fear of the brakeman. He considered himself safe down between the ends of the jolting cars, but once, as he chanced to look toward the sky, he saw a burly brakeman leaning on the brakewheel and regarding him.

"Come up here," said the brakeman.

Billie climbed painfully to the top of the car.

"Got any money?" said the brakeman.

"No," replied Billie.

"Well, then, gitoffahere," said the brakeman, and Billie received another installment of kicks. He went down the ladder and puckered his mouth and drew in his breath, preparatory to getting off the car, but the train had arrived at a small grade and Billie became frightened. The little wheels were all a-humming and the cars lurched like boats on the sea.

"Oh, please, mister," said Billie, "I can't git off. It's a-goin' too fast."

The brakeman swore and began the interesting operation of

treading, with his brass toed boots, on Billie's fingers. Billie hung hard. He cast glances of despair at the rapid fleeting ground and shifted his grip often. But presently the brakeman's heels came down with extraordinary force and Billie involuntarily released his hold.

He fell in a heap and rolled over and over. His face and body were scratched and bruised, and on the top of his head there was a contusion that fitted like a new derby. His clothes had been rags, but they were now exaggerated out of all semblance of clothes. He sat up and looked at the departing train. "Gawd-dernit," he said, "I'll never git t' Omaha at this rate."

Presently Billie developed a most superhuman hunger. He saw the houses of a village some distance away, and he made for them, resolved to have something to eat if it cost a life. But still he knew he would be arrested if he appeared on the streets of any well organized, respectable town in the trousers he was then obliged to wear. He was in a quandary until by good fortune he perceived a pair of brown overalls hanging on a line in the rear of an isolated house.

He "made a great sneak on 'em." This sort of thing requires patience, but not more than an hour later, he bore off a large square of cloth which he had torn from one leg of the overalls. At another house he knocked at the door and when a woman came he stood very carefully facing her and requested a needle and thread. She gave them to him, and he waited until she had shut the door before he turned and went away.

He retired then into a thick growing patch of sunflowers on the outskirts of the town and started in to sew the piece of overall to his trousers. He had not been engaged long at his task before "two hundred kids" accumulated in front of the sunflower patch and began to throw stones at him. For some time the sky was darkened by a shower of missiles of all sizes. Occasionally Billie, without his trousers, would make little forays, yelling savage threats. These would compel the boys to retire some distance, but they always returned again with renewed vigor. Billie thought he would never get his trousers mended.

But this adventure was the cause of his again meeting Black John Randolph, who Billie said was "th' whitest pardner" he ever had. While he was engaged in conflict with the horde of boys a negro came running down the road and began to belabor them with a boot blacking kit. The boys ran off, and Billie saw with delight that his rescuer was Black John Randolph, whom he had known in Memphis.

Billie, unmolested, sewed his trousers. Then he told Black

John that he was hungry, and the two swooped down on the town. Black John shined shoes until dark. He shined for all the available citizens of the place. Billie stood around and watched. The earnings were sixty cents. They spent it all for gingerbread, for it seems that Billie had developed a sudden marvelous longing for gingerbread.

Having feasted, Billie decided to make another attempt for Omaha. He and Black John went to the railroad yard and there they discovered an east-bound freight car that was empty save for one tramp and seven cans of peaches. They parleyed with the tramp and induced him to give up his claim on two-thirds of the car. They settled very comfortably, and that night Billie was again on his way to Omaha. The three of them lived for twenty-four hours on canned peaches, and would have been happy ever after no doubt if it had not happened that their freight car was presently switched off to a side line, and sent careering off in the wrong direction.

When Billie discovered this he gave a whoop and fell out of the car, for he was very particular about walking, and he did not wish to be dragged far from the main line. He trudged back to it, and there discovered a lumber car that contained about forty tramps.

This force managed to overawe the trainmen for a time and compel a free ride for a few miles, but presently the engine was stopped, and the trainmen formed in war array and advanced with clubs.

Billie had had experience in such matters. He "made a sneak." He repaired to a coal car and cuddled among the coal. He buried his body completely, and of his head only his nose and his eyes could have been seen.

The trainmen spread the tramps out over the prairie in a wide fleeing circle, as when a stone is hurled into a placid creek. They remained cursing in their beards, and the train went on.

Billie, snug in his bed, smiled without disarranging the coal that covered his mouth, and thought of Omaha.

But in an hour or two he got impatient, and upreared his head to look at the scenery. An eagle eyed brakeman espied him.

"Got any money?"

"No."

"Well, then, gitoffahere."

Billie got off. The brakeman continued to throw coal at him until the train had hauled him beyond range.

"Hully mack'rel," said Billie, "I'll never git t' Omaha."

He was quite discouraged. He lay down on a bank beside the

track to think, and while there he went to sleep. When he awoke a freight train was thundering past him. Still half asleep, he made a dash and a grab. He was up the ladder and on top of the car before he had recovered all of this faculties. A brakeman charged on him.

"Got any money?"

"No, but, please, mister, won't yeh please let me stay on yer train fer a little ways? I'm awful tired, an' I wanta git t' Omaha."

The brakeman reflected. Then he searched Billie's pockets, and finding half a plug of tobacco, took possession of it. He decided to let Billie ride for a time.

Billie perched on top of the car and admired the changing scenery while the train went twenty miles. Then the brakeman induced him to get off, considering no doubt that a twenty mile ride was sufficient in exchange for a half plug of tobacco.

The rest of the trip is incoherent, like the detailed accounts of great battles. Billie boarded trains and got thrown off on his head, on his left shoulder, on his right shoulder, on his hands and knees. He struck the ground slanting, straight from above and full sideways. His clothes were shredded and torn like the sails of a gale blown brig. His skin was tattooed with bloody lines, crosses, triangles, and all the devices known to geometry. But he wouldn't walk, and he was bound to reach Omaha. So he let the trainmen use him as a projectile with which to bombard the picturesque Western landscape.

And eventually he reached Omaha. One night, when it was snowing and cold winds whistled among the city's chimneys, he arrived in a coal car. He was filled with glee that he had reached the place of his endeavor. He could not repress his pride when he thought of the conquered miles. He went forth from the coal car with a blithe step.

The police would not let him stand on a corner nor sit down anywhere. They drove him about for two or three hours, until he happened to think of the railroad station. He went there, and was just getting into a nice doze by the warm red stove in the waiting room, when an official of some kind took him by the collar, and leading him calmly to the door, kicked him out into the snow. After that he was ejected from four saloons in rapid succession.

"Hully mack'rel!" he said, as he stood in the snow and quavered and trembled.

Until three o'colck in the morning various industrious police-men kept him moving from place to place as if he were pawn in a game of chess, until finally Billie became desperate and approached an officer in this fashion:

"Say, mister, won't yeh please arrest me? I wanta go t' jail so's I can sleep."

"What?"

"I say, won't yer please arrest me? I wanta go t' jail so I kin sleep."

The policeman studied Billie for a moment. Then he made an impatient gesture.

"Oh, can't yeh arrest yerself? The jail's a long ways from here, an' I don't wanta take yeh way up there."

"Sure — I kin," said Billie. "Where is it?"

The policeman gave him directions, and Billie started for the jail.

He had considerable difficulty in finding it. He was often obliged to accost people in the street.

"Please, mister, can yeh tell me where the jail is?"

At last he found it, and after a short parley, they admitted him. They gave him permission to sleep on a sort of an iron slab swung by four chains from the ceiling. Billie sank down upon this couch and arrayed his meager rags about his form. Before he was completely in the arms of the slumber god, however, he made a remark expressive of a new desire, a sudden born longing. "Hully mack'rel. I mus' start back fer Denver in th' mornin'."

THE GRATITUDE OF A NATION *

Gratitude, the sense of obligation, often comes very late to the mind of the world. It is the habit of humanity to forget her heroes, her well-doers, until they have passed on beyond the sound of earthly voices; then when the loud, praising cries are raised, there comes a regret and a sorrow that those ears are forever deaf to plaudits. It has almost become a great truth that the man who achieves an extraordinary benefit for the race shall go to death without the particular appreciation of his fellows. One by one they go, with no evident knowledge of the value of their services unless their own hearts tell them that in their fidelity to truth and to duty, they have gained a high success.

* Reprinted from Crane's manuscript — submitted to the New York Press but not published — in the Columbia University Crane Collection. The sketch was first published in Daniel G. Hoffman's edition of The Red Badge of Courage and Other Stories (1957). Here is an addition to the Crane canon.

The men who fought in the great war for freedom and union are disappearing. They are upon their last great march, a march that ceases to be seen at the horizon and whose end is death. We are now viewing the last of the procession, the belated ones, the stragglers. A vast body of them have thronged to the grave, regiment by regiment, brigade by brigade, and the others are hurrying after their fellows who have marched into the Hereafter. There, every company is gradually getting its men, no soldier but what will be there to answer his name, and upon earth there will remain but a memory of deeds well and stoutly done.

If in the past there is any reflection of the future, we can expect that when the last veteran has vanished there will come a time of great monuments, eulogies, tears. The boy in blue will have grown to heroic size, and painters, sculptors and writers will have been finally impressed, and strive to royally celebrate the deeds of the brave, simple, quiet men who crowded upon the opposing bayonets of their country's enemies. But no voice penetrates the grave, and the chants and shouts will carry no warmth to dead hearts.

Let us then struggle to defeat this ironical law of fate. Let us not wait to celebrate but consider that there are now before us the belated ones of the army that is marching over the horizon, off from the earth, into the sky, into history and tradition. The laws of the universe sometimes appear to be toying with compensations, holding back results until death closes the eyes to success, bludgeoning a man of benefactions, rewarding them who do evil. It is well that we do all in our power to defeat these things.

Do not then wait. Let not loud and full expression of gratitude come too late to the mind of the nation. Do not forget our heroes, our well-doers, until they have marched to where no little cheers of men can reach them. Remember them now, and if the men of the future forget, the sin is with them. They are ours, these boys in blue, their deeds and privations, their wondrous patience and endurance, their grim abiding faith and fortitude are ours. Let us expend our lungs then while they can hear; let us throw up our caps while they can see, these veterans whose feet are still sore from marches, in whose old grey hairs there still lingers the scent of victory. In the tremendous roll of events the pages and paragraphs of future histories are nothing. Our obligation exists in the present, and it is fit that we leave not too much to future historians.

Upon this day, those who are left go sadly, a little pitiable handful, to decorate the places of their comrades' rest. When the small solemn flower-laden processions start for the graves, it is well to be with them. There are to be learned there lessons of patriotism

that are good for us at this day. No harm would come if we allowed
the trucks to be less roaring and busy upon this day, nor if we
allowed the stores to have less rush and crowd. We cannot afford
to neglect the spectacle of our bearded, bronzed, and wrinkled men
in blue tramping slowly and haltingly to bestow their gifts upon
the sleeping places of those who are gone. And it is well then to
think of the times when these men were in the flush and vigor of
manhood and went with the firm-swinging steps of youth to do
their duty to their God, their homes and their country.

When they are gone, American society has lost its most valuable element for they have paid the price of patriotism, they know
the meaning of patriotism, and stars shot from guns would not
hinder their devotion to the flag which they rescued from dust and
oblivion. Let us watch with apprehension this departure of an army,
one by one, one by one. Let the last words that they hear from
us be words of gratitude and affection.

It is just and proper that we go with them to the graves, that
they may see that when they too are gone, there will be many to
come to their graves, that their camping grounds and battle fields
will be remembered places and that the lesson of their lives will be
taught to children who will never see their faces.

Great are the nation's dead who sleep in peace. May all old
comrades gather at an eternal camp-fire. May the sweet, wind-waved
rustle of trees be over them, may the long, lush grass and flowers be
about their feet. Peace and rest be with them forever, for they have
done well.

AN OMINOUS BABY.*

A baby was wandering in a strange country. He was a tattered
child with a frowsled wealth of yellow hair. His dress, of a checked
stuff, was soiled and showed the marks of many conflicts like the

---

* Published in The Arena: May 1894; reprinted in The Open
Boat and Other Stories (London, 1898). The sketch was written in 1893.

In a sequel, written on pink-lined pad sheets and entitled
"An Ominous Baby — Tommie's Home Coming," the child takes
home the booty acquired in "An Ominous Baby":

A baby wended along a street. His little tattered dress
showed the effects of some recent struggle. It disclosed his small thin shoulder. His blond hair was

chain-shirt of a warrior. His sun-tanned knees shone above wrinkled
stockings which he pulled up occasionally with an impatient movement when they entangled his feet. From a gaping shoe there appeared an array of tiny toes.

He was toddling along an avenue between rows of stolid,
brown houses. He went slowly, with a look of absorbed interest
on his small, flushed face. His blue eyes stared curiously. Carriages
went with a musical rumble over the smooth asphalt. A man with a
chrysanthemum was going up steps. Two nursery-maids chatted as
they walked slowly, while their charges hobnobbed amiably between perambulators. A truck wagon roared thunderously in the
distance.

The child from the poor district made way along the brown
street filled with dull gray shadows. High up, near the roofs, glanc-
ing sun-rays changed cornices to blazing gold and silvered the
fronts of windows. The wandering baby stopped and stared at the
two children laughing and playing in their carriages among the
heaps of rugs and cushions. He braced his legs apart in an attitude
of earnest attention. His lower jaw fell and disclosed his small, even
teeth. As they moved on, he followed the carriages with awe in his
face as if contemplating a pageant. Once one of the babies, with
twittering laughter, shook a gorgeous rattle at him. He smiled
jovially in return.

Finally a nursery maid ceased conversation and, turning, made
a gesture of annoyance.

"Go 'way, little boy," she said to him. "Go 'way. You're all
dirty."

He gazed at her with infant tranquillity for a moment and
then went slowly off, dragging behind him a bit of rope he had
acquired in another street. He continued to investigate the new
scenes. The people and houses struck him with interest as would
flowers and trees. Passengers had to avoid the small, absorbed

---

*tousled. His face was still wet with tears, but in his
hands he bore with an air of triumph a toy fire engine.*

*He avoided with care some men who were un-
loading some boxes from a truck, passed through
knots of children playing noisily in front of tenements
and went deeper into the slums. He kept his glittering possession concealed. . . .*

The "glittering possession" turns out to be a lemon in "A
Great Mistake" (1896) (see below), a companion piece to "An
Ominous Baby" and written the same year. Connected to them,
of course, are the paragraphs above quoted from Corwin
Knapp Linson's My Stephen Crane (1958), pp. 40, 41.

figure in the middle of the sidewalk. They glanced at the intent baby face covered with scratches and dust as with scars and powder smoke.

After a time, the wanderer discovered upon the pavement, a pretty child in fine clothes playing with a toy. It was a tiny fire engine painted brilliantly in crimson and gold. The wheels rattled as its small owner dragged it uproariously about by means of a string. The babe with his bit of rope trailing behind him paused and regarded the child and the toy. For a long while he remained motionless, save for his eyes, which followed all movements of the glittering thing.

The owner paid no attention to the spectator but continued his joyous imitations of phases of the career of a fire engine. His gleeful baby laugh rang against the calm fronts of the houses. After a little, the wandering baby began quietly to sidle nearer. His bit of rope, now forgotten, dropped at his feet. He removed his eyes from the toy and glanced expectantly at the other child.

"Say," he breathed, softly.

The owner of the toy was running down the walk at top speed. His tongue was clanging like a bell and his legs were galloping. An iron post on the corner was all ablaze. He did not look around at the coaxing call from the small, tattered figure on the curb.

The wandering baby approached still nearer and, presently, spoke again. "Say," he murmured, "le' me play wif it?"

The other child interrupted some shrill tootings. He bended his head and spoke disdainfully over his shoulder.

"No," he said.

The wanderer retreated to the curb. He failed to notice the bit of rope, once treasured. His eyes followed as before the winding course of the engine, and his tender mouth twitched.

"Say," he ventured at last, "is dat yours?"

"Yes," said the other, tilting his round chin. He drew his property suddenly behind him as if it were menaced. "Yes," he repeated, "it's mine."

"Well, le' me play wif it?" said the wandering baby, with a trembling note of desire in his voice.

"No," cried the pretty child with determined lips. "It's mine! My ma-ma buyed it."

"Well, tan't I play wif it?" His voice was a sob. He stretched forth little, covetous hands.

"No," the pretty child continued to repeat. "No, it's mine."

"Well, I want to play wif it," wailed the other. A sudden, fierce frown mantled his baby face. He clenched his thin hands and advanced with a formidable gesture. He looked some wee battler in a war.

"It's mine! It's mine," cried the pretty child, his voice in the treble of outraged rights.

"I want it," roared the wanderer.

"It's mine! It's mine!"

"I want it!"

"It's mine!"

The pretty child retreated to the fence, and there paused at bay. He protected his property with outstretched arms. The small vandal made a charge. There was a short scuffle at the fence. Each grasped the string to the toy and tugged. Their faces were wrinkled with baby rage, the verge of tears.

Finally, the child in tatters gave a supreme tug and wrenched the string from the other's hands. He set off rapidly down the street, bearing the toy in his arms. He was weeping with the air of a wronged one who has at last succeeded in achieving his rights. The other baby was squalling lustily. He seemed quite helpless. He wrung his chubby hands and railed.

After the small barbarian had got some distance away, he paused and regarded his booty. His little form curved with pride. A soft, gleeful smile loomed through the storm of tears. With great care, he prepared the toy for travelling. He stopped a moment on a corner and gazed at the pretty child whose small figure was quivering with sobs. As the latter began to show signs of beginning pursuit, the little vandal turned and vanished down a dark side street as into a swallowing cavern.

"YOUSE WANTS 'PETEY,' YOUSE DO." *

Three small boys with hardened faces stood at the bar of Jefferson Market Police Court yesterday morning, charged with breaking open a street stand at No. 455 Broadway and stealing several brushes and a can of corn.

The juvenile prisoners were Nathan Alstrumpt, seven years old, of No. 181 South Fifth avenue; Solomon Cashman, seven years old, of No. 507 Broome street, and Joseph Chriller, thirteen years old, of No. 41 Thompson street.

---

* From an undated article published in the New York Herald in 1892.

This is perhaps by Crane. It was first quoted in John Berryman, Stephen Crane (1950), but incorrectly noted.

"Yer see," said little Alstrumpt, the leader of the gang, to Justice Divver, "we was doin' notten but playen tag in der street when a blokie wat's called 'Petey' came along and says, 'Hi, fellers, let's go a swipen.' We went wid him — see? Youse wants 'Petey,' youse do. He did her swipen — not me nor de kids."

"Who's Petey?" asked Justice Divver.

"Why, he's 'Petey' Larkin, a mug wot lives in Thompson street," said the little reprobate.

The boys were committed to the care of Mr. Cerry's society.

MR. BINKS' DAY OFF/A STUDY OF A CLERK'S HOLIDAY *

When Binks was coming up town in a Broadway cable car one afternoon he caught some superficial glimpses of Madison square as he ducked his head to peek through between a young woman's bonnet and a young man's newspaper. The green of the little park vaguely astonished Binks. He had grown accustomed to a white and brown park; now, all at once, it was radiant green. The grass, the leaves, had come swiftly, silently, as if a great green light from the sky had shone suddenly upon the little desolate hued place.

The vision cheered the mind of Binks. It cried to him that nature was still supreme; he had begun to think the banking business to be the pivot on which the universe turned. Produced by this wealth of young green, faint, faraway voices called to him. Certain subtle memories swept over him. The million leaves looked into his soul and said something sweet and pure in an unforgotten song, the melody of his past. Binks began to dream.

When he arrived at the little Harlem flat he sat down to dinner with an air of profound dejection, which Mrs. Binks promptly construed into an insult to her cooking, and to the time and thought she had expended in preparing the meal. She promptly resented it. "Well, what's the matter now?" she demanded. Apparently she had asked this question ten thousand times.

"Nothin'," said Binks, shortly, filled with gloom. He meant by this remark that his ailment was so subtle that her feminine mind would not be enlightened by any explanation.

The head of the family was in an ugly mood. The little Binkses suddenly paused in their uproar and became very wary children. They knew that it would be dangerous to do anything irrelevant

* *Reprinted from New York Press: 8 July 1894.*

to their father's bad temper. They studied his face with their large eyes, filled with childish seriousness and speculation. Meanwhile they ate with the most extraordinary caution. They handled their little forks with such care that there was barely a sound. At each slight movement of their father they looked apprehensively at him, expecting the explosion.

The meal continued amid a somber silence. At last, however, Binks spoke, clearing his throat of the indefinite rage that was in it and looking over at his wife. The little Binkses seemed to inwardly dodge, but he merely said: "I wish I could get away into the country for awhile!"

His wife bristled with that brave anger which agitates a woman when she sees fit to assume that her husband is weak spirited. "If I worked as hard as you do, if I slaved over those old books the way you do, I'd have a vacation once in awhile or I'd tear their old office down." Upon her face was a Roman determination. She was a personification of all manner of courages and rebellions and powers.

Binks felt the falsity of her emotion in a vague way, but at that time he only made a sullen gesture. Later, however, he cried out in a voice of sudden violence: "Look at Tommie's dress! Why the dickens don't you put a bib on that child?"

His wife glared over Tommie's head at her husband, as she leaned around in her chair to tie on the demanded bib. The two looked as hostile as warring redskins. In the wife's eyes there was an intense opposition and defiance, an assertion that she now considered the man she had married to be beneath her in intellect, industry, valor. There was in this glance a jeer at the failures of his life. And Binks, filled with an inexpressible rebellion at what was to him a lack of womanly perception and sympathy in her, replied with a look that called his wife a drag, an uncomprehending thing of vain ambitions, the weight of his existence.

The baby meanwhile began to weep because his mother, in her exasperation, had yanked him and hurt his neck. Her anger, groping for an outlet, had expressed itself in the nervous strength of her fingers. "Keep still, Tommie," she said to him. "I didn't hurt you. You neen't cry the minute anybody touches you!" He made a great struggle and repressed his loud sobs, but the tears continued to fall down his cheeks and his under lip quivered from a baby sense of injury, the anger of an impotent child who seems as he weeps to be planning revenges.

"I don't see why you don't keep that child from eternally crying," said Binks, as a final remark. He then arose and went away to smoke, leaving Mrs. Binks with the children and the dishevelled table.

Later that night, when the children were in bed, Binks said to his wife: "We ought to get away from the city for awhile at least this spring. I can stand it in the summer, but in the spring — ." He made a motion with his hand that represented the new things that are born in the heart when spring comes into the eyes.

"It will cost something, Phil," said Mrs. Binks.

"That's true," said Binks. They both began to reflect, contemplating the shackles of their poverty. "And besides, I don't believe I could get off," said Binks after a time.

Nothing more was said of it that night. In fact, it was two or three days afterward that Binks came home and said: "Margaret, you get the children ready on Saturday noon and we'll all go out and spend Sunday with your Aunt Sarah!"

When he came home on Saturday his hat was far back on the back of his head from the speed he was in. Mrs. Binks was putting on her bonnet before the glass, turning about occasionally to admonish the little Binkses, who, in their new clothes, were wandering around, stiffly, and getting into all sorts of small difficulties. They had been ready since 11 o'clock. Mrs. Binks had been obliged to scold them continually, one after the other, and sometimes three at once.

"Hurry up," said Binks, immediately, "ain't got much time. Say, you ain't going to let Jim wear that hat, are you? Where's his best one? Good heavens, look at Margaret's dress! It's soiled already! Tommie, stop that, do you hear? Well, are you ready?"

Indeed, it was not until the Binkses had left the city far behind and were careering into New Jersey that they recovered their balances. Then something of the fresh quality of the country stole over them and cooled their nerves. Horse cars and ferryboats were maddening to Binks when he was obliged to convoy a wife and three children. He appreciated the vast expanses of green, through which ran golden hued roads. The scene accented his leisure and his lack of responsibility.

Near the track a little river jostled over the stones. At times the cool thunder of its roar came faintly to the ear. The Ramapo Hills were in the background, faintly purple, and surrounded with little peaks that shone with the luster of the sun. Binks began to joke heavily with the children. The little Binkses, for their part, asked the most superhuman questions about details of the scenery. Mrs. Binks leaned contentedly back in her seat and seemed to be at rest, which was a most extraordinary thing.

When they got off the train at the little rural station they created considerable interest. Two or three loungers began to view them in a sort of concentrated excitement. They were apparently fascinated by the Binkses and seemed to be indulging in all manner of wild and intense speculation. The agent, as he walked into his station, kept his head turned. Across the dusty street, wide at this place, a group of men upon the porch of a battered grocery store shaded their eyes with their hands. The Binkses felt dimly like a circus and were a trifle bewildered by it. Binks gazed up and down, this way and that; he tried to be unaware of the stare of the citizens. Finally, he approached the loungers, who straightened their forms suddenly and looked very expectant.

"Can you tell me where Miss Pattison lives?"

The loungers arose as one man. "It's th' third house up that road there."

"It's a white house with green shutters!"

"There, that's it — yeh can see it through th' trees!" Binks discerned that his wife's aunt was a well known personage, and also that the coming of the Binkses was an event of vast importance. When he marched off at the head of his flock, he felt like a drum-major. His course was followed by the unwavering, intent eyes of the loungers.

The street was lined with two rows of austere and solemn trees. In one way it was like parading between the plumes on an immense hearse. These trees, lowly sighing in a breath-like wind, oppressed one with a sense of melancholy and dreariness. Back from the road, behind flower beds, controlled by box-wood boarders, the houses were asleep in the drowsy air. Between them one could get views of the fields lying in a splendor of gold and green. A monotonous humming song of insects came from the regions of sunshine, and from some hidden barnyard a hen suddenly burst forth in a sustained cackle of alarm. The tranquillity of the scene contained a meaning of peace and virtue that was incredibly monotonous to the warriors from the metropolis. The sense of a city is battle. The Binkses were vaguely irritated and astonished at the placidity of this little town. This life spoke to them of no absorbing nor even interesting thing. There was something unbearable about it. "I should go crazy if I had to live here," said Mrs. Binks. A warrior in the flood-tide of his blood, going from the hot business of war to a place of utter quiet, might have felt that there was an insipidity in peace. And thus felt the Binkses from New York. They had always named the clash of the swords of commerce as sin, crime, but now they began to imagine something admirable in it. It was high wisdom. They put aside their favorite expressions: "The curse of gold," "A mad passion to get rich," "The rush for the spoils." In the light of their contempt for this stillness, the conflicts of the city were exalted. They were at any rate wondrously clever.

But what they did feel was the fragrance of the air, the radiance of the sunshine, the glory of the fields and the hills. With their ears still clogged by the tempest and fury of city uproars, they heard the song of the universal religion, the mighty and mystic hymn of nature, whose melody is in each landscape. It appealed to their elemental selves. It was as if the earth had called recreant and heedless children and the mother world, of vast might and significance, brought them to sudden meekness. It was the universal thing whose power no one escapes. When a man hears it he usually remains silent. He understands then the sacrilege of speech.

When they came to the third house, the white one with the green blinds, they perceived a woman, in a plaid sun bonnet, walking slowly down a path. Around her was a riot of shrubbery and flowers. From the long and tangled grass of the lawn grew a number of cherry trees. Their dark green foliage was thickly sprinkled with bright red fruit. Some sparrows were scuffling among the branches. The little Binkses began to whoop at the sight of the woman in the plaid sun bonnet.

"Hay-oh, Aunt Sarah, hay-oh!" they shouted.

The woman shaded her eyes with her hand. "Well, good gracious, if it ain't Marg'ret Binks! An' Phil, too! Well, I am surprised!"

She came jovially to meet them. "Why, how are yeh all? I'm awful glad t' see yeh!"

The children, filled with great excitement, babbled questions and ejaculations while she greeted the others.

"Say, Aunt Sarah, gimme some cherries!"

"Look at th' man over there!"

"Look at th' flowers!"

"Gimme some flowers, Aunt Sarah!"

And little Tommie, red faced from the value of his information, bawled out: "Aunt Sah-wee, dey have horse tars where I live!" Later he shouted: "We come on a twain of steam tars!"

Aunt Sarah fairly bristled with the most enthusiastic hospitality. She beamed upon them like a sun. She made desperate attempts to gain possession of everybody's bundles that she might carry them to the house. There was a sort of a little fight over the baggage. The children clamored questions at her; she tried heroically to answer them. Tommie, at times, deluged her with news.

The curtains of the dining room were pulled down to keep

out the flies. This made a deep, cool gloom in which corners of
the old furniture caught wandering rays of light and shone with
a mild luster. Everything was arranged with an unspeakable neat-
ness that was the opposite of comfort. A branch of an apple tree
moved by the gentle wind, brushed softly against the closed blinds.

"Take off yer things," said Aunt Sarah.

Binks and his wife remained talking to Aunt Sarah, but the
children speedily swarmed out over the farm, raiding in countless directions. It was only a matter of seconds before Jimmie discovered the brook behind the barn. Little Margaret roamed among
the flowers, bursting into little cries at sight of new blossoms, new
glories. Tommie gazed at the cherry trees for a few moments in
profound silence. Then he went and procured a pole. It was very
heavy, relatively. He could hardly stagger under it, but with infinite toil he dragged it to the proper place and somehow managed
to push it erect. Then with a deep earnestness of demeanor he
began a little onslaught upon the trees. Very often his blow missed
the entire tree and the pole thumped on the ground. This necessitated the most extraordinary labor. But then at other times he
would get two or three cherries at one wild swing of his weapon.

Binks and his wife spent the larger part of the afternoon out
under the apple trees at the side of the house. Binks lay down on
his back, with his head in the long lush grass. Mrs. Binks moved
lazily to and fro in a rocking chair that had been brought from the
house. Aunt Sarah, sometimes appearing, was strenuous in an account of relatives, and the Binkses had only to listen. They were
glad of it, for this warm, sleepy air, pulsating with the sounds of
insects, had enchained them in a great indolence.

It was to this place that Jimmie ran after he had fallen into
the brook and scrambled out again. Holding his arms out carefully from his dripping person, he was roaring tremendously. His
new sailor suit was a sight. Little Margaret came often to describe
the wonders of her journeys, and Tommie, after a frightful struggle
with the cherry trees, toddled over and went to sleep in the midst
of a long explanation of his operations. The breeze stirred the
locks on his baby forehead. His breath came in long sighs of content. Presently he turned his head to cuddle deeper into the grass.
One arm was thrown in childish abandon over his head. Mrs. Binks
stopped rocking to gaze at him. Presently she bended and noiselessly brushed away a spear of grass that was troubling the baby's
temple. When she straightened up she saw that Binks, too, was
absorbed in a contemplation of Tommie. They looked at each other
presently, exchanging a vague smile. Through the silence came the
voice of a plowing farmer berating his horses in a distant field.

The peace of the hills and the fields came upon the Binkses. They allowed Jimmie to sit up in bed and eat cake while his clothes were drying. Uncle Daniel returned from a wagon journey and recited them a ponderous tale of a pig that he had sold to a man with a red beard. They had no difficulty in feeling much interest in the story.

Binks began to expand with enormous appreciation. He would not go into the house until they compelled him. And as soon as the evening meal was finished he dragged his wife forth on a trip to the top of the hill behind the house. There was a great view from there, Uncle Daniel said.

The path, gray with little stones in the dusk, extended above them like a pillar. The pines were beginning to croon in a mournful key, inspired by the evening winds. Mrs. Binks had great difficulty in climbing this upright road. Binks was obliged to assist her, which he did with a considerable care and tenderness. In it there was a sort of a reminiscence of their courtship. It was a repetition of old days. Both enjoyed it because of this fact, although they subtly gave each other to understand that they disdained this emotion as an altogether un-American thing, for she, as a woman, was proud, and he had great esteem for himself as a man.

At the summit they seated themselves upon a fallen tree, near the edge of a cliff. The evening silence was upon the earth below them. Far in the west the sun lay behind masses of corn colored clouds, tumbled and heaved into crags, peaks and canyons. On either hand stood the purple hills in motionless array. The valley lay wreathed in somber shadows. Slowly there went on the mystic process of the closing of the day. The corn colored clouds faded to yellow and finally to a faint luminous green, inexpressibly vague. The rim of the hills was then an edge of crimson. The mountains became a profound blue. From the night, approaching in the east, came a wind. The trees of the mountain raised plaintive voices, bending toward the faded splendors of the day.

This song of the trees arose in low, sighing melody into the still air. It was filled with an infinite sorrow — a sorrow for birth, slavery, death. It was a wail telling the griefs, the pains of all ages. It was the symbol of agonies. It celebrated all suffering. Each man finds in this sound the expression of his own grief. It is the universal voice raised in lamentation.

As the trees huddled and bended as if to hide from their eyes a certain sight the green tints became blue. A faint suggestion of yellow replaced the crimson. The sun was dead.

The Binkses had been silent. These songs of the trees awe.[1]

1. As given in the text of the New York *Press*.

They had remained motionless during this ceremony, their eyes fixed upon the mighty and indefinable changes which spoke to them of the final thing — the inevitable end. Their eyes had an impersonal expression. They were purified, chastened by this sermon, this voice calling to them from the sky. The hills had spoken and the trees had crooned their song. Binks finally stretched forth his arm in a wondering gesture.

"I wonder why," he said; "I wonder why the dickens it — why it — why — "

Tangled in the tongue was the unformulated question of the centuries, but Mrs. Binks had stolen forth her arm and linked it with his. Her head leaned softly against his shoulder.

CONEY ISLAND'S/FAILING DAYS/WHAT ONE OF THEM HELD FOR A/STROLLING PHILOSOPHER./ NOT WHOLLY WITHOUT JOY/THE ADVANTAGES OF GREAT TOYS AND THE/UNIMPORTANCE OF BUGS. *

"Down here at your Coney Island, toward the end of the season, I am made to feel very sad," said the stranger to me. "The great mournfulness that settles upon a summer resort at this time always depresses me exceedingly. The mammoth empty buildings, planned by extraordinarily optimistic architects, remind me in an unpleasant manner of my youthful dreams. In those days of visions I erected huge castles for the reception of my friends and admirers, and discovered later that I could have entertained them more comfortably in a small two story frame structure. There is a mighty pathos in these gaunt and hollow buildings, impassively and stolidly suffering from an enormous hunger for the public. And the unchangeable, ever imperturbable sea pursues its quaint devices blithely at the feet of these mournful wooden animals, gabbling and frolicking, with no thought for absent man nor maid!"

As the stranger spoke, he gazed with considerable scorn at the emotions of the sea; and the breeze from the far Navesink hills gently stirred the tangled, philosophic hair upon his forehead. Presently he went on: "The buildings are in effect more sad than the men, but I assure you that some of the men look very sad. I

* Reprinted from New York Press: 14 October 1894.

watched a talented and persuasive individual who was operating in front of a tintype gallery, and he had only the most marvelously infrequent opportunities to display his oratory and finesse. The occasional stragglers always managed to free themselves before he could drag them into the gallery and take their pictures. In the long intervals he gazed about him with a bewildered air, as if he felt his world dropping from under his feet. Once I saw him spy a promising youth afar off. He lurked with muscles at a tension, and then at the proper moment he swooped. 'Look-a-here,' he said, with tears of enthusiasm in his eyes, 'the best picture in the world! An' on'y four fer a quarter. O'ny jest try it, an' you'll go away perfectly satisfied!'

"I'll go away perfectly satisfied without trying it," replied the promising youth, and he did. The tintype man wanted to dash his samples to the ground and whip the promising youth. He controlled himself, however, and went to watch the approach of two women and a little boy who were nothing more than three dots, away down the board walk.

"At one place I heard the voice of a popcorn man raised in a dreadful note, as if he were chanting a death hymn. It made me shiver as I felt all the tragedy of the collapsed popcorn market. I began to see that it was an insult to the pain and suffering of these men to go near to them without buying anything. I took new and devious routes sometimes.

"As for the railroad guards and station men, they were so tolerant of the presence of passengers that I felt it to be an indication of their sense of relief from the summer's battle. They did not seem so greatly irritated by patrons of the railroad as I have seen them at other times. And in all the beer gardens the waiters had opportunity to indulge that delight in each other's society and conversation which forms so important a part in a waiter's idea of happiness. Sometimes the people in a sparsely occupied place will fare more strange that those in a crowded one. At one time I waited twenty minutes for a bottle of the worst beer in Christendom while my waiter told a charmingly naive story to a group of his compatriots. I protested sotto voice at the time that such beer might at least have the merit of being brought quickly.

[CRABS THAT SEEMED FRESH.]

"The restaurants, however, I think to be quite delicious, being in a large part thoroughly disreputable and always provided with huge piles of red boiled crabs. These huge piles of provision around on the floor and on the oyster counters always give me the opinion that I am dining on the freshest food in the world, and I appreciate the sensation. If need be, it also allows a man to revel in dreams of unlimited quantity.

"I found countless restaurants where I could get things almost to my taste, and, as I ate, watch the grand, eternal motion of the sea and have the waiter come up and put the pepper castor on the menu card to keep the salt breeze from interfering with my order for dinner.

"And yet I have an occasional objection to the sea when dining in sight of it; for a man with a really artistic dining sense always feels important as a duke when he is indulging in his favorite pastime, and, as the sea always makes me feel that I am a trivial object, I cannot dine with absolute comfort in its presence. The conflict of the two perceptions disturbs me. This is why I have grown to prefer the restaurants down among the narrow board streets. I tell you this because I think an explanation is due to you."

As we walked away from the beach and around one of those huge buildings whose pathos had so aroused the stranger's interest, we came into view of two acres of merry-go-rounds, circular swings, roller coasters, observation wheels and the like. The stranger paused and regarded them.

"Do you know," he said, "I am deeply fascinated by all these toys. For, of course, I perceive that they are really enlarged toys. They reinforce me in my old opinion that humanity only needs to be provided for ten minutes with a few whirligigs and things of the sort, and it can forget at least four centuries of misery. I rejoice in these whirligigs," continued the stranger, eloquently, "and as I watch here and there a person going around and around or up and down, or over and over, I say to myself that whirligigs must be made in heaven.

"It is a mystery to me why some man does not provide a large number of wooden rocking horses and let the people sit and dreamfully rock themselves into temporary forgetfulness. There could be intense quiet enforced by special policemen, who, however, should allow subdued conversation on the part of the patrons of the establishment. Deaf mutes should patrol to and fro selling slumberous drinks. These things are none of them insane. They are particularly rational. A man needs a little nerve quiver, and he gets it by being flopped around in the air like a tailess kite. He needs the introduction of a reposeful element, and he procures it upon a swing that makes him feel like thiry-five emotional actresses all trying to swoon upon one rug. There are some people who stand apart and deride these machines. If you could procure a dark night for them and the total absence of their friends they would smile, many of them. I assure you that I myself would indulge in these forms of intoxication if I were not a very great philosopher."

[DREARINESS IN THE MUSIC HALLS.]

We strolled in the music hall district, where the sky lines of the row of buildings are wondrously near to each other, and the crowded little thoroughfares resemble the eternal "Street Scene in Cairo." There was an endless strumming and tooting and shrill piping in clamor and chaos, while at all times there were interspersed the sharp cracking sounds from the shooting galleries and the coaxing calls of innumerable fakirs. At the stand where one can throw at wooden cats and negro heads and be in danger of winning cigars, a self reliant youth bought a whole armful of base balls, and missed with each one. Everybody grinned. A heavily built man openly jeered. "You couldn't hit a church!" "Couldn't I?" retorted the young man, bitterly. Near them three bad men were engaged in an intense conversation. The fragment of a sentence suddenly dominated the noises. "He's got money to burn." The sun, meanwhile, was muffled in the clouds back of Staten Island and the Narrows. Softened tones of sapphire and carmine touched slantingly the sides of the buildings. A view of the sea, to be caught between two of the houses, showed it to be of a pale, shimmering green. The lamps began to be lighted, and shed a strong orange radiance. In one restaurant the only occupants were a little music hall singer and a youth. She was laughing and chatting in a light hearted way not peculiar to music hall girls. The youth looked as if he desired to be at some other place. He was singularly wretched and uncomfortable. The stranger said he judged from appearances that the little music hall girl must think a great deal of that one youth. His sympathies seemed to be for the music hall girl. Finally there was a sea of salt meadow, with a black train shooting across it.

"I have made a discovery in one of these concert halls," said the stranger, as we retraced our way. "It is an old gray haired woman, who occupies proudly the position of chief pianiste. I like to go and sit and wonder by what mighty process of fighting and drinking she achieved her position. To see her, you would think she was leading an orchestra of seventy pieces, although she alone composes it. It is a great reflection to watch that gray head. At those moments I am willing to concede that I must be relatively happy, and that is a great admission from a philosopher of my attainments.

"How seriously all these men out in front of the dens take

their vocations. They regard people with a voracious air, as if they contemplated any moment making a rush and a grab and mercilessly compelling a great expenditure. This scant and feeble crowd must madden them. When I first came to the part of the town I was astonished and delighted, for it was the nearest approach to a den of wolves that I had encountered since leaving the West. Oh, no, of course the Coney Island of to-day is not the Coney Island of the ancient days. I believe you were about to impale me upon that sentence, were you not?"

[THE PHILOSOPHY OF FRANKFURTERS.]

We walked along for some time in silence until the stranger went to buy a frankfurter. As he returned, he said: "When a man is respectable he is fettered to certain wheels, and when the chariot of fashion moves, he is dragged along at the rear. For his agony, he can console himself with the law that if a certain thing has not yet been respectable, he need only wait a sufficient time and it will eventually be so. The only disadvantage is that he is obliged to wait until other people wish to do it, and he is likely to lose his own craving. Now I have a great passion for eating frankfurters on the street, and if I were respectable I would be obliged to wait until the year 3365, when man will be able to hold their positions in society only by consuming immense quantities of frankfurters on the street. And by that time I would have undoubtedly developed some new pastime. But I am not respectable. I am a philosopher. I eat frankfurters on the street with the same equanimity that you might employ toward a cigarette.

"See those three young men enjoying themselves. With what rakish, daredevil airs they smoke those cigars. Do you know, the spectacle of three modern young men enjoying themselves is something that I find vastly interesting and instructive. I see revealed more clearly the purposes of the inexorable universe which plans to amuse us occasionally to keep us from the rebellion of suicide. And I see how simply and drolly it accomplishes its end. The insertion of a mild quantity of the egotism of sin into the minds of these young men causes them to wildly enjoy themselves. It is necessary to encourage them, you see, at this early day. After all, it is only great philosophers who have the wisdom to be utterly miserable."

[THE END OF IT ALL.]

As we walked toward the station the stranger stopped often to observe types which interested him. He did it with an unconscious calm insolence as if the people were bugs. Once a bug threatened to beat him. "What 'cher lookin' at?" he asked of him. "My friend," said the stranger, "if any one displays real interest in you in this world, you should take it as an occasion for serious study and reflection. You should be supremely amazed to find that a man can be interested in anybody but himself!" The belligerent seemed quite abashed. He explained to a friend: "He ain't right! What? I dunno. Something 'bout 'study' er something! He's got wheels in his head!"

On the train the cold night wind blew transversely across the reeling cars, and in the dim light of the lamps one could see the close rows of heads swaying and jolting with the motion. From directly in front of us peanut shells fell to the floor amid a regular and interminable crackling. A stout man, who slept with his head forward upon his breast, crunched them often beneath his uneasy feet. From some unknown place a drunken voice was raised in song.

"This return of the people to their battles always has a stupendous effect upon me," said the stranger. "The gayety which arises upon these Sunday night occasions is different from all other gayeties. There is an unspeakable air of recklessness and bravado and grief about it. The train load is going toward that inevitable, overhanging, devastating Monday. That singer there tomorrow will be a truckman, perhaps, and swearing ingeniously at his horses and other truckmen. He feels the approach of this implacable Monday. Two hours ago he was ingulfed in whirligigs and beer and had forgotten that there were Mondays. Now he is confronting it, and as he can't battle it, he scorns it. You can hear the undercurrent of it in that song, which is really as grievous as the cry of a child. If he had no vanity — well, it is fortunate for the world that we are not all great thinkers."

We sat on the lower deck of the Bay Ridge boat and watched the marvelous lights of New York looming through the purple mist. The little Italian band situated up one stairway, through two doors and around three corners from us, sounded in beautiful, faint and slumberous rhythm. The breeze fluttered again in the stranger's locks. We could hear the splash of the waves against the bow. The sleepy lights looked at us with hue of red and green and orange. Overhead some dust-colored clouds scudded across the deep indigo sky. "Thunderation," said the stranger, "if I did not know of so many yesterdays and have such full knowledge of to-morrows, I should be perfectly happy at this moment, and that would create a sensation among philosophers all over the world."

STORIES TOLD/BY AN ARTIST/A TALE ABOUT HOW "GREAT GRIEF"/GOT HIS HOLIDAY DINNER./AS TO PAYMENT OF THE RENT/HOW PENNOYER DISPOSED OF HIS SUNDAY/DINNER.*

Wrinkles had been peering into the little drygoods box that acted as a cupboard. "There is only two eggs and a half of a loaf of bread left," he announced brutally.

"Heavens!" said Warwickson from where he lay smoking on the bed. He spoke in his usual dismal voice. By it he had earned his popular name of Great Grief.

Wrinkles was a thrifty soul. A sight of an almost bare cupboard maddened him. Even when he was not hungry, the ghosts of his careful ancestors caused him to rebel against it. He sat down with a virtuous air. "Well, what are we going to do?" he demanded of

* *Reprinted from New York* Press: *20 October 1894. Unsigned.*

This sketch is obviously by Crane in that Pennoyer reappears in "The Silver Pageant" (see below), first published in Crane's posthumous Last Words *(1902), and in "The Cat's March," a lost tale written in Cuba in 1898.*

The artist's model in The Third Violet *(1897) reappears in "The Cat's March" to marry Pennoyer and settle in a small town, where she is given a hard time by respectable women. Crane in Cuba had anticipated what would happen if he brought Cora Taylor over from England to settle down with him in Port Jervis, a small New York town of petty gossips who would not tolerate an artist's model nor treat kindly the former madame of an establishment in Jacksonville, Florida, the Hotel de Dream, where Crane met her in 1896. She followed him to report the Greco-Turkish War for the New York* Journal *in 1897 and lived with him as his wife in England, 1897–1900.*

The scene in "Stories Told by an Artist" is the Art Students League building. Corinson is recast from the now familiar Corwin Knapp Linson. Great Grief is Stephen Crane, lying on the bed in Linson's studio (as photographed in Linson's My Stephen Crane), *smoking his pipe, and "waiting for fame."*

This sketch and "In a Park Row Restaurant" (see below) appeared in the same issue of the New York Press. *Crane very likely wrote both in 1892–1893.*

the others. It is good to be the thrifty man in a crowd of unsuccessful artists, for then you can keep the others from starving peace-
fully. "What are we going to do?"

"Oh, shut up, Wrinkles," said Grief from the bed. "You make
me think."

Little Pennoyer, with his head bended afar down, had been
busily scratching away at a pen and ink drawing. He looked up
from his board to utter his plaintive optimism.

"The Monthly Amazement may pay me to-morrow. They ought
to. I've waited over three months now. I'm going down there to-
morrow, and perhaps I'll get it."

His friends listened to him tolerantly, but at last Wrinkles
could not omit a scornful giggle. He was such an old man, almost
28, and he had seen so many little boys be brave. "Oh, no doubt,
Penny, old man." Over on the bed, Grief croaked deep down in his
throat. Nothing was said for a long time thereafter.

The crash of the New York streets came faintly. Occasionally
one could hear the tramp of feet in the intricate corridors of this
begrimed building that squatted, slumbering and aged between
two exalted commercial structures that would have had to bend
afar down to perceive it. The light snow beat pattering into the
window corners and made vague and gray the vista of chimneys
and roofs. Often, the wind scurried swiftly and raised a long cry.

Great Grief leaned upon his elbow. "See to the fire, will you,
Wrinkles?"

Wrinkles pulled the coal box out from under the bed and
threw open the stove door preparatory to shoveling some fuel. A
red glare plunged at the first faint shadows of dusk. Little Pennoyer threw down his pen and tossed his drawing over on the
wonderful heap of stuff that hid the table. "It's too dark to work."
He lit his pipe and walked about, stretching his shoulders like a
man whose labor was valuable.

When the dusk came it saddened these youths. The solemnity
of darkness always caused them to ponder. "Light the gas, Wrinkles," said Grief.

The flood of orange light showed clearly the dull walls lined
with sketches, the tousled bed in one corner, the mass of boxes
and trunks in another, the little fierce stove and the wonderful
table. Moreover, there were some wine colored draperies flung in
some places, and on a shelf, high up, there was a plaster cast dark
with dust in the creases. A long stovepipe wandered off in the
wrong direction and then twined impulsively toward a hole in the
wall. There were some extensive cobwebs on the ceiling.

"Well, let's eat," said Grief.

Later there came a sad knock at the door. Wrinkles, arranging a tin pail on the stove, little Pennoyer busy at slicing the bread, and Great Grief, affixing the rubber tube to the gas stove, yelled: "Come in!"

The door opened and Corinson entered dejectedly. His overcoat was very new. Wrinkles flashed an envious glance at it, but almost immediately he cried: "Hello, Corrie, old boy!"

Corinson sat down and felt around among the pipes until he found a good one. Great Grief had fixed the coffee to boil on the gas stove, but he had to watch it closely, for the rubber tube was short, and a chair was balanced on a trunk and then the gas stove was balanced on the chair. Coffee making was a feat.

"Well," said Grief, with his back turned, "how goes it, Corrie? How's Art, hey?" He fastened a terrible emphasis upon the word.

"Crayon portraits," said Corinson.

"What?" They turned toward him with one movement, as if from a lever connection. Little Pennoyer dropped his knife.

"Crayon portraits," repeated Corinson. He smoked away in profound cynicism. "Fifteen dollars a week, or more, this time of year, you know." He smiled at them calmly like a man of courage.

Little Pennoyer picked up his knife again. "Well, I'll be blowed," said Wrinkles. Feeling it incumbent upon him to think, he dropped into a chair and began to play serenades on his guitar and watch to see when the water for the eggs would boil. It was a habitual pose.

Great Grief, however, seemed to observe something bitter in the affair. "When did you discover that you couldn't draw?" he said, stiffly.

"I haven't discovered it yet," replied Corinson, with a serene air. "I merely discovered that I would rather eat."

"Oh!" said Grief.

"Hand me the eggs, Grief," said Wrinkles. "The water's boiling."

Little Pennoyer burst into the conversation. "We'd ask you to dinner, Corrie, but there's only three of us and there's two eggs. I dropped a piece of bread on the floor, too. I'm shy one."

"That's all right, Penny," said the other, "don't trouble yourself. You artists should never be hospitable. I'm going, anyway. I've got to make a call. Well, good night, boys, I've got to make a call. Drop in and see me."

When the door closed upon him, Grief said: "The coffee's done. I hate that fellow. That overcoat cost $30, if it cost a red cent. His egotism is so tranquil. It isn't like yours, Wrinkles. He — "

The door opened again and Corinson thrust in his head. "Say, you fellows, you know it's Thanksgiving to-morrow."

"Well, what of it?" demanded Grief.

Little Pennoyer said: "Yes, I know it is, Corrie. I thought of it this morning."

"Well, come out and have a table d'hote with me to-morrow night. I'll blow you off in good style."

While Wrinkles played an exuberant air on his guitar, little Pennoyer did part of a ballet. They cried ecstatically: "Will we? Well, I guess yes!"

When they were alone again Grief said: "I'm not going, anyhow. I hate that fellow."

"Oh, fiddle," said Wrinkles. "You're an infernal crank. And, besides, where's your dinner coming from to-morrow night if you don't go? Tell me that."

Little Pennoyer said: "Yes, that's so, Grief. Where's your dinner coming from if you don't go?"

Grief said: "Well, I hate him, anyhow."

[THE RENT.]

Little Pennoyer's four dollars could not last forever. When he received it he and Wrinkles and Great Grief went to a table d'hote. Afterward little Pennoyer discovered that only two dollars and a half remained. A small magazine away down town had accepted one out of the six drawings that he had taken them, and later had given him four dollars for it. Penny was so disheartened when he saw that his money was not going to last forever that, even with two dollars and a half in his pockets, he felt much worse than he had when he was penniless, for at that time he anticipated twenty-four. Wrinkles lectured upon 'Finance.'

Great Grief said nothing, for it was established that when he received $6 checks from comic weeklies he dreamed of renting studios at $75 per month, and was likely to go out and buy five dollars' worth of second hand curtains and plaster casts.

When he had money Penny always hated the cluttered den in the old building. He desired then to go out and breathe boastfully like a man. But he obeyed Wrinkles, the elder and the wise, and if you had visited that room about 10 o'clock of a morning or about 7 of an evening you would have thought that rye bread, frankfurters and potato salad from Second avenue were the only foods in the world.

Purple Sanderson lived there, too, but then he really ate. He had learned parts of the gasfitter's trade before he came to be such a great artist, and when his opinions disagreed with that of every art manager in New York he went to see a plumber, a friend of his, for whose opinion he had a great deal of respect. In consequence he frequented a very neat restaurant on Twenty-third street and sometimes on Saturday nights he openly scorned his companions.

Purple was a good fellow, Grief said, but one of his singularly bad traits was that he always remembered everything. One night, not long after little Pennoyer's great discovery Purple came in and as he was neatly hanging up his coat, said: "Well, the rent will be due in four days."

"Will it?" demanded Penny, astounded. Penny was always astounded when the rent came due. It seemed to him the most extraordinary occurrence.

"Certainly it will," said Purple with the irritated air of a superior financial man.

"My soul!" said Wrinkles.

Great Grief lay on the bed smoking a pipe and waiting for fame. "Oh, go home, Purple. You resent something. It wasn't me — it was the calendar."

"Try and be serious a moment, Grief."

"You're a fool, Purple."

Penny spoke from where he was at work. "Well, if those Amazement people pay me when they said they would I'll have money then."

"So you will, dear," said Grief, satirically. "You'll have money to burn. Did the Amazement people ever pay you when they said they would? You're wonderfully important all of a sudden, it seems to me. You talk like an artist."

Wrinkles, too, smiled at little Pennoyer. "The Established Magazine people wanted Penny to hire models and make a try for them, too. It will only cost him a big blue chip. By the time he has invested all the money he hasn't got and the rent is two weeks overdue he will be able to tell the landlord to wait seven months until the Monday morning after the day of publication. Go ahead, Penny."

It was the habit to make game of little Pennoyer. He was always having gorgeous opportunities, with no opportunity to take advantage of his opportunities.

Penny smiled at them, his tiny, tiny smile of courage.

"You're a confident little cuss," observed Grief, irrelevantly.

"Well, the world has no objection to your being confident, also, Grief," said Purple.

"Hasn't it?" said Grief. "Well, I want to know!"

Wrinkles could not be light spirited long. He was obliged to despair when occasion offered. At last he sank down in a chair and seized his guitar. "Well, what's to be done?" he said. He began to play mournfully.

"Throw Purple out," mumbled Grief from the bed.

"Are you fairly certain that you will have money then, Penny?" asked Purple.

Little Pennoyer looked apprehensive. "Well, I don't know," he said.

And then began that memorable discussion, great in four minds. The tobacco was of the "Long John" brand. It smelled like burning mummies.

[A DINNER ON SUNDAY EVENING.]

Once Purple Sanderson went to his home in St. Lawrence county to enjoy some country air, and, incidentally, to explain his life failure to his people. Previously, Great Grief had given him odds that he would return sooner than he then planned, and everybody said that Grief had a good bet. It is not a glorious pastime, this explaining of life failures.

Later, Great Grief and Wrinkles went to Haverstraw to visit Grief's cousin and sketch. Little Pennoyer was disheartened for it is bad to be imprisoned in brick and dust and cobbles when your ear can hear in the distance the harmony of the summer sunlight upon leaf and blade of green. Besides, he did not hear Wrinkles and Grief discoursing and quarreling in the den and Purple coming in a 6 o'clock with contempt.

On Friday afternoon he discovered that he only had fifty cents to last until Saturday morning, when he was to get his check from the Gamin. He was an artful little man by this time, however, and it is as true as the sky that when he walked toward the Gamin office on Saturday he had twenty cents remaining.

The cashier nodded his regrets. "Very sorry, Mr. — er — Pennoyer, but our pay day, you know, is on Monday. Come around any time after 10."

"Oh, it don't matter," said Penny. As he walked along on his return he reflected deeply how he could invest his twenty cents in food to last until Monday morning any time after 10. He bought two coffee cakes in a Third avenue bakery. They were very beautiful. Each had a hole in the center and a handsome scallop all around the edges.

Penny took great care of those cakes. At odd times he would rise from his work and go to see that no escape had been made. On Sunday he got up at noon and compressed breakfast and noon into one meal. Afterward he had almost three-quarters of a cake still left to him. He congratulated himself that with strategy he could make it endure until Monday morning, any time after 10.

At 3 in the afternoon there came a faint-hearted knock. "Come in," said Penny. The door opened and old Tim Connegan, who was trying to be a model, looked in apprehensively. "I beg pardon, sir," he said, at once.

"Come in, Tim, you old thief," said Penny. Tim entered, slowly and bashfully. "Sit down," said Penny. Tim sat down and began to rub his knees, for rheumatism had a mighty hold upon him.

Penny lit his pipe and crossed his legs. "Well, how goes it?"

Tim moved his square jaw upward and flashed Penny a little glance.

"Bad?" said Penny.

The old man raised his hand impressively. "I've been to every studio in the hull city and I never see such absences in my life. What with the seashore and the mountains, and this and that resort, I think all the models will be starved by fall. I found one man in up on Fifty-seventh street. He ses to me: 'Come around Tuesday — I may want yez and I may not.' That was last week. You know, I live down on the Bowery, Mr. Pennoyer, and when I got up there on Tuesday, he ses: 'Confound you, are you here again?' ses he. I went and sat down in the park, for I was too tired for the walk back. And there you are, Mr. Pennoyer. What with tramping around to look for men that are a thousand miles away, I'm near dead."

"It's hard," said Penny.

"It is, sir. I hope they'll come back soon. The summer is the death of us all, sir, it is. Sure, I never know where my next meal is coming until I get it. That's true."

"Had anything to-day?"

"Yes, sir — a little."

"How much?"

"Well, sir, a lady give me a cup of coffee this morning. It was good, too, I'm telling you."

Penny went to his cupboard. When he returned, he said: "Here's some cake.

Tim thrust forward his hands, palms erect. "Oh, now, Mr. Pennoyer, I couldn't. You — "

"Go ahead. What's the odds?"

"Oh, now — "

"Go ahead, you old bat."

Penny smoked.

When Tim was going out, he turned to grow eloquent again.

"Well, I can't tell you how much I'm obliged to you, Mr. Pennoyer.
You — "

"Don't mention it, old man."

Penny smoked.

IN A PARK ROW/RESTAURANT./THE NEVADAN SHERIFF WENT THERE/FOR EXCITEMENT./LIKE A BATTLE OF BAD MEN/HE SUGGESTS THAT RE-PEATING RIFLES/MIGHT TAKE THE PLACE OF SPOONS.*

"Whenever I come into a place of this sort, I am reminded of the
battle of Gettysburg," remarked the stranger. To make me hear
him he had to raise his voice considerably, for we were seated in
one of the Park Row restaurants during the noon hour rush. "I
think that if a squadron of Napoleon's dragoons charged into this
place they would be trampled under foot before they could get a
biscuit. They were great soldiers, no doubt, but they would at once
perceive that there were many things about sweep and dash and
fire of war of which they were totally ignorant.

"I come in here for the excitement. You know, when I was
Sheriff, long ago, of one of the gayest counties of Nevada, I lived
a life that was full of thrills, for the citizens could not quite comprehend the uses of a sheriff, and did not like to see him busy himself in other people's affairs continually. One man originated a
popular philosophy, in which he asserted that if a man required

* Reprinted from New York Press: 28 October 1894.

Crane wrote the first draft in his "Pocket Notebook,"
probably in 1892–1893. This restaurant, called "The Boeuf-
à-la-mode," was on Sixth Avenue, and Crane, Corwin Knapp
Linson, and the "Indians" of the Art Students League re-
christened it "The Buffalo Mud." They gathered there on
Saturday evenings. "It was a place to wallow in," says Linson
in My Stephen Crane (1958). "Scandalously cheap," it possessed "the allurement of the unexpected."

Crane also describes the restaurant in The Third Violet
(1897), Chapter XXVII being a variant on the opening paragraph of the section headed in the Press: "Like Distracted Water
Bugs." He describes Park Row in his Greco-Turkish War novel
Active Service (1899).

pastime, it was really better to shoot the sheriff than any other person, for then it would be quite impossible for the sheriff to organize a posse and pursue the assassin. The period which followed the promulgation of this theory gave me habits which I fear I can never outwear. I require fever and exhilaration in life, and when I come in here it carries me back to the old days."

I was obliged to put my head far forward, or I could never have heard the stranger's remarks. Crowds of men were swarming in from streets and invading the comfort of seated men in order that they might hang their hats and overcoats upon the long rows of hooks that lined the sides of the room. The finding of vacant chairs became a serious business. Men dashed to and fro in swift searches. Some of those already seated were eating with terrible speed, or else casting impatient or tempestuous glances at the waiters.

[LIKE DISTRACTED WATER BUGS.]

Meanwhile the waiters dashed about the room as if a monster pursued them, and they sought escape wildly through the walls. It was like the scattering and scampering of a lot of water bugs, when one splashes the surface of the brook with a pebble. Withal, they carried incredible masses of dishes and threaded their swift ways with rare skill. Perspiration stood upon their foreheads, and their breaths came strainedly. They served customers with such speed and violence that it often resembled a personal assault. The crumbs from the previous diner were swept off with one fierce motion of a napkin. A waiter struck two blows at the table and left there a knife and a fork. And then came the viands in a volley, thumped down in haste, causing men to look sharp to see if their trousers were safe.

There was in the air an endless clatter of dishes, loud and bewilderingly rapid, like the gallop of a thousand horses. From afar back, at the places of communication to the kitchen, there came the sound of a continual roaring altercation, hoarse and vehement, like the cries of the officers of a regiment under attack. A mist of steam fluttered where the waiters crowded and jostled about the huge copper coffee urns. Over in one corner a man who toiled there like a foundryman was continually assailed by sharp cries. "Brown th' wheat!" An endless string of men were already filing past the cashier, and, even in those moments, this latter was a marvel of self possession and deftness. As the spring doors clashed to and fro, one heard the interminable thunder of the street, and through the window, partially obscured by displayed vegetables and roasts and pies, could be seen the great avenue, a picture in gray tones, save where a bit of green park gleamed, the foreground occupied by this great typical turmoil of car and cab, truck and mail van, wedging their way through an opposing army of the same kind and surrounded on all sides by the mobs of hurrying people.

[THE HABIT OF GREAT SPEED.]

"A man might come in here with a very creditable stomach and lose his head and get indigestion," resumed the stranger, thoughtfully. "It is astonishing how fast a man can eat when he tries. This air is surcharged with appetites. I have seen very orderly, slow moving men become possessed with the spirit of this rush, lose control of themselves and all at once begin to dine like madmen. It is impossible not to feel the effect of this impetuous atmosphere.

"When consommé grows popular in these places all breweries will have to begin turning out soups. I am reminded of the introduction of canned soup into my town in the West. When the boys found that they could not get full on it they wanted to lynch the proprietor of the supply store for selling an inferior article, but a drummer who happened to be in town explained to them that it was a temperance drink.

"It is plain that if the waiters here could only be put upon a raised platform and provided with repeating rifles that would shoot corn muffins, butter cakes, Irish stews or any delicacy of the season, the strain of this strife would be greatly lessened. As long as the waiters were competent marksmen the meals here would be conducted with great expedition. The only difficulty would be when, for instance, a waiter made an error and gave an Irish stew to the wrong man. The latter would have considerable difficulty in passing it along to the right one. Of course the system would cause awkward blunders for a time. You can imagine an important gentleman in a white waistcoat getting up to procure the bill of fare from an adjacent table and by chance intercepting a Hamburger steak bound for a man down by the door. The man down by the door would refuse to pay for a steak that had never come into his possession.

[TO SAVE TIME.]

"In some such manner thousands of people could be accommodated in restaurants that at present during the noon hour can feed only a few hundred. Of course eloquent pickets would have to be stationed in the distance to intercept any unsuspecting gentleman from the West who might consider the gunnery of the waiters in a personal way and resent what would look to them like an assault. I remember that my old friend Jim Wilkinson, the ex-sheriff of Tin Can, Nevada, got very drunk one night and wandered into the business end of the bowling alley there. Of course he thought that they were shooting at him, and in reply he killed three of the best bowlers in Tin Can."

THE SILVER PAGEANT.*

"It's rotten," said Grief.

"Oh, it's fair, old man. Still, I would not call it a great contribution to American art," said Wrinkles.

"You've got a good thing, Gaunt, if you go at it right," said little Pennoyer.

These were all volunteer orations. The boys had come in one by one and spoken their opinions. Gaunt listened to them no more than if they had been so many match-peddlers. He never heard anything close at hand, and he never saw anything excepting that which transpired across a mystic wide sea. The shadow of his thoughts was in his eyes, a little grey mist, and, when what you said to him had passed out of your mind, he asked: "Wha — a — at?" It was understood that Gaunt was very good to tolerate the presence of the universe, which was noisy and interested in itself. All the younger men, moved by an instinct of faith, declared that he would one day be a great artist if he would only move faster than a pyramid. In the meantime he did not hear their voices. Occasionally when he saw a man take vivid pleasure in life, he faintly evinced an admiration. It seemed to strike him as a feat. As for him, he was watching that silver pageant across a sea.

When he came from Paris to New York somebody told him that he must make his living. He went to see some book publishers, and talked to them in his manner — as if he had just been stunned. At last one of them gave him drawings to do, and it did not surprise him. It was merely as if rain had come down.

_____

* *Reprinted from* Last Words (*London*, 1902).

Here appear the same characters as in "Stories Told by an Artist" (see above): Great Grief (Crane), Wrinkles, and Pennoyer. Corwin Knapp Linson is here the artist Gaunt who has been to Paris. Linson had been in Europe in 1888 to study art, but he was not gaunt. A portion of The Third Violet (1897) *recasts life in the Art Students League building as first sketched in this piece and in "Stories Told by an Artist."*

Great Grief went to see him in his studio, and returned to the den to say: "Gaunt is working in his sleep. Somebody ought to set fire to him."

It was then that the others went over and smoked, and gave their opinions of a drawing. Wrinkles said: "Are you really looking at it, Gaunt? I don't think you've seen it yet, Gaunt?"

"What?"

"Why don't you look at it?"

When Wrinkles departed, the model, who was resting at that time, followed him into the hall and waved his arms in rage. "That feller's crazy. Yeh ought t' see — " and he recited lists of all the wrongs that can come to models.

It was a superstitious little band over in the den. They talked often of Gaunt. "He's got pictures in his eyes," said Wrinkles. They had expected genius to blindly stumble at the perface[1] and ceremonies of the world, and each new flounder by Gaunt made a stir in the den. It awed them, and they waited.

At last one morning Gaunt burst into the room. They were all as dead men.

"I'm going to paint a picture." The mist in his eyes was pierced by a Coverian gleam. His gestures were wild and extravagant. Grief stretched out smoking on the bed, Wrinkles and little Pennoyer working at their drawing-boards tilted against the table — were suddenly frozen. If bronze statues had come and danced heavily before them, they could not have been thrilled further.

Gaunt tried to tell them of something, but it became knotted in his throat, and then suddenly he dashed out again.

Later they went earnestly over to Gaunt's studio. Perhaps he would tell them of what he saw across the sea.

He lay dead upon the floor. There was a little grey mist before his eyes.

When they finally arrived home that night they took a long time to undress for bed, and then came the moment when they waited for some one to put out the gas. Grief said at last, with the air of a man whose brain is desperately driven: "I wonder — I — what do you suppose he was going to paint?"

Wrinkles reached and turned out the gas, and from the sudden profound darkness, he said: "There is a mistake. He couldn't have had pictures in his eyes."

1. As given in the text of *Last Words* for the perhaps intended word "preface."

HOWELLS FEARS REALISTS MUST WAIT/AN IN-
TERESTING TALK WITH/WILLIAM DEAN HOW-
ELLS/THE EMINENT NOVELIST STILL HOLDS A
FIRM/FAITH IN REALISM, BUT CONFESSES A
DOUBT IF ITS DAY/HAS YET COME—HE HAS OB-
SERVED A CHANGE IN THE/LITERARY PULSE OF
THE COUNTRY WITHIN THE LAST FEW/MONTHS
—A REACTIONARY WAVE.*

William Dean Howells leaned his cheek upon the two outstretched
fingers of his right hand and gazed thoughtfully at the window —
the panes black from the night without, although studded once or
twice with little electric stars far up on the west side of the Park.
He was looking at something which his memory had just brought
to him.

"I have a little scheme," he at last said, slowly. "I saw a young
girl out in a little Ohio town once — she was the daughter of the
carpetwoman there — that is to say, her mother made ragcarpets
and rugs for the villagers. And this girl had the most wonderful
instinct in manner and dress. Her people were of the lowest of the
low in a way and yet this girl was a lady. It used to completely
amaze me — to think how this girl could grow there in that squalor.
She was as chic as chic could be, and yet the money spent and the
education was nothing — nothing at all. Where she procured her
fine taste you could not imagine. It was deeply interesting to me —
it overturned so many of my rooted social dogmas. It was the impossible, appearing suddenly. And then there was another in Cam-
bridge — a wonderful type. I have come upon them occasionally

---

* Published in New York Times: 28 October 1894. Reprinted
in R. W. Stallman, ed., Stephen Crane: An Omnibus (1952),
the article was first made known by George Arms and William
M. Gibson in Americana: April 1943. This is an addition to the
Crane canon.

Crane had first reported on Howells in 1891 when Crane
was on the Jersey Coast. Maggie (London, 1896) presents
"An Appreciation" by Howells (see below), which Heinemann,
Crane's London publisher, reprinted in Bowery Tales (1900).

here and there. I intend to write something of the kind if I can. I have thought of a good title, too, I think — a name of a flower — 'The Ragged Lady.'"

"I suppose this is a long way off," said the other man reflectively. "I am anxious to hear what you say in 'The Story of a Play.' Do you raise your voice toward reforming the abuses that are popularly supposed to hide in the manager's office for use upon the struggling artistic playwright and others? Do you recite the manager's divine misapprehension of art?"

"No, I do not," said Mr. Howells.

"Why?" said the other man.

"Well, in the first place, the manager is a man of business. He preserves himself. I suppose he judges not against art, but between art and act. He looks at art through the crowds."

"I don't like reformatory novels anyhow," said the other man.

"And in the second place," continued Mr. Howells, "it does no good to go at things hammer and tongs in this obvious way. I believe that every novel should have an intention. A man should mean something when he writes. Ah, this writing merely to amuse people — why, it seems to me altogether vulgar. A man may as well blacken his face and go out and dance on the street for pennies. The author is a sort of trained bear, if you accept certain standards. If literary men are to be the public fools, let us at any rate have it clearly understood, so that those of us who feel differently can take measures. But, on the other hand, a novel should never preach and berate and storm. It does no good. As a matter of fact, a book of that kind is ineffably tiresome. People don't like to have their lives half cudgeled out in that manner, especially in these days, when a man, likely enough, only reaches for a book when he wishes to be fanned, so to speak, after the heat of the daily struggle. When a writer desires to preach in an obvious way he should announce his intention — let him cry out then that he is in the pulpit. But it is the business of the novel — "

"Ah!" said the other man.

"It is the business of the novel to picture the daily life in the most exact terms possible, with an absolute and clear sense of proportion. That is the important matter — the proportion. As a usual thing, I think, people have absolutely no sense of proportion. Their noses are tight against life, you see. They perceive mountains where there are no mountains, but frequently a great peak appears no larger than a rat trap. An artist sees a dog down the street — well, his eye instantly relates the dog to its surroundings. The dog is proportioned to the buildings and the trees. Whereas, many people can conceive of that dog's tail resting upon a hill top."

"You have often said that the novel is a perspective," observed the other man.

"A perspective, certainly. It is a perspective made for the benefit of people who have no true use of their eyes. The novel, in its real meaning, adjusts the proportions. It preserves the balances. It is in this way that lessons are to be taught and reforms to be won. When people are introduced to each other they will see the resemblances, and won't want to fight so badly."

"I suppose that when a man tries to write 'what the people want' — when he tries to reflect the popular desire, it is a bad quarter of an hour for the laws of proportion."

"Do you recall any of the hosts of stories that began in love and ended a little further on? Those stories used to represent life to the people, and I believe they do now to a large class. Life began when the hero saw a certain girl, and it ended abruptly when he married her. Love and courtship was not an incident, a part of life — it was the whole of it. All else was of no value. Men of that religion must have felt very stupid when they were engaged at anything but courtship. Do you see the false proportion? Do you see the dog with his tail upon the hilltop? Somebody touched the universal heart with the fascinating theme — the relation of man to maid — and, for many years, it was as if no other relation could be recognized in fiction. Here and there an author raised his voice, but not loudly. I like to see the novelists treating some of the other important things of life — the relation of mother and son, of husband and wife, in fact all those things that we live in continually. The other can be but fragmentary."

"I suppose there must be two or three new literary people just back of the horizon somewhere," said the other man. "Books upon these lines that you speak of are what might be called unpopular. Do you think them to be a profitable investment?"

"From my point of view it is the right — it is sure to be a profitable investment. After that it is a question of perseverance, courage. A writer of skill cannot be defeated because he remains true to his conscience. It is a long, serious conflict sometimes, but he must win, if he does not falter. Lowell said to me one time: 'After all, the barriers are very thin. They are paper. If a man has his conscience and one or two friends who can help him, it becomes very simple at last.'"

"Mr. Howells," said the other man, suddenly, "have you observed a change in the literary pulse of the country within the last four months? Last Winter, for instance, it seemed that realism was about to capture things, but then recently I have thought that I saw coming a sort of counter wave, a flood of the other — a reaction, in fact. Trivial, temporary, perhaps, but a reaction, certainly."

Mr. Howells dropped his hand in a gesture of emphatic assent. "What you say is true. I have seen it coming. . . . I suppose we shall have to wait."

THE MEN IN THE STORM *

At about three o'clock of the February afternoon, the blizzard began to swirl great clouds of snow along the streets, sweeping it down from the roofs and up from the pavements until the faces of pedestrians tingled and burned as from a thousand needle-prickings. Those on the walks huddled their necks closely in the collars of their coats and went along stooping like a race of aged people. The drivers of vehicles hurried their horses furiously on their way. They were made more cruel by the exposure of their positions, aloft on high seats. The street cars, bound up-town, went slowly, the horses slipping and straining in the spongy brown mass that lay between the rails. The drivers, muffled to the eyes, stood erect and facing the wind, models of grim philosophy. Overhead the trains rumbled and roared, and the dark structure of the elevated railroad, stretching over the avenue, dripped little streams and drops of water upon the mud and snow beneath it.

All the clatter of the street was softened by the masses that lay upon the cobbles until, even to one who looked from a window, it became important music, a melody of life made necessary to the ear by the dreariness of the pitiless beat and sweep of the storm. Occasionally one could see black figures of men busily shovelling the white drifts from the walks. The sounds from their labor created new recollections of rural experiences which every man manages to have in a measure. Later, the immense windows of the shops became aglow with light, throwing great beams of orange and yellow upon the pavement. They were infinitely cheerful, yet in a way they accented the force and discomfort of the storm, and gave a meaning to the pace of the people and the vehicles, scores of

---

* Published in The Arena: October 1894. Elbert Hubbard reprinted the sketch in The Philistine in 1897; the Commercial Advertiser: 11 January 1898, remarked that Crane's sketch is "one of the most powerful pictures he has ever drawn of the tragedies of life among the poor of New York."

pedestrians and drivers, wretched with cold faces, necks and feet, speeding for scores of unknown doors and entrances, scattering to an infinite variety of shelters, to places which the imagination made warm with the familiar colors of home.

There was an absolute expression of hot dinners in the pace of the people. If one dared to speculate upon the destination of those who came trooping, he lost himself in a maze of social calculations; he might fling a handful of sand and attempt to follow the flight of each particular grain. But as to the suggestion of hot dinners, he was in firm lines of thought, for it was upon every hurrying face. It is a matter of tradition; it is from the tales of childhood. It comes forth with every storm.

However, in a certain part of a dark West-side street, there was a collection of men to whom these things were as if they were not. In this street was located a charitable house where for five cents the homeless of the city could get a bed at night and, in the morning, coffee and bread.

During the afternoon of the storm, the whirling snows acted as drivers, as men with whips, and at half-past three, the walk before the closed doors of the house was covered with wanderers of the street, waiting. For some distance on either side of the place they could be seen lurking in doorways and behind projecting parts of buildings, gathering in close bunches in an effort to get warm. A covered wagon drawn up near the curb sheltered a dozen of them. Under the stairs that led to the elevated railway station, there were six or eight, their hands stuffed deep in their pockets, their shoulders stooped, jiggling their feet. Others always could be seen coming, a strange procession, some slouching along with the characteristic hopeless gait of professional strays, some coming with hesitating steps wearing the air of men to whom this sort of thing was new.

It was an afternoon of incredible length. The snow, blowing in twisting clouds, sought out the men in their meagre hiding-places and skilfully beat in among them, drenching their persons with showers of fine, stinging flakes. They crowded together, muttering, and fumbling in their pockets to get their red, inflamed wrists covered by the cloth.

Newcomers usually halted at one of the groups and addressed a question, perhaps much as a matter of form, "Is it open yet?"

Those who had been waiting inclined to take the questioner seriously and become contemptuous. "No; do yeh think we'd be standin' here?"

The gathering swelled in numbers steadily and persistently. One could always see them coming, trudging slowly through the storm.

Finally, the little snow plains in the street began to assume a leaden hue from the shadows of evening. The buildings upreared gloomily save where various windows became brilliant figures of light that made shimmers and splashes of yellow on the snow. A street lamp on the curb struggled to illuminate, but it was reduced to impotent blindness by the swift gusts of sleet crusting its panes.

In this half-darkness, the men began to come from their shelter places and mass in front of the doors of charity. They were of all types, but the nationalities were mostly American, German and Irish. Many were strong, healthy, clear-skinned fellows with that stamp of countenance which is not frequently seen upon seekers after charity. There were men of undoubted patience, industry and temperance, who in time of ill-fortune, do not habitually turn to rail at the state of society, snarling at the arrogance of the rich and bemoaning the cowardice of the poor, but who at these times are apt to wear a sudden and singular meekness, as if they saw the world's progress marching from them and were trying to perceive where they had failed, what they had lacked, to be thus vanquished in the race. Then there were others of the shifting, Bowery lodging-house element who were used to paying ten cents for a place to sleep, but who now came here because it was cheaper.

But they were all mixed in one mass so thoroughly that one could not have discerned the different elements but for the fact that the laboring men, for the most part, remained silent and impassive in the blizzard, their eyes fixed on the windows of the house, statues of patience.

The sidewalk soon became completely blocked by the bodies of the men. They pressed close to one another like sheep in a winter's gale, keeping one another warm by the heat of their bodies. The snow came down upon this compressed group of men until, directly from above, it might have appeared like a heap of snow-covered merchandise, if it were not for the fact that the crowd swayed gently with a unanimous, rhythmical motion. It was wonderful to see how the snow lay upon the heads and shoulders of these men, in little ridges an inch thick perhaps in places, the flakes steadily adding drop and drop, precisely as they fall upon the unresisting grass of the fields. The feet of the men were all wet and cold and the wish to warm them accounted for the slow, gentle, rhythmical motion. Occasionally some man whose ears or nose tingled acutely from the cold winds would wriggle down until his head was protected by the shoulders of his companions.

There was a continuous murmuring discussion as to the probability of the doors being speedily opened. They persistently lifted their eyes toward the windows. One could hear little combats of opinion.

"There's a light in th' winder!"

"Naw; it's a reflection f'm across th' way."

"Well, didn't I see 'em lite it?"

"You did?"

"I did!"

"Well, then, that settles it!"

As the time approached when they expected to be allowed to enter, the men crowded to the doors in an unspeakable crush, jamming and wedging in a way that it seemed would crack bones. They surged heavily against the building in a powerful wave of pushing shoulders. Once a rumor flitted among all the tossing heads.

"They can't open th' doors! Th' fellers er smack up ag'in 'em."

Then a dull roar of rage came from the men on the outskirts; but all the time they strained and pushed until it appeared to be impossible for those that they cried out against to do anything but be crushed to pulp.

"Ah, git away f'm th' door!"

"Git outa that!"

"Throw 'em out!"

"Kill 'em!"

"Say, fellers, now, what th' 'ell? Give 'em a chanct t' open th' door!"

"Yeh damned pigs, give 'em a chanct t' open th' door!"

Men in the outskirts of the crowd occasionally yelled when a boot-heel of one of frantic trampling feet crushed on their freezing extremities.

"Git off me feet, yeh clumsy tarrier!"

"Say, don't stand on me feet! Walk on th' ground!"

A man near the doors suddenly shouted: "O-o-oh! Le' me out — le' me out!" And another, a man of infinite valor, once twisted his head so as to half face those who were pushing behind him. "Quit yer shovin', yeh" — and he delivered a volley of the most powerful and singular invective straight into the faces of the men behind him. It was as if he was hammering the noses of them with curses of triple brass. His face, red with rage, could be seen; upon it, an expression of sublime disregard of consequences. But nobody cared to reply to his imprecations; it was too cold. Many of them snickered and all continued to push.

In occasional pauses of the crowd's movement the men had opportunity to make jokes; usually grim things, and no doubt very uncouth. Nevertheless, they are notable — one does not expect to find the quality of humor in a heap of old clothes under a snow-drift.

The winds seemed to grow fiercer as time wore on. Some of the gusts of snow that came down on the close collection of heads cut like knives and needles, and the men huddled, and swore, not like dark assassins, but in a sort of an American fashion, grimly and desperately, it is true, but yet with a wondrous under-effect, indefinable and mystic, as if there was some kind of humor in this catastrophe, in this situation in a night of snow-laden winds.

Once, the window of the huge dry-goods shop across the street furnished material for a few moments of forgetfulness. In the brilliantly-lighted space appeared the figure of a man. He was rather stout and very well clothed. His whiskers were fashioned charmingly after those of the Prince of Wales. He stood in an attitude of magnificent reflection. He slowly stroked his moustache with a certain grandeur of manner, and looked down at the snow-encrusted mob. From below, there was denoted a supreme complacence in him. It seemed that the sight operated inversely, and enabled him to more clearly regard his own environment, delightful relatively.

One of the mob chanced to turn his head and perceive the figure in the window. "Hello, lookit 'is whiskers," he said genially.

Many of the men turned then, and a shout went up. They called to him in all strange keys. They addressed him in every manner, from familiar and cordial greetings to carefully-worded advice concerning changes in his personal appearance. The man presently fled, and the mob chuckled ferociously like ogres who had just devoured something.

They turned then to serious business. Often they addressed the stolid front of the house.

"Oh, let us in fer Gawd's sake!"

"Let us in or we'll all drop dead!"

"Say, what's th' use o' keepin' all us poor Indians out in th' cold?"

And always some one was saying, "Keep off me feet."

The crushing of the crowd grew terrific toward the last. The men, in keen pain from the blasts, began almost to fight. With the pitiless whirl of snow upon them, the battle for shelter was going to the strong. It became known that the basement door at the foot of a little steep flight of stairs was the one to be opened, and they jostled and heaved in this direction like laboring fiends. One could hear them panting and groaning in their fierce exertion.

Usually some one in the front ranks was protesting to those in the rear: "O — o — ow! Oh, say, now, fellers, let up, will yeh? Do yeh wanta kill somebody?"

A policeman arrived and went into the midst of them, scolding and berating, occasionally threatening, but using no force but that of his hands and shoulders against these men who were only struggling to get in out of the storm. His decisive tones rang out sharply: "Stop that pushin' back there! Come, boys, don't push! Stop that! Here, you, quit yer shovin'! Cheese that!"

When the door below was opened, a thick stream of men forced a way down the stairs, which were of an extraordinary narrowness and seemed only wide enough for one at a time. Yet they somehow went down almost three abreast. It was a difficult and painful operation. The crowd was like a turbulent water forcing itself through one tiny outlet. The men in the rear, excited by the success of the others, made frantic exertions, for its seemed that this large band would more than fill the quarters and that many would be left upon the pavements. It would be disastrous to be of the last, and accordingly men with the snow biting their faces, writhed and twisted with their might. One expected that from the tremendous pressure, the narrow passage to the basement door would be so choked and clogged with human limbs and bodies that movement would be impossible. Once indeed the crowd was forced to stop, and a cry went along that a man had been injured at the foot of the stairs. But presently the slow movement began again, and the policeman fought at the top of the flight to ease the pressure on those who were going down.

A reddish light from a window fell upon the faces of the men when they, in turn, arrived at the last three steps and were about to enter. One could then note a change of expression that had come over their features. As they thus stood upon the threshold of their hopes, they looked suddenly content and complacent. The fire had passed from their eyes and the snarl had vanished from their lips. The very force of the crowd in the rear, which had previously vexed them, was regarded from another point of view, for it now made it inevitable that they should go through the little doors into the place that was cheery and warm with light.

The tossing crowd on the sidewalk grew smaller and smaller. The snow beat with merciless persistence upon the bowed heads of those who waited. The wind drove it up from the pavements in frantic forms of winding white, and it seethed in circles about the huddled forms, passing in, one by one, three by three, out of the storm.

WHEN EVERY ONE IS PANIC STRICKEN/A REALISTIC PEN PICTURE OF A FIRE/IN A TENEMENT./ THE PHILOSOPHY OF WOMEN/FRIGHT AND FLIGHT—THE MISSING BABY/—A COMMONPLACE HERO.*

[FIRE!]

We were walking on one of the shadowy side streets, west of Sixth avenue. The midnight silence and darkness was upon it save where at the point of intersection with the great avenue, there was a broad span of yellow light. From there came the steady monotonous jingle of streetcar bells and the weary clatter of hoofs on the cobbles. While the houses in this street turned black and mystically silent with the night, the avenue continued its eternal movement and life, a great vein that never slept nor paused. The gorgeous orange-hued lamps of a saloon flared plainly, and the figures of some

---

* Reprinted from New York Press: 25 November 1894.
  This Greenwich Village fire never occurred. Crane's signed report was a hoax on the New York Press.

  The facts are: there was no fire at all, no baby, no hysterical mother, no brave policeman, no nothing, except Crane's magnificent and, in this instance, impish imagination, and the great William Dean Howells was so taken in that he pronounced Crane's article "a piece of realistic reporting." It is fiction, not reporting. Anyone who consults the New York newspapers around the date 25 November 1894 "will find nothing at all about any fire having taken place, much less anything about any policeman rescuing a child from a burning building." (John S. Mayfield, American Book Collector: January 1957.)

  The Sunday Editor of the New York Press, Edward Marshall, expressed himself years later about Crane's tenement house fire report: "one of the best things that he or any other man ever did." And so it is, although it is pure fiction. Crane had duped the man who had hired him. But Crane redeemed himself during the Spanish-American War when he filed the dispatch of Marshall for a rival newspaper, when Marshall had been shot through the spine.

loungers could be seen as they stood on the corner. Passing to and fro, the tiny black figures of people made an ornamental border on this fabric of yellow light.

The stranger was imparting to me some grim midnight reflections upon existence, and in the heavy shadows and in the great stillness pierced only by the dull thunder of the avenue, they were very impressive.

Suddenly the muffled cry of a woman came from one of those dark, impassive houses near us. There was the sound of the splinter and crash of broken glass, falling to the pavement. "What's that," gasped the stranger. The scream contained that ominous quality, that weird timber which denotes fear of imminent death.

A policeman, huge and panting, ran past us with glitter of buttons and shield in the darkness. He flung himself upon the fire alarm box at the corner where the lamp shed a flicker of carmine tints upon the pavement. "Come on," shouted the stranger. He dragged me excitedly down the street. We came upon an old four story structure, with a long sign of a bakery over the basement windows, and the region about the quaint front door plastered with other signs. It was one of those ancient dwellings which the churning process of the city had changed into a hive of little industries.

At this time some dull gray smoke, faintly luminous in the night, writhed out from the tops of the second story windows, and from the basement there glared a deep and terrible hue of red, the color of satanic wrath, the color of murder. "Look! Look!" shouted the stranger.

It was extraordinary how the street awakened. It seemed but an instant before the pavements were studded with people. They swarmed from all directions, and from the dark mass arose countless exclamations, eager and swift.

"Where is it? Where is it?"

"No. 135."

"It's that old bakery."

"Is everybody out?"

"Look — gee — say, lookut 'er burn, would yeh?"

The windows of almost every house became crowded with people, clothed and partially clothed, many having rushed from their beds. Here were many woman, and as their eyes fastened upon that terrible growing mass of red light one could hear their little cries, quavering with fear and dread. The smoke oozed in greater clouds from the spaces between the sashes of the windows, and urged by the fervor of the heat within, ascended in more rapid streaks and curves.

Upon the sidewalk there had been a woman who was fumbling mechanically with the buttons at the neck of her dress. Her features were lined in anguish; she seemed to be frantically searching her memory — her memory, that poor feeble contrivance that had deserted her at the first of the crisis, at the momentous time. She really struggled and tore hideously at some frightful mental wall that upreared between her and her senses, her very instincts. The policeman, running back from the fire alarm box, grabbed her, intending to haul her away from danger of falling things. Then something came to her like a bolt from the sky. The creature turned all grey, like an ape. A loud shriek rang out that made the spectators bend their bodies, twisting as if they were receiving sword thrusts.

"My baby! My baby! My baby!"

The policeman simply turned and plunged into the house. As the woman tossed her arms in maniacal gestures about her head, it could then be seen that she waved in one hand a little bamboo easel, of the kind which people sometimes place in corners of their parlors. It appeared that she had with great difficulty saved it from the flames. Its cost should have been about 30 cents.

A long groaning sigh came from the crowd in the street, and from all the thronged windows. It was full of distress and pity, and a sort of cynical scorn for their impotency. Occasionally the woman screamed again. Another policeman was fending her off from the house, which she wished to enter in the frenzy of her motherhood, regardless of the flames. These people of the neighborhood, aroused from their beds, looked at the spectacle in a half-dazed fashion at times, as if they were contemplating the ravings of a red beast in a cage. The flames grew as if fanned by tempests, a sweeping, inexorable appetite of a thing, shining, with fierce, pitiless brilliancy, gleaming in the eyes of the crowd that were upturned to it in an ecstasy of awe, fear and, too, half barbaric admiration. They felt the human helplessness that comes when nature breaks forth in passion, overturning the obstacles, emerging at a leap from the position of a slave to that of a master, a giant. There became audible a humming noise, the buzzing of curious machinery. It was the voices of the demons of the flame. The house, in manifest heroic indifference to the fury that raged in its entrails, maintained a stolid and imperturbable exterior, looming black and immovable against the turmoil of crimson.

Eager questions were flying to and fro in the street.

"Say, did a copper go in there?"

"Yeh! He come out again, though."

"He did not! He's in there yet!"

"Well, didn't I see 'im?"

"How long ago was the alarm sent it?"

" 'Bout a minute."

A woman leaned perilously from a window of a nearby apartment house and spoke querulously into the shadowy, jostling crowd beneath her, "Jack!"

And the voice of an unknown man in an unknown place answered her gruffly and short in the tones of a certain kind of downtrodden husband who revels upon occasion, "What?"

"Will you come up here?" cried the woman, shrilly irritable. "Supposin' this house should get afire" — It came to pass that during the progress of the conflagration these two held a terse and bitter domestic combat, infinitely commonplace in language and mental maneuvers.

The blaze had increased with a frightful vehemence and swiftness. Unconsciously, at times, the crowd dully moaned, their eyes fascinated by this exhibition of the strength of nature, their master after all, that ate them and their devices at will whenever it chose to fling down their little restrictions. The flames changed in color from crimson to lurid orange as glass was shattered by the heat, and fell crackling to the pavement. The baker, whose shop had been in the basement, was running about, weeping. A policeman had fought interminably to keep the crowd away from the front of the structure.

"Thunderation!" yelled the stranger, clutching my arm in a frenzy of excitement, "did you ever see anything burn so? Why, it's like an explosion. It's only been a matter of seconds since it started."

In the street, men had already begun to turn toward each other in that indefinite regret and sorrow, as if they were not quite sure of the reason of their mourning.

"Well, she's a goner!"

"Sure — went up like a box of matches!"

"Great Scott, lookut 'er burn!"

Some individual among them furnished the inevitable grumble. "Well, these — " It was a half-coherent growling at conditions, men, fate, law.

Then, from the direction of the avenue there suddenly came a tempestuous roar, a clattering, rolling rush and thunder, as from the headlong sweep of a battery of artillery. Wild and shrill, like a clangorous noise of war, arose the voice of a gong.

One could see a sort of a delirium of excitement, of ardorous affection, go in a wave of emotion over this New York crowd, usually so stoical. Men looked at each other. "Quick work, eh?" They crushed back upon the pavements, leaving the street almost clear. All eyes were turned toward the corner, where the lights of the avenue glowed.

The roar grew and grew until it was as the sound of an army, charging. That policeman's hurried fingers sending the alarm from the box at the corner had aroused a tornado, a storm of horses, machinery, men. And now they were coming in clamor and riot of hoofs and wheels, while over all rang the piercing cry of the gong, tocsin-like, a noise of barbaric fights.

It thrilled the blood, this thunder. The stranger jerked his shoulders nervously and kept up a swift muttering. "Hear 'em come!" he said, breathlessly.

Then in an instant a fire patrol wagon, as if apparitional, flashed into view at the corner. The lights of the avenue gleamed for an instant upon the red and brass of the wagon, the helmets of the crew and the glassy sides of the galloping horses. Then it swung into the dark street and thundered down upon its journey, with but a half-view of a driver making his reins to be steel ribbons over the backs of his horses, mad from the fervor of their business.

The stranger's hand tightened convulsively upon my arm. His enthusiasm was like the ardor of one who looks upon the pageantry of battles. "Ah, look at 'em! Look at 'em! Ain't that great? Why it hasn't been any time at all since the alarm was sent in, and now look!" As this clanging, rolling thing, drawn swiftly by the beautiful might of the horses, clamored through the street, one could feel the cheers, wild and valorous, at the very lips of these people habitually so calm, cynical, impassive. The crew tumbled from their wagon and ran toward the house. A hoarse shout arose high above the medley of noises.

Other roars, other clangings, were to be heard from all directions. It was extraordinary, the loud rumblings of wheels and the pealings of gongs aroused by a movement of the policeman's fingers.

Of a sudden, three white horses dashed down the street with their engine, a magnificent thing of silver-like glitter, that sent a storm of red sparks high into the air and smote the heart with the wail of its whistle.

A hosecart swept around the corner and into the narrow lane, whose close walls made the reverberations like the crash of infantry volleys. There was shine of lanterns, of helmets, of rubber coats, of the bright, strong trappings of the horses. The driver had been confronted by a dreadful little problem in street cars and elevated railway pillars just as he was about to turn into the street, but there had been no pause, no hesitation. A clever dodge, a shrill grinding of the wheels in the street-car tracks, a miss of this and an escape of that by a beautifully narrow margin, and the hose-cart went on its headlong way. When the gleam-white and gold of the cart stopped in the shadowy street it was but a moment before a stream of water, of a cold steel color, was plunging through a window into the yellow glare, into this house which was now a den of fire wolves, lashing, carousing, leaping, straining. A wet snake-like hose trailed underfoot to where the steamer was making the air pulsate with its swift vibrations.

From another direction had come another thunder that developed into a crash of sounds, as a hook-and-ladder truck, with long and graceful curves, spun around the other corner, with the horses running with steady leaps toward the place of the battle. It was always obvious that these men who drove were drivers in blood and fibre, charioteers incarnate.

When the ladders were placed against the side of the house, firemen went slowly up them, dragging their hose. They became outlined like black beetles against the red and yellow expanses of flames. A vast cloud of smoke, sprinkled thickly with sparks, went coiling heavily toward the black sky. Touched by the shine of the blaze, the smoke sometimes glowed dull red, the color of bricks. A crowd that, it seemed, had sprung from the cobbles, born at the sound of the wheels rushing through the night, thickly thronged the walks, pushed here and there by the policemen who scolded them roundly, evidently in an eternal state of injured surprise at their persistent desire to get a view of things.

As we walked to the corner we looked back and watched the red glimmer from the fire shine on the dark surging crowd over which towered at times the helmets of police. A billow of smoke swept away from the structure. Occasionally, burned out sparks, like fragments of dark tissue, fluttered in the air. At the corner a streamer was throbbing, churning, shaking in its power as if overcome with rage. A fireman was walking tranquilly about it scrutinizing the mechanism. He wore a blasé air. They all, in fact, seemed to look at fires with the calm, unexcited vision of veterans. It was only the populace with their new nerves, it seemed, who could feel the thrill and dash of these attacks, these furious charges made in the dead of night, at high noon, at any time, upon the common enemy, the loosened flame.

HEARD ON THE STREET/ELECTION NIGHT/PASSING REMARKS GATHERED IN FRONT/OF "THE PRESS" STEREOPTICON./HOW THEY TOOK THE GOOD NEWS/HUMAN NATURE HAD FULL SWING ON/PARK ROW TUESDAY EVENING.*

"Hully chee! Everything's dumped!"

"S'cuse me, g'l'men, fer bein' s'noisy, but, fact is, I'm Repu'lican! What? Yessir! Morton by seventy-fi' thousan'. Yessir! I'm goin' holler thish time 'til I bust m' throat — tha's what I am."

"Can you tell me, please, if the returns indicate that Goff has a chance?"
"Who? Goff? Well, I guess! He's running like a race-horse. He's dead in it."

"That's all right. Wait 'til later. Then, you'll see. Morton never had a show. Hill will swamp him." [1]

1. Research discloses that these are actual figures in the election rout of the autumn of 1894. David Bennett Hill, who had been governor of New York, 1885–1891, ran again. He was defeated by Republican Levi P. Morton. In the same election, William L. Strong, Republican, was the successful candidate for mayor of the city of New York. John W. Goff, Republican, was elected city recorder. Hugh J. Grant, unsuccessful Tammany candidate for mayor, is the "Hughie" referred to in the sketch. Richard Croker was the Tammany Hall boss.

"Oh, hurry up with your old slide. Put on another. Good thing — push it along. Ah, there we are. 'Morton's — plurality — over — Hill — is — estimated — at — 10,135.' Say, look at that, would you?

* Published in New York Press: ? November 1894; reprinted from an undated clipping in the Columbia University Crane Collection.

A portion of this sketch, six pages, appears in Crane's "Pocket Notebook," the Press version being an expanded draft. The "Notebook" version first appeared in R. W. Stallman, "Stephen Crane: Some New Stories," Bulletin of the New York Public Library: September 1956.

Don't talk to me about the unterrified Democracy. The unterrified
Democracy can be dog goned. There's more run than fight in them
this trip. Hey, hurry up, Willie, give us another one. It's a good
thing, but push it along."

"Say, that magic lantern man is a big fakir. Lookatim pushin'
ads in on us. Hey, take that out, will yeh? You ain't no bill-poster,
are yeh?"

"Strong has got a cinch. He wins in a walk. Ah there, Hughie,
ah there."

"Well, I guess not. If Hill wins this time, he's got to have ice-
boats on his feet. He ain't got a little chance."

"Down in Fourteenth street,
"Hear that mournful sound;
"All the Indians are a-weeping,
"Davie's in the cold, cold ground."

"If Tammany wins this time, we might as well all quit the
town and go to Camden. If we don't beat 'em now, we're a lot of
duffers and we're only fit to stuff mattresses with."

"Say, hear 'em yell 'Goff.' Popular? I guess yes."
"He won't, hey? You just wait, me boy. If Hill can't carry this
State at any time in any year, I'll make you a present of the
Brooklyn bridge, and paint it a deep purple with gold stripes, all
by myself."

"Goff! Goff! John — W — Goff!
"Goff! Goff! John — W — Goff!"

"Voorhis and Taintor! They're the only two. The rest — "
"Well, this is what comes from monkeyin' with the people. You
think you've got 'em all under a board when, first thing you know,
they come out and belt you in the neck."

"Oh, everything's conceded. Yes, they admit the whole thing.
They didn't get a taste. It's a walk-over."

"Hully chee!
"Who are we?
"The men who did up Tammanee!"

"I've only seen two Tammany Democrats to-night. There's another. That makes three."

"Oh, my, what a surprise! Little David Bennett Hill is now going down the back-stairs in his stocking-feet."

"Who said Tammany couldn't be thrown down? Grady did. Ah there, Grady."

"There never was a minute
"Little Goffie wasn't in it."

"I'd like to see Dickie Croker now and ask him how he knew when to get in out of the wet. I tell you what it is—there's no use saying anything about Dickie's eyesight."

"Don't be too sure, sonny. I tell you, Dave Hill is a foxey man, and you better wait until it's a dead sure thing before you holler. I've seen a good deal of this sort of thing. In 1884 — "

"Strong's got a regular pie."

"Ta-ra-ra-ra-boom-de-aye,
"Hughie Grant has had his day,
"Safely now at home he'll stay,
"Ta-ra-ra-boom-de-aye."

"Now, I'll tell you just one thing — if this don't prove to politicians that a man has got to be always on the level if he wants to hold his snap. Why, they're about as thick-headed a gang as there is on the face of the earth. The man who is always on the level is the man who gets there in the end. If you ain't on the level, you get a swift, hard throw-down sooner or later — dead sure."

"Hurray for Goff!"

" 'Eternal vigilance is the price of liberty.' That's what it is. The people lost their liberty because they went to sleep. Then all of a sudden they wake up and slug around and surprise all of the men who thought they were in a trance. They ought to have done it long ago. And now they are awake, they don't want to do a thing but sit up night and day and lay for robbers. This waking up every ten or twelves years gives me a pain."

"There never was a doubt of it. No, sir. It was playing a sure thing from start to finish. I tell you, when the avalanche starts, you want to climb a hill near by and put all your money on the avalanche."

"I'm a Tammany Hall man, but I put my vote on John W. Goff. I did. What? Hill. Well, any man would tumble if a brick steeple fell on him."

"Parkhurst was his Jonah."

"Who's all right? Strong! Hurrah for Strong!"

"Say, lookut d' blokie flashin' er patent-medicine ad. on d' canvas. He's a Dimmy-crat. Who won't be 'lected? Goff? I bet 'che he will. Soitently! Say, Jimmie, gimme change for a nick! Ah, I bet'che Goff'll leave 'm at d' post. Say, who 'er yez fer, anyhow? Ah, he'll git it in d'troat. Goff'll smother 'im."

"By colly, I bed you Morton is elected by a hundret thousand votes. Suah! I am a Republican effery leetle minnet. I am so excited my hand shake."

"Oh, what a cinch they thought they had. Say, those fellers thought they had New York locked in a box. And they got left, didn't they?"

"Good-bye, Hughie! Good-bye, Hughie!
"Good-bye, Hughie, you'll have to leave us now."

"Well, they monkeyed with the band wagon and they got slumped. Good job. Very surprising way the American people have of throttling a man just when he thinks he's got 'em dead under his thumb."

"It was easy, after all, wasn't it? Truth is, New York has been held down by a great big, wire-edged bluff. Tammany said she couldn't be beaten, and everybody believed it."

"What? Git out! Entire Republican ticket, cit and State? Well, for the love of Mike! Holy smoke, ain't we in it!"

"Is they any Democrats left?"

"Where's all the Tammany men?"

"Somebody tell Hill where he's at."

"Tammany's in the soup."

"Oh, what a roast!"

"Hully chee! Everyt'ing's dumped!"

WHEN MAN FALLS/A CROWD GATHERS/A GRAPHIC STUDY OF NEW YORK/HEARTLESSNESS. /GAZING WITH PITILESS EYES/"WHAT'S THE MATTER?" THAT TOO FAMILIAR QUERY.*

A man and a boy were trudging slowly along an East Side street. It was nearly 6 o'clock in the evening and this street which led to one of the East River ferries was crowded with laborers, shop men and shop women hurrying to their dinners. The store windows were a-glare.

The man and the boy conversed in Italian mumbling the soft syllables and making little quick egostitical gestures. They walked with the lumbering peasant's gait, slowly, and blinking their black eyes at the passing show of the street.

Suddenly the man wavered on his limbs and glared bewildered and helpless as if some blinding light had flashed before his vision. Then he swayed like a drunken man and fell. The boy grasped his companion's arm frantically and made an attempt to support him so that the limp form slid to the sidewalk with an easy motion as a body sinks in the sea. The boy screamed.

Instantly, from all directions, people turned their gaze upon the prone figure. In a moment there was a dodging, pushing, peer-

* *Reprinted from New York Press: 2 December 1894.*

A first draft portion of this sketch appears in Crane's "Pocket Notebook." A press clipping in the Columbia University Crane Collection bears in Crane's script: "When Men Stumble"; this would indicate that the title in the Press is not Crane's. In Last Words (1902) a shortened version of the sketch is entitled "A Street Scene in New York."

ing group about the man. A volley of questions, replies, specula-
tions flew to and fro above all the bobbing heads.

"What's th' matter? What's th' matter?"

Two streams of people coming from different directions met
at this point to form a crowd. Others came from across the street.

Down under their feet, almost lost under this throng, lay the
man, hidden in the shadows caused by their forms, which, in fact,
barely allowed a particle of light to pass between them. Those in
the foremost rank bended down, shouldering each other, eager,
anxious to see everything. Others, behind them, crowded savagely
for a place like starving men fighting for bread. Always the question could be heard flying in the air: "What's the matter?" Some
near to the body and perhaps feeling the danger of being forced
over upon it, twisted their heads and protested violently to those
unheeding ones who were scuffling in the rear. "Say, quit yer
shovin', can't yeh? Wat d' yeh want, anyhow? Quit!"

A man back in the crowd suddenly said: "Say, young feller,
you're a peach wid dose feet o' yours. Keep off me!"

Another voice said, "Well, dat's all right!"

The boy who had been walking with the man who fell was
standing helplessly, a terrified look in his eyes. He held the man's
hand. Sometimes he gave it a little jerk that was at once an appeal,
a reproach, a caution. And, withal, it was a timid calling to the limp
and passive figure as if he half expected to arouse it from its coma
with a pleading touch of his fingers. Occasionally he looked about
him with swift glances of indefinite hope, as if assistance might
come from the clouds. The men near him questioned him, but he
did not seem to understand. He answered them "Yes" or "No,"
blindly, with no apparent comprehension of their language. They
frequently jostled him until he was obliged to put his hand upon
the breast of the body to maintain his balance.

Those that were nearest to the man upon the sidewalk at first
saw his body go through a singular contortion. It was as if an in-
visible hand had reached up from the earth and had seized him
by the hair. He seemed dragged slowly, relentlessly backward,
while his body stiffened convulsively; his hand clenched, and his
arms swung rigidly upward. A slight froth was upon his chin.
Through his pallid, half closed lids could be seen the steel colored
gleam of his eyes that were turned toward all the bending, swaying faces and this inanimate thing upon the pavement burned
threateningly, dangerously, whining with a mystic light, as a corpse
might glare at those live ones who seemed about to trample it
under foot.

As for the men near, they hung back, appearing as if they

expected it to spring erect and clutch at them. Their eyes, however, were held in a spell of fascination. They seemed scarcely to breathe. They were contemplating a depth into which a human being had sunk, and the marvel of this mystery of life or death held them chained.

Occasionally from the rear a man came thrusting his way impetuously, satisfied that there was a horror to be seen and apparently insane to get a view of it. Less curious persons swore at these men when they trod upon their toes. The loaded street cars jingled past this scene in endless parade. Occasionally, from where the elevated railroad crossed the street, there came a rhythmical roar, suddenly begun and suddenly ended. Over the heads of the crowd hung an immovable canvas sign, "Regular dinner, twenty cents."

After the first spasm of curiosity had passed away there were those in the crowd who began to consider ways to help. A voice called: "Rub his wrists." The boy and some one on the other side of the man began to rub his wrists and slap his palms, but still the body lay inert, rigid. When a hand was dropped the arm fell like a stick. A tall German suddenly appeared and resolutely began to push the crowd back. "Get back there — get back," he continually repeated as he pushed them. He had psychological authority over this throng: they obeyed him. He and another knelt by the man in the darkness and loosened his shirt at the throat. Once they struck a match and held it close to the man's face. This livid visage suddenly appearing under their feet in the light of the match's yellow glare made the throng shudder. Half articulate exclamations could be heard. There were men who nearly created a battle in the madness of their desire to see the thing.

Meanwhile others with magnificent passions for abstract statistical information were questioning the boy. "What's his name?" "Where does he live?"

Then a policeman appeared. The first part of the little play had gone on without his assistance, but now he came swiftly, his helmet towering above the multitude of black derbys and shading that confident, self reliant police face. He charged the crowd as if he were a squadron of Irish lancers. The people fairly withered before this onslaught. He shouted: "Come, make way there! Make way!" He was evidently a man whose life was half pestered out of him by the inhabitants of the city who were sufficiently unreasonable and stupid as to insist on being in the streets. His was the rage of a placid cow, who wishes to lead a life of tranquility, but who is eternally besieged by flies that hover in clouds.

When he arrived at the center of the crowd he first demanded, threateningly: "Well, what's th' matter here?" And then, when he saw that human bit of wreckage at the bottom of the sea of men, he said to it: "Come, git up out a-that! Git out a-here!"

Whereupon hands were raised in the crowd and a volley of decorated information was blazed at the officer.

"Ah, he's got a fit! Can't yeh see?"

"He's got a fit!"

"He's sick!"

"What yeh doin'? Leave 'm be!"

The policeman menaced with a glance the crowd from whose safe interior the defiant voices had emerged.

A doctor had come. He and the policeman bended down at the man's side. Occasionally the officer upreared to create room. The crowd fell way before his threats, his admonitions, his sarcastic questions and before the sweep of those two huge buckskin gloves.

At last the peering ones saw the man on the sidewalk begin to breathe heavily, with the strain of overtaxed machinery, as if he had just come to the surface from some deep water. He uttered a low cry in his foreign tongue. It was a babyish squeal, or like the sad wail of a little storm-tossed kitten. As this cry went forth to all those eager ears, the jostling and crowding recommenced until the doctor was obliged to yell warningly a dozen times. The policeman had gone to send an ambulance call.

When a man struck another match and in its meager light the doctor felt the skull of the prostrate one to discover if any wound or fracture had been caused by his fall to the stone sidewalk, the crowd pressed and crushed again. It was as if they fully anticipated a sight of blood in the gleam of the match and they scrambled and dodged for positions. The policeman returned and fought with them. The doctor looked up frequently to scold at them and to sharply demand more space.

At last out of the golden haze made by the lamps far up the street, there came the sound of a gong beaten rapidly, impatiently. A monstrous truck loaded to the sky with barrels scurried to one side with marvelous agility. And then the black ambulance with its red light, its galloping horse, its dull gleam of lettering and bright shine of gong clattered into view. A young man, as imperturbable always as if he were going to a picnic, sat thoughtfully upon the rear seat.

When they picked up the limp body, from which came little moans and howls, the crowd almost turned into a mob, a silent mob, each member of which struggled for one thing. Afterward some resumed their ways with an air of relief, as if they themselves had been in pain and were at last recovered. Others still continued to stare at the ambulance on its banging, clanging return journey until it vanished into the golden haze. It was as if they had been cheated. Their eyes expressed discontent at this curtain which had been rung down in the midst of the drama. And this impenetrable fabric, suddenly intervening between a suffering creature and their curiosity, seemed to appear to them as an injustice.

THE DUEL THAT WAS NOT FOUGHT.*

Patsy Tulligan was not as wise as seven owls, but his courage could throw a shadow as long as the steeple of a cathedral. There were men on Cherry Street who had whipped him five times, but they all knew that Patsy would be as ready for the sixth time as if nothing had happened.

Once he and two friends had been away up on Eighth Avenue, far out of their country, and upon their return journey that evening they stopped frequently in saloons until they were as independent of their surroundings as eagles, and cared much less about thirty days on Blackwell's.

On Lower Sixth Avenue they paused in a saloon where there was a good deal of lamp-glare and polished wood to be seen from the outside, and within, the mellow light shone on much furbished brass and more polished wood. It was a better saloon than they were in the habit of seeing, but they did not mind it. They sat down at one of the little tables that were in a row parallel to the bar and ordered beer. They blinked stolidly at the decorations, the bar-tender, and the other customers. When anything transpired they discussed it with dazzling frankness, and what they said of it was as free as air to the other people in the place.

At midnight there were few people in the saloon. Patsy and his friends still sat drinking. Two well-dressed men were at another table, smoking cigars slowly and swinging back in their chairs. They occupied themselves with themselves in the usual manner, never betraying by a wink of an eyelid that they knew that other

---

* *Published in New York* Press: *9 December 1894; reprinted from* The Open Boat and Other Stories *(London, 1898).*

A portion of this sketch appears in Crane's "Pocket Notebook," and it links with other Sixth Avenue sketches, such as "Sixth Avenue" (see below) and "In a Park Row Restaurant" (see above). Another link with these pieces and very likely written at the same time is "A Detail" (see above).

folk existed. At another table directly behind Patsy and his companions was a slim little Cuban, with miraculously small feet and hands, and with a youthful touch of down upon his lip. As he lifted his cigarette from time to time his little finger was bended in dainty fashion, and there was a green flash when a huge emerald ring caught the light. The bar-tender came often with his little brass tray. Occasionally Patsy and his two friends quarrelled.

Once this little Cuban happened to make some slight noise and Patsy turned his head to observe him. Then Patsy made a careless and rather loud comment to his two friends. He used a word which is no more than passing the time of day down in Cherry Street, but to the Cuban it was a dagger-point. There was a harsh scraping sound as a chair was pushed swiftly back.

The little Cuban was upon his feet. His eyes were shining with a rage that flashed there like sparks as he glared at Patsy. His olive face had turned a shade of grey from his anger. Withal his chest was thrust out in portentous dignity, and his hand, still grasping his wine-glass, was cool and steady, the little finger still bended, the great emerald gleaming upon it. The others, motionless, stared at him.

"Sir," he began ceremoniously. He spoke gravely and in a slow way, his tone coming in a marvel of self-possessed cadences from between those lips which quivered with wrath. "You have insult me. You are a dog, a hound, a cur. I spit upon you. I must have some of your blood."

Patsy looked at him over his shoulder.

"What's th' matter wi' che?" he demanded. He did not quite understand the words of this little man who glared at him steadily, but he knew that it was something about fighting. He snarled with the readiness of his class and heaved his shoulders contemptuously. "Ah, what's eatin' yeh? Take a walk! You h'ain't got nothin' t' do with me, have yeh? Well, den, go sit on yerself."

And his companions leaned back valorously in their chairs, and scrutinized this slim young fellow who was addressing Patsy.

"What's de little Dago chewin' about?"

"He wants t' scrap!"

"What!"

The Cuban listened with apparent composure. It was only when they laughed that his body cringed as if he was receiving lashes. Presently he put down his glass and walked over to their table. He proceeded always with the most impressive deliberation.

"Sir," he began again. "You have insult me. I must have s-s-satis-fac-shone. I must have your body upon the point of my sword.

In my country you would already be dead. I must have s-s-satisfac-shone."

Patsy had looked at the Cuban with a trifle of bewilderment. But at last his face began to grow dark with belligerency, his mouth curved in that wide sneer with which he would confront an angel of darkness. He arose suddenly in his seat and came towards the little Cuban. He was going to be impressive too.

"Say, young feller, if yeh go shootin' off yer face at me, I'll wipe d' joint wid yeh. What'cher gaffin' about, hey? Are yeh givin' me er jolly? Say, if yeh pick me up fer a cinch, I'll fool yeh. Dat's what! Don't take me fer no dead easy mug." And as he glowered at the little Cuban, he ended his oration with one eloquent word, "Nit!"

The bar-tender nervously polished his bar with a towel, and kept his eyes fastened upon the men. Occasionally he became trans-fixed with interest, leaning forward with one hand upon the edge of the bar and the other holding the towel grabbed in a lump, as if he had been turned into bronze when in the very act of polishing.

The Cuban did not move when Patsy came toward him and delivered his oration. At its conclusion he turned his livid face toward where, above him, Patsy was swaggering and heaving his shoulders in a consummate display of bravery and readiness. The Cuban, in his clear, tense tones, spoke one word. It was the bitter insult. It seemed to fairly spin from his lips and crackle in the air like breaking glass.

Every man save the little Cuban made an electric movement. Patsy roared a black oath and thrust himself forward until he towered almost directly above the other man. His fists were doubled into knots of bone and hard flesh. The Cuban had raised a steady finger.

"If you touch me wis your hand, I will keel you."

The two well-dressed men had come swiftly, uttering pro-testing cries. They suddenly intervened in this second of time in which Patsy had sprung forward and the Cuban had uttered his threat. The four men were now a tossing, arguing, violent group, one well-dressed man lecturing the Cuban, and the other holding off Patsy, who was now wild with rage, loudly repeating the Cuban's threat, and manœuvring and struggling to get at him for revenge's sake.

The bar-tender, feverishly scouring away with his towel, and at times pacing to and fro with nervous and excited tread, shouted out —

"Say, for heaven's sake, don't fight in here. If yeh wanta fight, go out in the street and fight all yeh please. But don't fight in here."

Patsy knew only one thing, and this he kept repeating —

"Well, he wants t' scrap! I didn't begin dis! He wants t' scrap."

The well-dressed man confronting him continually replied —

"Oh, well, now, look here, he's only a lad. He don't know what he's doing. He's crazy mad. You wouldn't slug a kid like that."

Patsy and his aroused companions, who cursed and growled, were persistent with their argument. "Well, he wants t' scrap!" The whole affair was as plain as daylight when one saw this great fact. The interference and intolerable discussion brought the three of them forward, battleful and fierce.

"What's eatin' you, anyhow?" they demanded. "Dis ain't your business, is it? What business you got shootin' off your face?"

The other peacemaker was trying to restrain the little Cuban, who had grown shrill and violent.

"If he touch me wis his hand I will keel him. We must fight like gentlemen or else I keel him when he touch me wis his hand."

The man who was fending off Patsy comprehended these sentences that were screamed behind his back, and he explained to Patsy —

"But he wants to fight you with swords. With swords, you know."

The Cuban, dodging around the peacemakers, yelled in Patsy's face —

"Ah, if I could get you before me wis my sword! Ah! Ah! A-a-ah!" Patsy made a furious blow with a swift fist, but the peacemakers bucked against his body suddenly like football players.

Patsy was greatly puzzled. He continued doggedly to try to get near enough to the Cuban to punch him. To these attempts the Cuban replied savagely —

"If you touch me wis your hand, I will cut your heart in two piece."

At last Patsy said — "Well, if he's so dead stuck on fightin' wid swords, I'll fight 'im. Soitenly! I'll fight 'im." All this palaver had evidently tired him, and he now puffed out his lips with the air of a man who is willing to submit to any conditions if he can only bring on the row soon enough. He swaggered, "I'll fight 'im wid swords. Let 'im bring on his swords, an' I'll fight 'im 'til he's ready t' quit."

The two well-dressed men grinned. "Why, look here," they said to Patsy, "he'd punch you full of holes. Why, he's a fencer. You can't fight him with swords. He'd kill you in 'bout a minute."

"Well, I'll giv' 'im a go at it, anyhow," said Patsy, stout-hearted and resolute. "I'll giv' 'im a go at it, anyhow, an' I'll stay wid 'im long as I kin."

As for the Cuban, his lithe little body was quivering in an ecstasy of the muscles. His face radiant with a savage joy, he fastened his glance upon Patsy, his eyes gleaming with a gloating, murderous light. A most unspeakable, animal-like rage was in his expression.

"Ah! ah! He will fight me! Ah!" He bended unconsciously in the posture of a fencer. He had all the quick, springy movements of a skilful swordsman. "Ah, the b-r-r-rute! The b-r-r-rute! I will stick him like a pig!"

The two peacemakers, still grinning broadly, were having a great time with Patsy.

"Why, you infernal idiot, this man would slice you all up. You better jump off the bridge if you want to commit suicide. You wouldn't stand a ghost of a chance to live ten seconds."

Patsy was as unshaken as granite. "Well, if he wants t' fight wid swords, he'll get it. I'll giv' 'im a go at it, anyhow."

One man said — "Well, have you got a sword? Do you know what a sword is? Have you got a sword?"

"No, I ain't got none," said Patsy honestly, "but I kin git one." Then he added valiantly — "An' quick too."

The two men laughed. "Why, can't you understand it would be sure death to fight a sword duel with this fellow?"

"Dat's all right! See? I know me own business. If he wants t' fight one of dee d — n duels, I'm in it, understan'?"

"Have you ever fought one, you fool?"

"No, I ain't. But I will fight one, dough! I ain't no muff. If he want t' fight a duel, by Gawd, I'm wid 'im! D'yeh understan' dat!" Patsy cocked his hat and swaggered. He was getting very serious.

The little Cuban burst out — "Ah, come on, sirs: come on! We can take cab. Ah, you big cow, I will stick you, I will stick you. Ah, you will look very beautiful, very beautiful. Ah, come on, sirs. We will stop at hotel — my hotel. I there have weapons."

"Yeh will, will yeh? Yeh bloomin' little black Dago," cried Patsy in hoarse and maddened reply to the personal part of the Cuban's speech. He stepped forward. "Git yer d — n swords," he commanded. "Git yer swords. Git 'em quick! I'll fight wi' che! I'll fight wid anyting, too! See? I'll fight yeh wid a knife an' fork if yeh say so! I'll fight yer standin' up er sittin' down!" Patsy delivered this intense oration with sweeping, intensely emphatic gestures, his hands stretched out eloquently, his jaw thrust forward, his eyes glaring.

"Ah," cried the little Cuban joyously. "Ah, you are in very

pretty temper. Ah, how I will cut your heart in two piece, my dear, d-e-a-r friend." His eyes, too, shone like carbuncles, with a swift, changing glitter, always fastened upon Patsy's face.

The two peacemakers were perspiring and in despair. One of them blurted out —

"Well, I'll be blamed if this ain't the most ridiculous thing I ever saw."

The other said — "For ten dollars I'd be tempted to let these two infernal blockheads have their duel."

Patsy was strutting to and fro, and conferring grandly with his friends.

"He took me for a muff. He tought he was goin' t' bluff me out, talkin' 'bout swords. He'll get fooled." He addressed the Cuban — "You're a fine little dirty picter of a scrapper, ain't che? I'll chew yez up, dat's what I will."

There began then some rapid action. The patience of well-dressed men is not an eternal thing. It began to look as if it would at last be a fight with six corners to it. The faces of the men were shining red with anger. They jostled each other defiantly, and almost every one blazed out at three or four of the others. The bartender had given up protesting. He swore for a time, and banged his glasses. Then he jumped the bar and ran out of the saloon, cursing sullenly.

When he came back with a policeman, Patsy and the Cuban were preparing to depart together. Patsy was delivering his last oration —

"I'll fight yer wid swords! Sure I will! Come ahead, Dago! I'll fight yeh anywheres wid anyting! We'll have a large, juicy scrap, an' don't yeh forgit dat! I'm right wid yez. I ain't no muff! I scrap wid a man jest as soon as he ses scrap, an' if yeh wanta scrap, I'm yer kitten. Understan' dat?"

The policeman said sharply — "Come, now; what's all this?" He had a distinctly business air.

The little Cuban stepped forward calmly. "It is none of your business."

The policeman flushed to his ears. "What?"

One well-dressed man touched the other on the sleeve. "Here's the time to skip," he whispered. They halted a block away from the saloon and watched the policeman pull the Cuban through the door. There was a minute of scuffle on the sidewalk, and into this deserted street at midnight fifty people appeared at once as if from the sky to watch it.

At last the three Cherry Hill men came from the saloon, and swaggered with all their old valour toward the peacemakers.

"Ah," said Patsy to them, "he was so hot talkin' about this duel business, but I would a-given 'im a great scrap, an' don't yeh forgit it."

For Patsy was not as wise as seven owls, but his courage could throw a shadow as long as the steeple of a cathedral.

SIXTH AVENUE *

Sixth Avenue is a street that leads a dual existence. It typifies the man who walks very primly in the observing light of the sun but who, when in the shadows, cuts many and strange pranks. The day finds it thronged with shoppers; the doors of the great shops clash to and fro in endless motion. Huge windows disclose wonderful masses of goods that have been dragged from all corners of the earth. Hosts of women crowd the side-walks. The elevated trains and the street-cars unload battalions of them. The huge stores uprear their austere fronts to glance across the street at little saloons that in this white light of respectability remain subdued and silent. It is the time of the marching and counter-marching of the feminine buyers; it is the time when Sixth Avenue is profoundly busy but profoundly decorous.

MISS LOUISE GERARD—SOPRANO †

Miss Louise Gerard first became prominent as a child violinist. She was but eight years of age when she attracted the attention of the public with her violin, and the prints of a dozen years ago contained frequent expressions of admiration for the talent of this little

---

* Published here for the first time from a single-sheet holograph manuscript in the Columbia University Crane Collection. It is the opening paragraph of a sketch intended for the New York Press but never published. This is an addition to the Crane canon.

   Crane lived with Charles J. Pike on and off for eighteen months during 1895–1896 in Pike's third-floor studio on the corner of Sixth Avenue and 33rd Street. Sixth Avenue figures in several of Crane's sketches in this collection.

---

† Published in The Musical News: December 1894. Unsigned. The sketch is reprinted from a press clipping pasted into

girl, who indicated in no way, save by the tiny torchlike points in her large eyes, the power, the maturity of thought necessary to comprehend fully the music that she played. The *St. Nicholas Magazine*, which, true to the publishing instinct, only adopts that which has been clamorously adopted by the public, printed a very charming picture of her. Since she has become well-known as a soprano, the result of her violin study still is evident in intonation and phrasing. Moreover, it is undoubtedly her early experiences upon the concert stage that enable her to appear now with an utter absence of the affectations and stupid mannerisms that so mar the performances of many famous people. She sings the quaint little English ballads as a girl might sing in the garden: not as if she knew she was an accomplished soprano, alone in a blaze of yellow light, with a multitude of eyes upon her. It is the finesse of experienced wisdom in a girl of twenty-two.

Miss Gerard has had opportunity for making a reputation in the musical capitals of Europe; her voice has easily gained for her a conquest enviably complete and final. Upon her first trip to London, the journals of the city were astonished out of their lassitude, and ceased to wear a bored air. They cried in chorus of the sweetness of her voice and of the excellence of her concerts. One newspaper enthusiastically advised British artists that they might to great advantage copy her method, informing them, in a frank way, that they had much to learn from her. In the meantime, the concerts at St. James Hall were well crowded by the critical people of London. The fact that the American colony appeared in force is a great proof that London was charmed with her, since the American colony are usually fearful of disclosing their patriotism until after they learn the attitude of the fashionable set. She returned to America from this first trip with a memory of the applause of London, and with the great prestige that a success across the sea gives to an American singer. Afterward, in London, she has been always assured of that profound attention that was granted her by the most intelligently critical part of London upon her first journey.

Later, in Paris, she was received with acclaim by the artistic French public. The Parisians crowded the fashionable drawing-rooms to hear her sing. The American colony, which, in Paris, is a free agent, and quite different from the American colony in London,

---

Crane's Scrapbook in the Columbia University Crane Collection.
    In Crane's writing in the margin is: "The Musical News/ Dec., 94." The themes here had a significance for Crane's own life. Also Cranesque is the critical remark about the St. Nicholas Magazine, which had rejected a dog story that Crane had submitted there.

welcomed her loudly. Galignani's *Messenger* said, in its review of her first recital: "Miss Gerard is the possessor of a pure soprano voice of excellent quality . . . She was warmly applauded for her artistic rendering of Scotch and English ballads. Santuzza's Aria, from Cavalleria Rusticana, was delivered with great dramatic power." Each Paris paper was obliged to conclude its review with a list of titled people and representative musicians who were in the audience. Less conservative journals than the *Messenger* caused intensely laudatory reviews to be written.

Miss Gerard has made quite a name for herself as a writer on both social and musical subjects. Her recent article in the *American Art Journal*, summing up all that is possible in musical interpretation under eleven philosophical rules, has been copied and indorsed by the leading musical papers of both Europe and America.

The dramatic quality is particularly strong in Miss Gerard's singing. She is careful of the meaning of those curious little cries of love, grief, war, which grow upon the hillsides of Scotland and in the meadows of England. She understands that they are not merely clever collections of notes to be faultlessly sung, but that they have a significance, a meaning, that is as wide as the world, as universal as love, grief, war: that these songs, so often called "simple," are as simple as the human heart, and no more. Hence, she sings them with an intelligent comprehension. It is because of such interpretations that one is able to discern between the artist and the machinist.

The training which she has given her voice, allows her to sing with no apparent effort, and the tale of the composer's reverie comes to the ear clear and pure as silver.

A CHRISTMAS DINNER/WON IN BATTLE./A TALE BY STEPHEN CRANE.*

Tom had set up a plumbing shop in the prairie town of Levelville as soon as the people learned to care more about sanitary conditions than they did about the brand of tobacco smoked by the in-

---

* *Reprinted from* The Plumbers' Trade Journal, Gas, Steam and Hot Water Fitters' Review: *1 January 1895.*
    Crane's name appeared occasionally in the headlines, but much more frequently at the end of the piece, and in these latter instances the Editors have deleted it.

habitants of Mars. Nevertheless he was a wise young man for he
was only one week ahead of the surveyors. A railroad, like a magic
wand, was going to touch Levelville and change it to a great city.
In an incredibly short time, the town had a hotel, a mayor, a board
of alderman and more than a hundred real estate agents, besides
a blue print of the plans for a street railway three miles long. When
the cow boys rode in with their customary noise to celebrate the
fact that they had been paid, their efforts were discouraged by new
policemen in uniform. Levelville had become a dignified city.

As the town expanded in marvelous circles out over the prairies,
Tom bestrode the froth of the wave of progress. He was soon one
of the first citizens. These waves carry men to fortune with sudden
sweeping movements, and Tom had the courage, the temerity and
the assurance to hold his seat like a knight errant.

In the democratic and genial atmosphere of this primary boom,
he became an intimate acquaintance of Colonel Fortman, the president of the railroad, and with more courage, temerity and assurance, had already fallen violently in love with his daughter, the
incomparable Mildred. He carried his intimacy with the colonel
so far as to once save his life from the flying might of the 5:30
express. It seems that the colonel had ordered the engineer of the
5:30 to make his time under all circumstances; to make his time
if he had to run through fire, blood and earthquake. The engineer
decided that the usual rule relating to the speed of trains when
passing through freight yards could not concern an express that
was ordered to slow down for nothing but the wrath of heaven
and in consequence, at the time of this incident, the 5:30 was
shrieking through the Levelville freight yard at fifty miles an hour,
roaring over the switches and screaming along the lines of box cars.
The colonel and Tom were coming from the shops. They had just
rounded the corner of a car and stepped out upon the main track
when this whirring, boiling, howling demon of an express came
down upon them. Tom had an instant in which to drag his companion off the rails; the train whistled past them like an enormous
projectile. "Damn that fellow — he's making his time," panted the
old colonel gazing after the long speeding shadow with its two
green lights. Later he said very soberly: "I'm much obliged to you
for that Tom, old boy."

When Tom went to him a year later, however, to ask for the
hand of Mildred, the colonel replied: "My dear man, I think you
are insane. Mildred will have over a million dollars at my death,
and while I don't mean to push the money part of it too far forward, yet Mildred with her beauty, her family name and her
wealth, can marry the finest in the land. There isn't anyone too

great for her. So you see, my dear man, it is impossible that she could consider you for a moment."

Whereupon Tom lost his temper. He had the indignation of a good, sound minded, fearless eyed young fellow who is assured of his love and assured almost of the love of the girl. Moreover, it filled him with unspeakable rage to be called:

"My dear man."

They then accused each other of motives of which neither were guilty, and Tom went away. It was a serious quarrel. The colonel told Tom never to dare to cross his threshold. They passed each other on the street without a wink of an eye to disclose the fact that one knew that the other existed. As time went on the colonel became more massively aristocratic and more impenetrably stern. Levelville had developed about five grades of society, and the Fortman's mingled warily with the dozen families that formed the highest and iciest grades. Once when the colonel and Mildred were driving through town, the girl bowed to a young man who passed them.

"Who the deuce was that?" said the colonel airily. "Seems to me I ought to know that fellow."

"That's the man that saved your life from the 5:30," replied Mildred.

"See here, young lady," cried the colonel angrily. "Don't you take his part against me."

About a year later came the great railway strike. The papers of the city foreshadowed it vaguely from time to time, but no one apparently took the matter in a serious way. There had been threats and rumors of threats but the general public had seemed to view them as idle bombast. At last, however, the true situation displayed itself suddenly and vividly. Almost the entire force of the great P.C.C. and W.U. system went on strike. The people of the city awoke one morning to find the gray sky of dawn splashed with a bright crimson color. The strikers had set ablaze one of the company's shops in the suburbs and the light from it flashed out a red ominous signal of warning foretelling the woe and despair of the struggle that was to ensue. Rumors came that the men usually so sober, industrious and imperturbable were running in a wild mob, raving and destroying. Whereupon, the people who had laughed to scorn any idea of being prepared for this upheaval began to assiduously abuse the authorities for not being ready to meet it.

That morning Tom, in his shirt sleeves, went into the back part of his shop to direct some of his workmen about a certain job, and when he came out he was well covered by as honest a coating of grime and soot as was ever worn by journeymen. He went to the sink to dispose of this adornment and while there he heard his men talking of the strike. One was saying: "Yes, sir; sure as th' dickens! They say they're goin' t' burn th' president's house an' everybody in it." Tom's body stiffened at these words. He felt himself turn cold. A moment later he left the shop forgetting his coat, forgetting his covering of soot and grime.

In the main streets of the city there was no evident change. The horses of the jangling street cars still slipped and strained in the deep mud into which the snow had been churned. The store windows were gay with the color of Christmas. Innumerable turkeys hung before each butcher's shop. Upon the walks the business men had formed into little eager groups discussing the domestic calamity. Against the leaden-hued sky, over the tops of the buildings, arose a great leaning pillar of smoke marking the spot upon which stood the burning shop.

Tom hurried on through that part of town which was composed of little narrow streets with tiny gray houses on either side. There he saw a concourse of Slavs, Polacs, Italians and Hungarians, laborers of the company, floundering about in the mud and raving, conducting a riot in their own inimitable way. They seemed as blood thirsty, pitiless, mad, as starved wolves. And Tom presented a figure no less grim as he ran through the crowd, coatless and now indeed hatless, with pale skin showing through the grime. He went until he came to a stretch of commons across which he could see the Fortman's house standing serenely with no evidences of riot about it. He moderated his pace then.

When he had gone about half way across this little snow-covered common, he looked back, for he heard cries. Across the white fields, winding along the muddy road, there came a strange procession. It resembled a parade of Parisians at the time of the first revolution. Fists were wildly waving and at times hoarse voices rang out. It was as if this crowd was delirious from drink. As it came nearer Tom could see women — gaunt and ragged creatures with inflamed visages and rolling eyes. There were men with dark sinister faces whom Tom had never before seen. They had emerged from the earth, so to speak, to engage in this carousal of violence. And from this procession there came continual threatening ejaculations, shrill cries for revenge, and querulous voices of hate, that made a sort of barbaric hymn, a pagan chant of savage battle and death.

Tom waited for them. Those in the lead evidently considered him to be one of their number since his face was grimed and his garments dishevelled. One gigantic man with bare and brawny arms and throat, gave him invitation with a fierce smile. "Come ahn, Swipsey, while we go roast 'em."

A raving grey-haired woman, struggling in the mud, sang a song which consisted of one endless line:

> "We'll burn th' foxes out,
> We'll burn th' foxes out
> We'll burn th' foxes out."

As for the others, they babbled and screamed in a vast variety of foreign tongues. Tom walked along with them listening to the cries that came from the terrible little army, marching with clenched fists and with gleaming eyes fastened upon the mansion that up-reared so calmly before them.

When they arrived, they hesitated a moment, as if awed by the impassive silence of the structure with closed shutters and barred doors, which stolidly and indifferently confronted them.

Then from the centre of the crowd came the voice of the grey-headed old woman: "Break in th' door! Break in th' door!" And then it was that Tom displayed the desperation born of his devotion to the girl within the house. Although he was perhaps braver than most men, he had none of that magnificent fortitude, that gorgeous tranquility amid upheavals and perils which is the attribute of people in plays; but he stepped up on the porch and faced the throng. His face was wondrously pallid and his hands trembled but he said: "You fellows can't come in here."

There came a great sarcastic howl from the crowd. "Can't we?" They broke into laughter at this wildly ridiculous thing. The brawny, bare-armed giant siezed Tom by the arm. "Get outa th' way, you yap," he said between his teeth. In an instant Tom was punched and pulled and knocked this way and that way, and amid the pain of these moments he was conscious that members of the mob were delivering thunderous blows upon the huge doors. Directly indeed they crashed down and he felt the crowd sweep past him and into the house. He clung to a railing; he had no more sense of balance than a feather. A blow in the head had made him feel that the ground swirled and heaved around him. He had no further interest in rioting, and such scenes of excitement. Gazing out over the common he saw two patrol wagons, loaded with policemen, and the lashed horses galloping in the mud. He wondered dimly why they were in such a hurry.

But at that moment a scream rang from the house out through the open doors. He knew the voice and, like an electric shock it aroused him from his semi-stupor. Once more alive, he turned and charged into the house as valiant and as full of rage as a Roman. Pandemonium reigned within. There came yells and roars, splinter-

ings, cracklings, crashes. The scream of Mildred again rang out;
this time he knew it came from the dining-room before whose
closed door, four men were as busy as miners with improvised
pick and drill.

Tom grasped a heavy oaken chair that stood ornamentally in
the hall and, elevating it above his head, ran madly at the four
men. When he was almost upon them, he let the chair fly. It
seemed to strike all of them. A heavy oak chair of the old English
type is one of the most destructive of weapons. Still, there seemed
to be enough of the men left for they flew at him from all sides
like dragons. In the dark of the hallway, Tom put down his head
and half-closed his eyes and plied his fists. He knew he had but a
moment in which to stand up, but there was a sort of grim joy in
knowing that the most terrific din of this affray was going straight
through the dining-room door, and into the heart of Mildred and
when she knew that her deliverer was — He saw a stretch of blood-
red sky flame under his lids and then sank to the floor, blind, deaf,
and nerveless.

When the old colonel arrived in one of the patrol wagons, he
did not wait to see the police attack in front but ran around to the
rear. As he passed the dining room windows he saw his wife's face.
He shouted, and when they opened a window he clambered with
great agility into the room. For a minute they deluged each other
with shouts of joy and tears. Then finally the old colonel said:
"But they did not get in here. How was that?"

"Oh, papa," said Mildred, "they were trying to break in when
somebody came and fought dreadfully with them and made them
stop."

"Heavens, who could it have been?" said the colonel. He went
to the door and opened it. A group of police became visible hurrying about the wide hall but near the colonel's feet lay a body with
a white still face.

"Why, it's — it's — " ejaculated the colonel in great agitation.

"It's Tom," cried Mildred.

When Tom came to his senses he found that his fingers were
clasped tightly by a soft white hand which by some occult power
of lovers he knew at once.

"Tom," said Mildred.

And the old colonel from further away said: "Tom, my boy!"

But Tom was something of an obstinate young man. So as
soon as he felt himself recovered sufficiently, he arose and went
unsteadily toward the door.

"Tom, where are you going?" cried Mildred.

"Where are you going, Tom?" called the colonel.

"I'm going home," said Tom doggedly. "I didn't intend to cross this threshold — I —" He swayed unsteadily and seemed almost about to fall. Mildred screamed and ran toward him. She made a prisoner of him. "You shall not go home," she told him.

"Well," began Tom weakly yet persistently, "I —"

"No, no, Tom," said the colonel, "you are to eat a Christmas dinner with us to-morrow and then I wish to talk with you about — about —"

"About what?" said Tom.

"About — about — damnitall, about marrying my daughter," cried the colonel.

A LOVELY JAG/IN A CROWDED CAR/A BLITHE EPISODE OF THE BUSY/SHOPPING DAYS./JOY UN-CORKED AND EXUBERANT/THIS MAN HAD A GREAT TIME ALL BY/HIMSELF.*

The crosstown car was bound for the great shopping district, and one side of it was lined with women who sat in austere silence regarding each other in occasional furtive glances and preserving their respectability with fierce vigilance. A solitary man sat in a corner meekly pretending that he was interested in his newspaper. The conductor came and went without discussion, like a wellbred servant. The atmosphere of the car was as decorous as that of the most frigid of drawing rooms.

However, the decorous atmosphere was doomed to be destroyed by a wild red demon of drink and destruction. He was standing on a street corner, swaying gently on his wavering legs and blinking at the cobbles. Frequently he regarded the passing people with an expression of the most benign amiability.

As the car came near to him he tottered greatly in his excitement. He waved his umbrella and shouted: "Stop sh' car! Stop sh' car!"

The driver pulled stoutly at the reins with his gloved left hand, and with his right one swung the polished brass of the brake lever. The car halted and, upon the rear platform, the conductor reached down to help the wild, red demon of drink and destruc-

---

* Reprinted from New York Press: 6 January 1895.

tion aboard the car. He climbed up the steps with an important
and serious air, as if he were boarding a frigate; then he went
smiling in jovial satisfaction into the car. As he was about to sit
down there were two sharp, clanging notes on the bell, the driver
released his brake and again tightened his reins, and the car started
with a sudden jerk that caused the man to be precipitated violently into a seat as if some one had struck him. He seemed to feel
a keen humor in the situation for, upon recovering himself, he
looked at the other passengers and laughed.

As for the women bound for the shopping district, they had
suddenly turned into so many statues of ice. They stared out of
the little windows which cut the street scenes in half and allowed
but the upper parts of people to be seen, moving curiously without any legs. Whenever the eyes of the women were obliged to
encounter the man they assumed at once an expression of the most
heroic disgust and disdain. The man over in the corner grinned,
urchin-like.

The drunken man put his hands on his knees and beamed
about him in absolute unalloyed happiness. He seemed to believe
that he was engaged in carousing with a convivial party and these
friends were represented to his mind by the silent row of women
who were going shopping. He had not the air of a man who was on
a solitary spree; he was conducting a great celebration. The universe was engaged with him in a vast rakish song to flagon and
cup, the sun had its hat over its eye, all of humanity staggered
and smiled.

Presently his excited spirits overflowed to such an extent that
he was obliged to sing. He began to beat time with his fore-finger
as if he was leading a grand chorus.

> But th' younger shon was er shon-of-a-gun,
>   He was! He was!
> 'E shuffle' cards an' 'e play fer mon,
>   He did! He did!
> He wore shilk hat an' er high stannin' collar,
> He'd go out with'er boys an' gi' full an' then holler.
>   Oh, he was er ——

He was interrupted by the conductor, who came in and said
in a heavy, undertone: "Close that trap now or I'll put'che off!"

The injustice of the conductor was both an astonishment and
a grief to the man. He had been on the best of terms with each
single atom in space, and now here suddenly appeared a creature
who gruffly stated a dampening fact. He spoke very loudly in his
pain and disappointment:

"Pu' me off? What 'che go pu' me off fer? We ain't doin' er shing! G'wan way! Go shtand on er end z'car! Thash where you b'long! You ain' got no business talk me."

The conductor returned scowling to the rear platform. He turned and looked at the man with a glance that was full of menace.

Meanwhile, within the car, the inebriated passenger continued to conduct the grand celebration. "Hurray!" he said, at the conclusion of one of his little ballads. "le's all haver drink! Le's all haver noz' drink! Shay! Shay, look here a minute." He began to pound on the floor with his umbrella and make earnest gestures at the conductor. "Shay, look here!"

The conductor, watchful eyed but self contained, came forward. "Well," he said.

"Bringesh noz' round drinkshs," said the man. "Bringesh noz' round drinkshs."

"Say, you'll have to cool down some or I'll put'che off th' car. What d'yeh think?" said the conductor.

But the man was busy trying to find out the preference of each of the passengers. "What'll yeh take?" he demanded of each one, smiling genially. Whereupon the women opposite to him stared at the floor, at the ceiling, at the forward end of the car and at the rear end of the car, their lips set in stern lines.

Notwithstanding all these icy expressions, his face remained lit with a sunny grin, as if he were convinced that every one regarded him affectionately. He insisted that they should all take something.

"What'll you take? What? Ain'che drinkin'? What? Shay, yeh mus' take somethin'. What? Well, all ri', I'll order Manhattan fer yeh! Shay, Jim," he called loudly to the conductor, "bringesh noz' Manhattan."

With infinite pains and thoroughness he canvassed the passengers, putting to each one the formidable question: "What'll yeh drink?" The faces of the women were set in lines of horror, dismay and disgust. No one uttered a syllable in reply save the man over in the corner, who said indulgently: "Oh, I guess I'll take a beer."

At the conclusion of his canvass the man spent some anxious moments in reflection, calculating carefully upon his fingers. Then he triumphantly ordered one beer and nine Manhattan cocktails of the conductor.

The latter, who was collecting fares at the time, turned and said: "Say, lookahere, now, you've got t' quit this thing. Just close your face or I'll throw yeh out in th' street."

"Tha's all ri'," said the other, nodding his head portentously and wisely. "Tha's all ri'. You ain't go' throw me out. I ain't doin' er shing. Wha' you throw me out fer? Tha's all ri'." Then he returned to his demeanor of command. "Come. Hur' up! Bringesh nine Manhattans an' — an' — le's see — somebody order beer, didn' they? Who order beer?" He gazed inquiringly at the imperturbable faces. Finally he addressed the man over in the corner. "Shay, didn' you order beer?"

The man in the corner grinned. "Well, yes, I guess it was me."

"Look here, bringesh nine Manhattans an' er beer," called the celebrating man to the conductor. "Hur' up! Bringesh 'em quick."

The conductor looked scornfully away.

As the car passed through the region of the great stores the group of women gradually diminished until finally they disappeared altogether, and, as the car went on its way toward a distant ferry, there remained within only the celebrating individual and the man over in the corner. The celebrator became more jovial as time went forward. He rejoiced that the world was to him one vast landscape of pure rose color. The humming of the wheels and the clatter of the horses' hoofs did not drown the sound of this high quavering voice that sang of the pearl-hued joys of life as seen through a pair of strange, oblique, temporary spectacles. The conductor, musing upon the rear platform, had grown indifferent.

At last the celebrator seemed overcome by the wild thought that the car had passed the point where he had intended to leave it. He broke off in the midst of a ballad and scrambled for the door. "Stop sh' car," he yelled. The conductor reached for the bell strap, but before the car stopped the celebrator sprawled out upon the cobbles. He arose instantly and began a hurried and unsteady journey back up the street, retracing the way over which the car had just brought him. He seemed overwhelmed with anxiety.

The man in the corner came to the rear platform and gazed after the form of the celebrator. "Well, he was a peach," he said.

"That's what he was," said the conductor.

They both turned to watch him and they remained there deep in reflection, absorbed in contemplation of this wavering figure in the distance, until observation was no longer possible.

THE JUDGMENT OF THE SAGE*

A beggar crept wailing through the streets of a city. A certain man came to him there and gave him bread, saying: "I give you this loaf, because of God's word." Another came to the beggar and gave him bread, saying: "Take this loaf; I give it because you are hungry."

Now there was a continual rivalry among the citizens of this town as to who should appear to be the most pious man, and the event of the gifts to the beggar made discussion. People gathered in knots and argued furiously to no particular purpose. They appealed to the beggar, but he bowed humbly to the ground, as befitted one of his condition, and answered: "It is a singular circumstance that the loaves were of one size and of the same quality. How, then, can I decide which of these men gave bread more piously?"

The people heard of a philosopher who travelled through their country, and one said: "Behold, we who give not bread to beggars are not capable of judging those who have given bread to beggars. Let us, then, consult this wise man."

"But," said some, "mayhap this philosopher, according to your rule that one must have given bread before judging they who give bread, will not be capable."

"That is an indifferent matter to all truly great philosophers." So they made search for the wise man, and in time they came upon him, strolling along at his ease in the manner of philosophers.

"Oh, most illustrious sage," they cried.

"Yes," said the philosopher promptly.

"Oh, most illustrious sage, there are two men in our city, and one gave bread to a beggar, saying: 'Because of God's word.' And the other gave bread to the beggar, saying: 'Because you are hungry.' Now, which of these, oh, most illustrious sage, is the more pious man?"

---

* *Reprinted from* The Bookman: *January 1896.*

This prose parable is a variant of the characteristic Crane poem in The Black Riders *(1895). As a prose parable, it links also with his fables such as "How the Donkey Lifted the Hills" (1897). Its subject links it with "An Experiment in Misery" (1894) (see above).*

"Eh?" said the philosopher.

"Which of these, oh, most illustrious sage, is the more pious man?"

"My friends," said the philosopher suavely addressing the concourse, "I see that you mistake me for an illustrious sage. I am not he whom you seek. However, I saw a man answering my description pass here some time ago. With speed you may overtake him. Adieu."

A GREAT MISTAKE*

An Italian kept a fruit-stand on a corner where he had good aim at the people who came down from the elevated station, and at those who went along two thronged streets. He sat most of the day in a backless chair that was placed strategically.

There was a babe living hard by, up five flights of stairs, who regarded this Italian as a tremendous being. The babe had investigated this fruit-stand. It had thrilled him as few things he had met with in his travels had thrilled him. The sweets of the world had laid there in dazzling rows, tumbled in luxurious heaps. When he gazed at this Italian seated amid such splendid treasures, his lower lip hung low and his eyes, raised to the vendor's face, were filled with deep respect, worship, as if he saw omnipotence.

The babe came often to this corner. He hovered about the stand and watched each detail of the business. He was fascinated by the tranquillity of the vendor, the majesty of power and possession. At times he was so engrossed in his contemplation that people, hurrying, had to use care to avoid bumping him down.

He had never ventured very near to the stand. It was his habit to hang warily about the curb. Even there he resembled a babe who looks unbidden at a feast of gods.

One day, however, as the baby was thus staring, the vendor arose, and going along the front of the stand, began to polish oranges with a red pocket handkerchief. The breathless spectator moved across the sidewalk until his small face almost touched the

* Reprinted from The Open Boat and Other Stories (London, 1898). The sketch was first published in Elbert Hubbard's The Philistine: 2 March 1896, and then in his Roycroft Quarterly: May 1896. It was reprinted yet again that same month in A Souvenir and a Medley.

This sketch of a child and his venture relates to "A Dark-Brown Dog" (see below) and "An Ominous Baby" (see above).

vendor's sleeve. His fingers were gripped in a fold of his dress.

At last, the Italian finished with the oranges and returned to his chair. He drew a newspaper printed in his language from behind a bunch of bananas. He settled himself in a comfortable position, and began to glare savagely at the print. The babe was left face to face with the massed joys of the world. For a time he was a simple worshipper at this golden shrine. Then tumultuous desires began to shake him. His dreams were of conquest. His lips moved. Presently into his head there came a little plan. He sidled nearer, throwing swift and cunning glances at the Italian. He strove to maintain his conventional manner, but the whole plot was written upon his countenance.

At last he had come near enough to touch the fruit. From the tattered skirt came slowly his small dirty hand. His eyes were still fixed upon the vendor. His features were set, save for the under lip, which had a faint fluttering movement. The hand went forward.

Elevated trains thundered to the station and the stairway poured people upon the sidewalks. There was a deep sea roar from feet and wheels going ceaselessly. None seemed to perceive the babe engaged in a great venture.

The Italian turned his paper. Sudden panic smote the babe. His hand dropped, and he gave vent to a cry of dismay. He remained for a moment staring at the vendor. There was evidently a great debate in his mind. His infant intellect had defined this Italian. The latter was undoubtedly a man who would eat babes that provoked him. And the alarm in the babe when this monarch had turned his newspaper brought vividly before him the consequences if he were detected. But at this moment the vendor gave a blissful grunt, and tilting his chair against a wall, closed his eyes. His paper dropped unheeded.

The babe ceased his scrutiny and again raised his hand. It was moved with supreme caution toward the fruit. The fingers were bent, claw-like, in the manner of great heart-shaking greed. Once he stopped and chattered convulsively, because the vendor moved in his sleep. The babe, with his eyes still upon the Italian, again put forth his hand, and the rapacious fingers closed over a round bulb.

And it was written that the Italian should at this moment open his eyes. He glared at the babe a fierce question. Thereupon the babe thrust the round bulb behind him, and with a face expressive of the deepest guilt, began a wild but elaborate series of gestures declaring his innocence. The Italian howled. He sprang to his feet, and with three steps overtook the babe. He whirled him fiercely, and took from the little fingers a lemon.

A DARK-BROWN DOG *

A child was standing on a street-corner. He leaned with one shoulder against a high board fence and swayed the other to and fro, the while kicking carelessly at the gravel.

Sunshine beat upon the cobbles, and a lazy summer wind raised yellow dust which trailed in clouds down the avenue. Clattering trucks moved with indistinctness through it. The child stood dreamily gazing.

After a time, a little dark-brown dog came trotting with an intent air down the sidewalk. A short rope was dragging from his neck. Occasionally he trod upon the end of it and stumbled.

He stopped opposite the child, and the two regarded each other. The dog hesitated for a moment, but presently he made some little advances with his tail. The child put out his hand and called him. In an apologetic manner the dog came close, and the two had an interchange of friendly pattings and waggles. The dog became more enthusiastic with each moment of the interview, until with his gleeful caperings he threatened to overturn the child. Whereupon the child lifted his hand and struck the dog a blow upon the head.

This thing seemed to overpower and astonish the little dark-brown dog, and wounded him to the heart. He sank down in despair at the child's feet. When the blow was repeated, together with an admonition in childish sentences, he turned over upon his back, and held his paws in a peculiar manner. At the same time with his ears and his eyes he offered a small prayer to the child.

He looked so comical on his back, and holding his paws peculiarly, that the child was greatly amused and gave him little taps repeatedly, to keep him so. But the little dark-brown dog took this chastisement in the most serious way, and no doubt considered that he had committed some grave crime, for he wriggled contritely and showed his repentance in every way that was in his power.

---

* Published in Cosmopolitan Magazine: *March 1901; reprinted here from Vincent Starrett, ed.,* Men, Women and Boats *(1921).*

This sketch of a child and his dog can be compared with "A Great Mistake" (see above), published in March 1896. Crane sent "A Dark Brown Dog" in early 1900 to his London agent James B. Pinker, but probably he had written it along with "A Desertion" (see below) in his New York City days, 1892–1896.

He pleaded with the child and petitioned him, and offered more prayers.

At last the child grew weary of this amusement and turned toward home. The dog was praying at the time. He lay on his back and turned his eyes upon the retreating form.

Presently he struggled to his feet and started after the child. The latter wandered in a perfunctory way toward his home, stopping at times to investigate various matters. During one of these pauses he discovered the little dark-brown dog who was following him with the air of a footpad.

The child beat his pursuer with a small stick he had found. The dog lay down and prayed until the child had finished, and resumed his journey. Then he scrambled erect and took up the pursuit again.

On the way to his home the child turned many times and beat the dog, proclaiming with childish gestures that he held him in contempt as an unimportant dog, with no value save for a moment. For being this quality of animal the dog apologized and eloquently expressed regret, but he continued stealthily to follow the child. His manner grew so very guilty that he slunk like an assassin.

When the child reached his doorstep, the dog was industriously ambling a few yards in the rear. He became so agitated with shame when he again confronted the child that he forgot the dragging rope. He tripped upon it and fell forward.

The child sat down on the step and the two had another interview. During it the dog greatly exerted himself to please the child. He performed a few gambols with such abandon that the child suddenly saw him to be a valuable thing. He made a swift, avaricious charge and seized the rope.

He dragged his captive into a hall and up many long stairways in a dark tenement. The dog made willing efforts, but he could not hobble very skilfully up the stairs because he was very small and soft, and at last the pace of the engrossed child grew so energetic that the dog became panic-stricken. In his mind he was being dragged toward a grim unknown. His eyes grew wild with the terror of it. He began to wiggle his head frantically and to brace his legs.

The child redoubled his exertions. They had a battle on the stairs. The child was victorious because he was completely absorbed in his purpose, and because the dog was very small. He dragged his acquirement to the door of his home, and finally with triumph across the threshold.

No one was in. The child sat down on the floor and made overtures to the dog. These the dog instantly accepted. He beamed with affection upon his new friend. In a short time they were firm and abiding comrades.

When the child's family appeared, they made a great row. The dog was examined and commented upon and called names. Scorn was leveled at him from all eyes, so that he became much embarrassed and drooped like a scorched plant. But the child went sturdily to the center of the floor, and, at the top of his voice, championed the dog. It happened that he was roaring protestations, with his arms clasped about the dog's neck, when the father of the family came in from work.

The parent demanded to know what the blazes they were making the kid howl for. It was explained in many words that the infernal kid wanted to introduce a disreputable dog into the family.

A family council was held. On this depended the dog's fate, but he in no way heeded, being busily engaged in chewing the end of the child's dress.

The affair was quickly ended. The father of the family, it appears, was in a particularly savage temper that evening, and when he perceived that it would amaze and anger everybody if such a dog were allowed to remain, he decided that it should be so. The child, crying softly, took his friend off to a retired part of the room to hobnob with him, while the father quelled a fierce rebellion of his wife. So it came to pass that the dog was a member of the household.

He and the child were associated together at all times save when the child slept. The child became a guardian and a friend. If the large folk kicked the dog and threw things at him, the child made loud and violent objections. Once when the child had run, protesting loudly, with tears raining down his face and his arms outstretched, to protect his friend, he had been struck in the head with a very large saucepan from the hand of his father, enraged at some seeming lack of courtesy in the dog. Ever after, the family were careful how they threw things at the dog. Moreover, the latter grew very skilful in avoiding missiles and feet. In a small room containing a stove, a table, a bureau and some chairs, he would display strategic ability of a high order, dodging, feinting and scuttling about among the furniture. He could force three or four people armed with brooms, sticks and handfuls of coal, to use all their ingenuity to get in a blow. And even when they did, it was seldom that they could do him a serious injury or leave any imprint.

But when the child was present these scenes did not occur.

It came to be recognized that if the dog was molested, the child would burst into sobs, and as the child, when started, was very riotous and practically unquenchable, the dog had therein a safeguard.

However, the child could not always be near. At night, when he was asleep, his dark-brown friend would raise from some black corner a wild, wailful cry, a song of infinite loneliness and despair, that would go shuddering and sobbing among the buildings of the block and cause people to swear. At these times the singer would often be chased all over the kitchen and hit with a great variety of articles.

Sometimes, too, the child himself used to beat the dog, although it is not known that he ever had what truly could be called a just cause. The dog always accepted these thrashings with an air of admitted guilt. He was too much of a dog to try to look to be a martyr or to plot revenge. He received the blows with deep humility, and furthermore he forgave his friend the moment the child had finished, and was ready to caress the child's hand with his little red tongue.

When misfortune came upon the child, and his troubles overwhelmed him, he would often crawl under the table and lay his small distressed head on the dog's back. The dog was ever sympathetic. It is not to be supposed that at such times he took occasion to refer to the unjust beatings his friend, when provoked, had administered to him.

He did not achieve any notable degree of intimacy with the other members of the family. He had no confidence in them, and the fear that he would express at their casual approach often exasperated them exceedingly. They used to gain a certain satisfaction in underfeeding him, but finally his friend the child grew to watch the matter with some care, and when he forgot it, the dog was often successful in secret for himself.

So the dog prospered. He developed a large bark, which came wondrously from such a small rug of a dog. He ceased to howl persistently at night. Sometimes, indeed, in his sleep, he would utter little yells, as from pain, but that occurred, no doubt, when in his dreams he encountered huge flaming dogs who threatened him direfully.

His devotion to the child grew until it was a sublime thing. He wagged at his approach; he sank down in despair at his departure. He could detect the sound of the child's step among all the noises of the neighborhood. It was like a calling voice to him.

The scene of their companionship was a kingdom governed by this terrible potentate, the child; but neither criticism nor rebellion ever lived for an instant in the heart of the one subject. Down in the mystic, hidden fields of his little dog-soul bloomed flowers of love and fidelity and perfect faith.

The child was in the habit of going on many expeditions to observe strange things in the vicinity. On these occasions his friend usually jogged aimfully along behind. Perhaps, though, he went ahead. This necessitated his turning around every quarter-minute to make sure the child was coming. He was filled with a large idea of the importance of these journeys. He would carry himself with such an air! He was proud to be the retainer of so great a monarch.

One day, however, the father of the family got quite exceptionally drunk. He came home and held carnival with the cooking utensils, the furniture and his wife. He was in the midst of this recreation when the child, followed by the dark-brown dog, entered the room. They were returning from their voyages.

The child's practised eye instantly noted his father's state. He dived under the table, where experience had taught him was a rather safe place. The dog, lacking skill in such matters, was, of course, unaware of the true condition of affairs. He looked with interested eyes at his friend's sudden dive. He interpreted it to mean: Joyous gambol. He started to patter across the floor to join him. He was the picture of a little dark-brown dog en route to a friend.

The head of the family saw him at this moment. He gave a huge howl of joy, and knocked the dog down with a heavy coffee-pot. The dog, yelling in supreme astonishment and fear, writhed to his feet and ran for cover. The man kicked out with a ponderous foot. It caused the dog to swerve as if caught in a tide. A second blow of the coffee-pot laid him upon the floor.

Here the child, uttering loud cries, came valiantly forth like a knight. The father of the family paid no attention to these calls of the child, but advanced with glee upon the dog. Upon being knocked down twice in swift succession, the latter apparently gave up all hope of escape. He rolled over on his back and held his paws in a peculiar manner. At the same time with his eyes and his ears he offered up a small prayer.

But the father was in a mood for having fun, and it occurred to him that it would be a fine thing to throw the dog out of the window. So he reached down and, grabbing the animal by a leg, lifted him, squirming, up. He swung him two or three times hilariously about his head, and then flung him with great accuracy through the window.

The soaring dog created a surprise in the block. A woman watering plants in an opposite window gave an involuntary shout and dropped a flower-pot. A man in another window leaned perilously out to watch the flight of the dog. A woman who had been hanging out clothes in a yard began to caper wildly. Her mouth was filled with clothes-pins, but her arms gave vent to a sort of exclamation. In appearance she was like a gagged prisoner. Children ran whooping.

The dark-brown body crashed in a heap on the roof of a shed five stories below. From thence it rolled to the pavement of an alleyway.

The child in the room far above burst into a long, dirge-like cry, and toddled hastily out of the room. It took him a long time to reach the alley, because his size compelled him to go downstairs backward, one step at a time, and holding with both hands to the step above.

When they came for him later, they found him seated by the body of his dark-brown friend.

A TALE OF MERE CHANCE./BEING AN ACCOUNT OF THE PURSUIT OF THE TILES, STATEMENT OF THE CLOCK,/AND THE GRIP OF A COAT OF ORANGE SPOTS, TOGETHER WITH SOME CRITICISM/OF A DETECTIVE SAID TO BE CARVED FROM AN OLD TABLE-LEG. *

By Stephen Crane

Yes, my friend, I killed the man; but I would not have been detected in it were it not for some very extraordinary circumstances. I had long considered this deed, but I am a delicate and sensitive person, you understand, and I hesitated over it as the diver hesitates on the brink of a dark and icy mountain pool. A thought of the shock of contact holds one back.

As I was passing his house one morning I said to myself, "Well, at any rate, if she loves him it will not be for long." And after that decision I was not myself, but a sort of machine.

I rang the bell, and the servants admitted me to the drawing-room. I waited there while the tall old clock placidly ticked its

---

* *Reprinted from* The English Illustrated Magazine: *March 1896.*

speech of time. The rigid and austere chairs remained in possession of their singular imperturbability, although, of course, they were aware of my purpose. But the little white tiles of the floor whispered one to another, and looked at me.

Presently he entered the room, and I, drawing my revolver, shot him. He screamed — you know that scream, mostly amazement — and as he fell forward his blood was upon the little white tiles. They huddled, and covered their eyes from this rain. It seemed to me that the old clock stopped ticking, as a man may gasp in the middle of a sentence, and a chair threw itself in my way as I sprang toward the door.

A moment later I was walking down the street — tranquil, you understand — and I said to myself: "It is done! Long years from this day I will say to her that it was I who killed him. After time has eaten the conscience of the thing she will admire my courage."

I was elated that the affair had gone off so smoothly, and I felt like returning home and taking a long, full sleep, like a tired working man. When people passed me I contemplated their stupidity with a sense of satisfaction.

But those accursed little white tiles!

I heard a shrill crying and chattering behind me, and looking back I saw them, blood-stained and impassioned, raising their little hands and screaming, "Murder! It was he!" I have said that they had little hands. I am not so sure of it, but they had some means of indicating me as unerringly as pointing fingers. As for their movement, they swept along as easily as dry, light leaves are carried by the wind. Always they were shrilly piping their song of my guilt.

My friend, may it never be your fortune to be pursued by a crowd of little blood-stained tiles. I used a thousand means to be free from the clash, clash, of those tiny feet. I ran through the world at my best speed, but it was no better than that of an ox, while they, my pursuers, were always fresh, eager, relentless.

I am an ingenious person, and I used every trick that a desperately fertile man can invent. Hundreds of times I had almost evaded them when some smouldering, neglected spark would blaze up and discover me.

I felt that the eye of conviction would have no terrors for me; but the eye of suspicion, which I saw in city after city, on road after road, drove me to the verge of going forward and saying, "Yes, I have murdered."

People would see the following, clamorous troupe of blood-stained tiles and give me piercing glances, so that these swords played continually at my heart. But we are a decorous race, thank God! It is very vulgar to apprehend murderers on the public street.

We have learned correct manners from the English. Besides, who can be sure of the meaning of clamouring tiles? It might be merely a trick in politics.

Detectives? What are detectives? Oh, yes, I have read of them and their deeds when I come to think of it. The prehistoric races must have been remarkable. I have never been able to understand how the detectives navigated in stone boats. Still, specimens of their pottery excavated in Taumanipas show a remarkable knowledge of mechanics. I remember the little hydraulic — what's that? Well, what you say may be true, my friend, but I think you dream.

The little stained tiles. My friend, I stopped in an inn at the end of the earth, and in the morning they were there flying like birds and pecking at my window.

I should have escaped. Heavens! I should have escaped! What was more simple? I murdered, and then walked into the world, which is wide and intricate.

Do you know that my own clock assisted in the hunt of me? They asked what time I left my home that morning and it replied at once: "Half-past eight." The watch of a man I had chanced to pass near the house of the crime told the people "Seven minutes after nine." And of course the tall old clock in the drawing-room went about day after day repeating: "Eighteen minutes after nine."

Do you say that the man who caught me was very clever? My friend, I have lived long, and he was the most incredible blockhead of my experience. An enslaved, dust-eating Mexican vaquero wouldn't hitch his pony to such a man. Do you think he deserves credit for my capture? If he had been as pervading as the atmosphere he would never have caught me. If he was a detective, as you say, I could carve a better one from an old table-leg. But the tiles! That is another matter. At night I think they flew in a long, high flock, like pigeons. In the day, little mad things, they murmured on my trail like frothy-mouthed weasels.

I see that you note these great, round, vividly orange spots on my coat. Of course, even if the detective was really carved from an old table-leg, he could hardly fail to apprehend a man thus badged. As sores come upon one in the plague, so came these spots upon my coat. When I discovered them I made efforts to free myself of this coat. I tore, tugged, wrenched at it, but around my shoulders it was like the grip of a dead man's arms. Do you know that I have plunged in a thousand lakes? I have smeared this coat with a thousand paints, but day and night the spots burn like lights. I might walk from this jail to-day if I could rid myself of this coat, but it clings — clings — clings.

At any rate, the person you call a detective is not so clever to discover a man in a coat of spotted orange, followed by shrieking blood-stained tiles.

Yes, that noise from the corridor is most peculiar; but they are always there, muttering and watching, clashing and jostling. It sounds as if the dishes of Hades were being washed. Yet I have become used to it. Once, indeed, in the night, I cried out to them: "In God's name, go away, little blood-stained tiles!" But they doggedly answered: "It is the law."

SAILING DAY SCENES/ON THE DOCK OF A BIG OCEAN LINER/JUST BEFORE THE START./SMILES AND TEARS MINGLE/ROAR, BUSTLE, CONFUSION, CONVIVIALITY/AND ACHING HEARTS.*

The interior of the huge pier had been long thronged with trucks, merchandise and people. A great babble of voices and roar of wheels arose from it. Over all rang the wild incoherent shouts of the bosses, who directed the stevedores. These latter marched in endless procession, with bales and bags upon their shoulders. It was the last of the cargo. They ferreted their way stolidly through the noisy crowds of visitors and then up a wide gangplank in steady and monotonous procession.

Through the wide doors in the side of the pier could be seen the mighty sides of the steamer, and above little stretches of white deck, whereon people stood in rows gazing fixedly at the shore as if they expected at any moment to see it vanish. At the end of the passenger gangplank two sailors remained imperturbably at their station. An officer leaned on the railing near them. Near the shoreward end swarmed countless stewards, mingling their blue uniforms in with the gay colored clothes of the crowd and wondering assiduously about everybody's business.

From a position near the doors one could see that the enormous funnels of the steamship were emitting continual streams of black, curling smoke.

---

* Reprinted from an undated clipping in Crane's Scrapbook in the Columbia University Crane Collection, on which he wrote "The Press, New York."

Some of Crane's friends sailed for Europe on 29 February 1896, and Crane no doubt saw them off. This sketch was perhaps written then.

Gradually there was a vanishing of the stewards. The two sailors at the gangplank began to look serious and rather wild, as if the responsibility of their positions and the eye of the adjacent officer was too much for them. Rows of stevedores manned ropes and prepared to tug at the gangplanks. Meanwhile, from all along the line of the pier, extraordinary conversations were being held with people who leaned upon the railings of the decks above. A preliminary thrill went through the throng. The talk began to grow hurried, excited. People spoke wildly and with great speed, conscious that the last moments were upon them. And it devolved upon certain individuals to lose their friends at the final minute in the chaos of heads upon the decks, so that one could often hear the same typical formula coming from a dozen different sources, as if everybody was interested in the same person and had missed him. Two grayheaded New Yorkers held a frantic argument.

"There he is! There he is! Hurray! Goodby, ol' man!"

"Darn it all, I tell you that it isn't him at all!"

"It is, too!"

"It ain't, I tell you!"

"Ah, there he is now. Down there further! Goodby, ol' man, goodby!"

A man upon the steamer suddenly burst out in a fury of gesticulation. "Where's Tommie?" he bawled. "I can't see Tommie!"

His excitement was communicated to two women upon the pier. "Heavens!" said one with a nervous cry, "Where is that boy!" She could not omit some complainings of motherhood. "He's the greatest plague! Here's his father sailing for Europe and he's off somewhere! Tommie! Tommie! Come here!" They began to glance frenziedly through the crevices of the crowd. It was plain that they expected to detect him in some terrible, irrelevant crime.

Then suddenly above the clamor of farewells arose the wild shout of a little boy, undismayed by the crowds. "Papa! Papa! Papa! Here I am! Goodby, papa!" The man on the steamship made a tremendous gesture. The two women on the pier began to weep vaguely.

The faces on all sides beamed with affection and some sort of a suggestion of mournful reminiscence. There were plentiful smiles, but they expressed always a great tender sorrow. It was surprising to see how full of expression the face of a blunt, every day American business man could become. They were suddenly angels.

As for the women, they were sacred from stare through the purity of their grief. Many of them allowed the tears to fall unheeded down their faces. Theirs was a quality of sorrow that has a certain valor, a certain boldness.

The crowd began to swarm toward the end of the pier to get the last gesture and glance of their friends as the steamer backed out. It was coming toward the supreme moment.

At last some indefinite mechanism set the sailors and the stevedores in motion. Ropes were flung away and the heavy gang-planks were pulled back onto the dock with loud shouts. "Look out! Look out there!" The people were unheeding, for now uprose a great tumult of farewells, a song of affection that swelled into a vast incoherent roar. They had waited long for this moment, and now with a sense of its briefness they were frantic in an effort to think how best to use it. Handkerchiefs waved in white clouds. Men bawled in a last futile struggle to express their state of mind. Over all could often be heard the shrill wail of the little boy! "Oh, papa! Papa! Here I am!"

Back from the surging crowd around the huge doors was the motionless figure of a beautiful woman. She had been gazing long at the steamship with clear and unswerving eye and face as stoical as a warrior's. She remained carven, expressionless, as the huge panorama of black and white went slowly past the doors. When the bow went by with its burden of a few tranquil sailors busy with ropes, a faint flutter went over her rose tinted under lip. She put up her hands and took a long time to arrange the laces about her throat.

Out at the end of the pier the whole final uproar was in full motion. A tug loaded with gesturing, howling people bustled to and fro, celebrating everything with a barbaric whistle. A last great cry arose as steel hued water began to show between the craft and the pier. It was a farewell with an undercurrent of despair of ex-pression. The inadequacy of the goodbys seemed suddenly appar-ent to the crowd. The forlorn pathos of the thing struck their minds anew and many of the women began to weep again in that vague way, as if overcome by a sadness that was subtly more than the tangible grief of parting. A pompous officer, obviously vain of his clothes, strode before the agitated faces upon the ship and looked complacently at the pier. It was an old story to him, and he thought it rather silly. He regarded all such moments with the contempt of a man of very strong nature.

When the steamer had passed out of shouting distance a woman spoke to a man who was bowing in a profuse foreign fashion. "Well, he is gone. It was good of you to come this morning. You can't think how he liked the flowers." She was one of those women whose grief had a quality of valor. She did not understand

that tears were shameful things to be hidden in houses. Her veil
was high upon her forehead. She paid no heed to the tears upon
her eyelids.

Further back within the pier a woman sat weeping discon-
solately. A group of four children stood around her in an awed
and puzzled circle. A little babe kept repeating in a dumb, uncomprehending tone: "Ma-ma ky! ma-ma ky!"

The beautiful woman who had stared imperturbably at the
ship walked slowly by. The weeping woman looked up. They
exchanged a long, friendly glance. It was the free masonry of two
sorrows.

OPIUM'S VARIED DREAMS./THE HABIT, THE VIC-TIM, THE RE-/LIEF, AND THE DESPAIR./THIS CITY'S 25,000 OPIUM SMOKERS AND/THEIR WAYS SINCE REFORM BROKE UP/THEIR RESORTS—THE PIPE AND ITS HAN-/DLING, AND THE HABITUE'S DEFENCE.*

Opium smoking in this country is believed to be more particularly
a pastime of the Chinese, but in truth the greater number of the
smokers are white men and white women. Chinatown furnishes the
pipe, lamp, and yen-nock, but let a man once possess a layout, and
a common American drug store furnishes him with the opium, and
China is discernible only in the traditions that cling to the habit.

There are 25,000 opium smokers in the city of New York alone.
At one time there were two great colonies, one in the Tenderloin,
one, of course, in Chinatown. This was before the hammer of reform struck them. Now the two colonies are splintered into some-

---

* Reprinted from New York Sun: 17 May 1896. Unsigned.

This article prepares for Crane's sketch "A Tenderloin
Story" about Yen-Nock Bill (see below) in New York Journal:
29 November 1896. It was not included in Bowery Tales (London, 1900) nor in Wilson Follett, ed., The Work of Stephen
Crane (1925–1927).

Crane purchased an opium layout in order to experience
firsthand "opium's varied dreams" before writing this sketch,
and it was found in his boardinghouse by the police after they
arrested Dora Clark as a streetwalker in his company.

thing less than 25,000 fragments. The smokers are disorganized, but they still exist.

The Tenderloin district of New York fell an early victim to opium. That part of the population which is known as the "sporting" class adopted the habit quickly. Cheap actors, race track touts, gamblers, and the different kinds of confidence men took to it generally. Opium raised its yellow banner over the Tenderloin, attaining the dignity of a common vice.

Splendid joints were not uncommon then in New York. There was one on Forty-second street which would have been palatial if it were not for the bad taste of the decorations. An occasional man from Fifth avenue or Madison avenue would have there his private layout, an elegant equipment of silver, ivory, and gold. The bunks which lined all sides of the two rooms were nightly crowded, and some of the people owned names which are not altogether unknown to the public. This place was raided because of sensational stories in the newspapers, and the little wicket no longer opens to allow the fiend to enter.

Upon the appearance of reform, opium retired to private flats. Here it now reigns, and it will be undoubtedly an extremely long century before the police can root it from these little strongholds. Once Billie Hostetter got drunk on whiskey and emptied three scuttles of coal down the dumb-waiter shaft. This made a noise, and, Billie, naturally, was arrested. But opium is silent. The smokers do not rave. They dream, or talk in low tones.

People who declare themselves able to pick out opium smokers on the street usually are deluded. An opium smoker may look like a deacon or a deacon may look like an opium smoker. The fiends easily conceal their vice. They get up from the layout, adjust their cravats, straighten their coat tails, and march off like ordinary people, and the best kind of an expert would not be willing to bet that they were or were not addicted to the habit.

It would be very hard to say just exactly what constitutes a habit. With the fiends it is an elastic word. Ask a smoker if he has a habit and he will deny it. Ask him if some one who smokes the same amount has a habit and he will admit it. Perhaps the ordinary smoker consumes 25 cents' worth of opium each day. There are others who smoke $1 worth. This is rather extraordinary, and in this case at least it is safe to say that it is a habit. The $1 smokers usually indulge in high hats, which is the term for a large pill. The ordinary smoker is satisfied with pinheads. Pinheads are of about the size of a French pea.

Habit smokers have a contempt for the sensation smoker, who has been won by the false glamour which surrounds the vice, and goes about really pretending that he has a ravenous hunger for the pipe. There are more sensation smokers than one would imagine.

It is said to take one year of devotion to the pipe before one can contract a habit; but probably it does not take any such long time. Sometimes an individual who has smoked only a few months will speak of nothing but pipe, and when a man talks pipe persistently it is a pretty sure sign that the drug has fastened its grip so that he is not able to stop its use easily. When a man arises from his first trial of the pipe, the nausea that clutches him is something that can give cards and spades and big cassino to seasickness. If he had swallowed a live chimney sweep he could not feel more like dying. The room and everything in it whirls like the inside of an electric light plant. There comes a thirst, a great thirst, and this thirst is so sinister and so misleading that if the novice drank spirits to satisfy it he would presently be much worse. The one thing that will make him feel again that life may be a joy is a cup of strong black coffee.

If there is a sentiment in the pipe for him, he returns to it after this first unpleasant trial. Gradually the power of the drug sinks into his heart. It absorbs his thought. He begins to lie with more and more grace to cover the shortcomings and little failures of his life. And then, finally, he may become a full-fledged pipe fiend, a man with a yen-yen.

A yen-yen, be it known, is the hunger, the craving. It comes to a fiend when he separates himself from his pipe and it takes him by the heart strings. If, indeed, he will not buck through a brick wall to get to the pipe, he at least will become the most disagreeable, sour-tempered person on earth until he finds a way to satisfy his craving.

When the victim arrives at the point where his soul calls for the drug, he usually learns to cook. The operation of rolling the pill and cooking it over the little lamp is a delicate task, and it takes time to learn it. When a man can cook for himself and buys his own layout, he is gone, probably. He has placed upon his shoulders an elephant which he may carry to the edge of forever. The Chinese have a preparation which they call a cure, but the first difficulty is to get the fiend to take the preparation, and the second difficulty is to cure anything with this cure.

The fiend will defend opium with eloquence and energy. He very seldom drinks spirits, and so he gains an opportunity to make the most ferocious parallels between the effects of rum and the effects of opium. Ask him to free his mind and he will probably say:

"Opium does not deprive you of your senses. It does not make a madman of you. But drink does. See? Who ever heard of a man committing murder when full of hop. Get him full of whiskey and he might kill his father. I don't see why people kick so about opium smoking. If they knew anything about it, they wouldn't talk that way. Let anybody drink rum who cares to, but as for me, I would rather be what I am."

As before mentioned, there were at one time gorgeous opium dens in New York, but now there is probably not a den with any pretence to splendid decoration. The Chinamen will smoke in a cellar, bare, squalid, occupied by an odor that will float wooden chips. The police took the adornments from the vice and left nothing but the pipe itself. Yet the pipe is sufficient for its slant-eyed lover.

When prepared for smoking purposes, opium is a heavy liquid much like molasses. Ordinarily it is sold in hollow li-shi nuts or in little round tins resembling the old percussion cap boxes. The pipe is a curious affair, particularly notable for the way in which it does not resemble the drawings of it that appear in print. The stem is of thick bamboo, the mouthpiece usually of ivory. The bowl crops out suddenly about four inches from the end of the stem. It is a heavy affair of clay or stone. The cavity is a mere hole, of the diameter of a lead pencil, drilled through the centre. The yen-nock is a sort of sharpened darning needle. With it the cook takes the opium from the box. He twirls it dexterously with his thumb and forefinger until enough of the gummy substance adheres to the sharp point. Then he holds it over the tiny flame of the lamp which burns only peanut oil or sweet oil. The pill now exactly resembles boiling molasses. The clever fingers of the cook twirl it above the flame. Lying on his side comfortably, he takes the pipe in his left hand and transfers the cooked pill from the yen-nock to the bowl of the pipe, where he again moulds it with the yen-nock until it is a little button-like thing with a hole in the centre fitting squarely over the hole in the bowl. Dropping the yen-nock, the cook now uses two hands for the pipe. He extends the mouthpiece toward the one whose turn it is to smoke, and as the smoker leans forward in readiness, the cook draws the bowl toward the flame until the heat sets the pill to boiling. Whereupon the smoker takes a long, deep draw at the pipe, the pill sputters and fries, and a moment later the smoker sinks back tranquilly. An odor, heavy, aromatic, agreeable, and yet disagreeable, hangs in the air and makes its way with peculiar powers of penetration. The group about the layout talk in low voices, and watch the cook deftly moulding another pill. The little flame casts a strong yellow light on their faces as they huddle about the layout. As the pipe passes and passes around the circle, the voices drop to a mere indolent cooing, and the eyes that so lazily watch the cook at his work, glisten and glisten from the influence of the drug until they resemble flashing bits of silver.

There is a similarity in coloring and composition in a group of men about a midnight camp fire in a forest and a group of smokers about the layout tray with its tiny light. Everything, of course, is on a smaller scale with the smoking. The flame is only an inch and a half, perhaps, in height, and the smokers huddle closely in order that every person may smoke undisturbed. But there is something in the abandon of the poses, the wealth of light on the faces, and the strong mystery of shadow at the backs of the people that bring the two scenes into some kind of artistic resemblance. And just as the lazy eyes about a camp fire fasten themselves dreamfully upon the blaze of logs, so do the lazy eyes about an opium layout fasten themselves upon the little flame.

There is but one pipe, one lamp, and one cook to each smoking layout. Pictures of nine or ten persons sitting in armchairs and smoking various kinds of curiously carved tobacco pipes probably serve well enough, but when they are named "Interior of an Opium Den" and that sort of thing, it is absurd. Opium could not be smoked like tobacco. A pill is good for one long draw. After that the cook moulds another. A smoker would just as soon choose a gallows as an armchair for smoking purposes. He likes to curl down on a mattress placed on the floor in the quietest corner of a Tenderloin flat, and smoke there with no light but the tiny yellow spear from the layout lamp.

It is a curious fact that it is rather the custom to purchase for a layout tray one of those innocent black tin affairs which are supposed to be placed before a baby as he takes his high chair for dinner.

If a beginner expects to have dreams of an earth dotted with white porcelain towers and a sky of green silk, he will be much mistaken. "The Opium Smoker's Dream" seems to be mostly a mistake. The influence of dope is evidently a fine languor, a complete mental rest. The problems of life no longer appear. Existence is peace. The virtues of a man's friends, for instance, loom beautifully against his own sudden perfection. The universe is readjusted. Wrong departs, injustice vanishes: there is nothing but a quiet harmony of all things — until the next morning.

And who should invade this momentary land of rest, this dream country, if not the people of the Tenderloin; they who are at once supersensitive and hopeless, the people who think more upon death and the mysteries of life, the chances of the hereafter than any other class, educated or uneducated? Opium holds out to them its

lie, and they embrace it eagerly, expecting to find a consummation
of peace, but they awake to find the formidable labors of life grown
more formidable. And if the pipe should happen to ruin their lives
they cling the more closely to it because then it stands between
them and thought.

A PROLOGUE.*

A gloomy stage. Slender curtains at a window, centre. Before the
window, a table, and upon the table, a large book, opened. A
moonbeam, no wider than a sword-blade, pierces the curtains and
falls upon the book.

A moment of silence.

From without, then — an adjacent room in intention — come
sounds of celebration, of riotous drinking and laughter. Finally, a
swift quarrel. The din and crash of a fight. A little stillness. Then
a woman's scream. "Ah, my son, my son."

A moment of silence.

Curtain.

---

* *Published in* Roycroft Quarterly: *May 1896; reprinted in*
The Philistine: *July 1896.*

    *Crane from the start hankered to attain a name for him-
self not only as a fiction and sketch writer but also as a dramatist. He cast some of his early sketches in dramatic dialogue
form, as in "At Clancy's Wake" (1893) (see above), which
links with "A Prologue" in that both poke fun at contemporary
melodramas.*

    *"A Prologue" was written probably in the autumn of 1895
when Crane had hopes of becoming drama critic for the Philadelphia Press. Reprinted here for the first time.*

NEW YORK'S BICYCLE SPEEDWAY./THE BOULE-
VARD, ONCE A QUIET AVENUE, NOW/THE SCENE
OF NIGHTLY CARNIVALS—HERE/ALL GOTHAM
COMES TOGETHER AND/ROLLS ALONG IN AN
ENDLESS,/SHIMMERING PANORAMA./BY STEPHEN
CRANE.*

New York, July 3, 1896. — The Bowery has had its day as a famous
New York street. It is now a mere tradition. Broadway will long
hold its place as the chief vein of the city's life. No process of ex-
pansion can ever leave it abandoned to the cheap clothing dealers
and dime museum robbers. It is too strategic in position. But lately
the Western Boulevard which slants from the Columbus monument at the southwest corner of Central Park to the river has
vaulted to a startling prominence and is now one of the sights of
New York. This is caused by the bicycle. Once the Boulevard was
a quiet avenue whose particular distinctions were its shade trees
and its third foot-walk which extended in Parisian fashion down
the middle of the street. Also it was noted for its billboards and its
huge and slumberous apartment hotels. Now, however, it is the
great thoroughfare for bicycles. On these gorgeous spring days they
appear in thousands. All mankind is a-wheel apparently and a person on nothing but legs feels like a strange animal. A mighty army
of wheels streams from the brick wilderness below Central Park and
speeds over the asphalt. In the cool of the evening it returns with
swaying and flashing of myriad lamps.

The bicycle crowd has completely subjugated the street. The
glittering wheels dominate it from end to end. The cafes and dining rooms or the apartment hotels are occupied mainly by people

---

* Reprinted from an unidentified press clipping dated "For
July 5" in Crane's Scrapbook in the Columbia University Crane
Collection. The text is identical with his "Transformed Boule-
vard" in the New York Sun: 5 July 1896. Only the title differs.
The Sun apparently published the sketch under a different title
on the same day, "New York's Bicycle Speedway."

Crane very likely knew of "Brooklyn's Big Bicycle Parade,"
Harper's Weekly: 20 June 1895, an illustrated article about the
new bicycle path.

in bicycle clothes. Even the billboards have surrendered. They advertise wheels and lamps and tires and patent saddles with all the flaming vehemence of circus art. Even when they do condescend to still advertise a patent medicine, you are sure to confront a lithograph of a young person in bloomers who is saying in large type: "Yes, George, I find that Willowrum always refreshes me after these long rides."

Down at the Circle where stands the patient Columbus, the stores are crowded with bicycle goods. There are innumerable repair shops. Everything is bicycle. In the afternoon the parade begins. The great discoverer, erect on his tall grey shaft, must feel his stone head whirl when the battalions come swinging and shining around the curve.

It is interesting to note the way in which the blasphemous and terrible truck-drivers of the lower part of the city will hunt a bicyclist. A truck-driver, of course, believes that a wheelman is a pest. The average man could not feel more annoyance if nature had suddenly invented some new kind of mosquito. And so the truck-driver resolves in his dreadful way to make life as troublous and thrilling for the wheelman as he possibly can. The wheelman suffers under a great handicap. He is struggling over the most uneven cobbles which bless a metropolis. Twenty horses threaten him and forty wheels miss his shoulder by an inch. In his ears there is a hideous din. It surrounds him, envelopes him.

Add to this trouble, then, a truckman with a fiend's desire to see dead wheelmen. The situation affords deep excitement for everyone concerned.

But when a truck-driver comes to the Boulevard the beautiful balance of the universe is apparent. The teamster sits mute, motionless, casting sidelong glances at the wheels which spin by him. He still contrives to exhibit a sort of a sombre defiance, but he has no oath nor gesture nor wily scheme to drive a 3 ton wagon over the prostrate body of some unhappy cyclist. On the Boulevard this roaring lion from down town is so subdued, so isolated that he brings tears to the sympathetic eye.

There is a new game on the Boulevard. It is the game of Bicycle Cop and Scorcher. When the scorcher scorches beyond the patience of the law, the bicycle policeman, if in sight, takes after him. Usually the scorcher has a blissful confidence in his ability to scorch and thinks it much easier to just ride away from the policeman than to go to court and pay a fine. So they go flying up the Boulevard with the whole mob of wheelmen and wheelwomen, eager to see the race, sweeping after them. But the bicycle police are mighty hard riders and it takes a flier to escape them. The affair usually ends in calamity for the scorcher, but in the meantime fifty or sixty cyclists have had a period of delirious joy.

Bicycle Cop and Scorcher is a good game, but after all it is not as good as the game that was played in the old days when the suggestion of a corps of bicycle police in neat knickerbockers would have scandalized Mulberry street. This was the game of Fat Policeman on Foot Trying to Stop a Spurt. A huge, unwieldy officer rushing out into the street and wildly trying to head off and grab some rider who was spinning along in just one silver flash was a sight that caused the populace to turn out in a body. If some madman started at a fierce gait from the Columbus monument, he could have the consciousness that at frequent and exciting intervals, red-faced policemen would gallop out at him and frenziedly clutch at his coat-tails. And owing to a curious dispensation, the majority of the policemen along the boulevard were very stout and could swear most graphically in from two to five languages.

But they changed all that. The un-police-like bicycle police are wonderfully clever and the vivid excitement of other days is gone. Even the scorcher seems to feel depressed and narrowly looks over the nearest officer before he starts on his frantic career.

The girl in bloomers is, of course, upon her native heath when she steers her steel steed into the Boulevard. One becomes conscious of a bewildering variety in bloomers. There are some that fit and some that do not fit. There are some that were not made to fit and there are some that couldn't fit anyhow. As a matter of fact the bloomer costume is now in one of the primary stages of its evolution. Let us hope so at any rate. Of course every decent citizen concedes that women shall wear what they please and it is supposed that he covenants with himself not to grin and nudge his neighbor when anything particularly amazing passes him on the street but resolves to simply and industriously mind his own affairs. Still the situation no doubt harrows him greatly. No man was ever found to defend bloomers. His farthest statement, as an individual, is to advocate them for all women he does not know and cares nothing about. Most women become radical enough to say: "Why shouldn't I wear 'em, if I choose." Still, a second look at the Boulevard convinces one that the world is slowly, solemnly, inevitably coming to bloomers. We are about to enter an age of bloomers, and the bicycle, that machine which has gained an economic position of the most tremendous importance, is going to be responsible for more than the bruises on the departed fat policemen of the Boulevard.

AN APPRECIATION *

By W. D. Howells

I think that what strikes me most in the story of "Maggie" is that quality of fatal necessity which dominates Greek tragedy. From the conditions it all had to be, and there were the conditions. I felt this in Mr. Hardy's "Jude," where the principle seems to become conscious in the writer; but there is apparently no consciousness of any such motive in the author of "Maggie." Another effect is that of an ideal of artistic beauty which is as present in the working out of this poor girl's squalid romance as in any classic fable. This will be foolishness, I know, to the many foolish people who cannot discriminate between the material and the treatment in art, and think that beauty is inseparable from daintiness and prettiness, but I do not speak to them. I appeal rather to such as feel themselves akin with every kind of human creature, and find neither high nor low when it is a question of inevitable suffering, or of a soul struggling vainly with an inexorable fate.

My rhetoric scarcely suggests the simple terms the author uses to produce the effect which I am trying to repeat again. They are simple, but always most graphic, especially when it comes to the personalities of the story; the girl herself, with her bewildered wish to be right and good, with her distorted perspective, her clinging and generous affections, her hopeless environments; the horrible old drunken mother, a cyclone of violence and volcano of vulgarity; the mean and selfish lover, dandy, rowdy, with his gross ideals and ambitions; her brother, an Ishmaelite from the cradle, who with his warlike instincts beaten back into cunning, is what the b'hoy of former times has become in our more strenuously policed days. He is, indeed, a wonderful figure in a group which betrays no faltering in the artist's hand. He, with his dull hates, his warped good-will, his cowed ferocity, is almost as fine artistically as Maggie, but he could not have

---

* *Published in* Maggie: A Girl of the Streets (*London, 1896*); *reprinted in* Bowery Tales (*London, 1900*).

  Except for a changed turn of phrase in the opening sentence, "An Appreciation" is identical with what Howells first issued in his "New York Low Life in Fiction," New York World: 26 July 1896.

been so hard to do, for all the pathos of her fate is rendered without one maudlin touch. So is that of the simple-minded and devoted and tedious old woman who is George's mother in the book of that name. This is scarcely a study at all, while Maggie is really and fully so. It is the study of a situation merely; a poor inadequate woman, of a commonplace religiosity, whose son goes to the bad. The wonder of it is the courage which deals with persons so absolutely average, and the art which graces them with the beauty of the author's compassion for everything that errs and suffers. Without this feeling the effects of his mastery would be impossible, and if it went further, or put itself into the pitying phrases, it would annul the effects. But it never does this; it is notable how in all respects the author keeps himself well in hand. He is quite honest with his reader. He never shows his characters or his situations in any sort of sentimental glamour; if you will be moved by the sadness of common fates you will feel his intention; but he does not flatter his portraits of people on conditions to take your fancy.

EVENING ON THE ROOF/FLASHING SPOTS IN DARKNESS WHERE/NEW YORK GETS FRESH AIR./ GOLDEN HAIRED SOUBRETTE/THE GIRL WITH A COPPER VOICE AND THE IRISH-/MAN WITH CIRCULAR WHISKERS HAVE THEIR/INNINGS AT ENTERTAINING AND THE CROWDS/GUZZLE BEER, WHILE WAITERS OBSTRUCT THE/VIEW—GAR-DENS WHERE PEOPLE MOST DO/CONGREGATE —INVENTION OF ARAB AND MOOR.*

New York, Aug. 7 — When the hot weather comes the roof-gardens burst into full bloom, and if an inhabitant of Chicago should take flight on his wings over this city he would observe six or eight flashing spots in the darkness, spots as radiant as crowns. These are the roof-gardens and if a giant had flung a handful of monstrous

---

* *Reprinted from Washington* Post: 9 *August 1896.*
    The sketch appeared in Last Words (1902) *as "The Roof Gardens and Gardeners of New York."*

golden coins upon the somber-shadowed city he could not have
benefited the metropolis more, although he would not have given
the same opportunity to various commercial aspirants to charge a
price and a half for everything. There are two classes of men — reporters and Central Office detectives — who do not mind these
prices because they are very prodigal of their money.

Now is the time of the girl with the copper voice, the Irishman
with circular whiskers, and the minstrel who had a reputation in
1833. To the street the noise of the band comes down on the wind
in fitful gusts and at the brilliantly illuminated rail there is suggestion of many straw hats.

One of the main features of a roof-garden is the waiter, who
stands directly in front of you whenever anything interesting tran-
spires on the stage. This waiter is 300 feet high and 72 feet wide.
His little finger can block your view of the golden-haired soubrette,
and when he waves his arm the stage disappears as if by a miracle.

[FORGETFUL OF HIS PROPORTIONS.]

What particularly fascinates you is his lack of self-appreciation.
He doesn't know that his length over all is 300 feet and that his
beam is 72 feet. He only knows that while the golden-haired
soubrette is singing her first verse he is depositing beer on the
table before some thirsty New Yorkers. He only knows that during
the second verse he is making change. He only knows that during
the third verse the thirsty New Yorkers object to the roof-garden
prices. He does not know that behind him are some fifty citizens
who ordinarily would not give three whoops to see the golden-
haired soubrette, but who under these particular circumstances are
kept from swift assassination by sheer force of the human will.
He gives an impressive exhibition of a man who is regardless of
consequences oblivious to everything save his task which is to provide beer. Some day there may be a wholesale massacre of roof-
garden waiters, but they will die with astonished faces and with
questions on their lips. Skulls so steadfastly opaque defy axes or
any of the other methods which the populace occasionally use to
cure colossal stupidity.

Between numbers on an ordinary roof-garden programme the
orchestra sometimes plays what the more enlightened and wary
citizens of the town call a "beer overture." But for reasons which
no civil service commission could give the waiter does not choose
this time to serve the thirsty. No; he waits until the golden-haired
soubrette appears; he waits until the haggard audience has goaded
itself into some interest in the proceedings. Then he gets under
way; then he comes forth and blots out the stage. In case of war

all roof-garden waiters should be recruited in a special regiment and sent out in advance of everything. There is a peculiar quality of bullet-proofness about them which would turn a projectile pale.

[GAINING GLIMPSES BY STRATEGY.]

If you have strategy enough in your soul you may gain furtive glimpses of the stage despite the efforts of the waiters, and then with something to engage the attention when the attention grows weary of the mystic wind, the flashing yellow lights, the music, and the undertone of the far street's roar you should be happy.

Far up into the night there is a wildness, a temper to the air which suggests tossing tree boughs and the swift rustle of grass. The New Yorker whose business will not allow him to go out to nature perhaps appreciates these little opportunities to go up to nature, although doubtless he thinks he goes to see the show.

This season two new roof gardens have opened. The one at the top of Grand Central Palace is large enough for a regimental drill room. The band is imprisoned still higher in a turreted affair and a person who prefers gentle and unobtrusive amusement can gain deep pleasure and satisfaction from watching the leader of this band gesticulating upon the heavens. His figure is silhouetted beautifully against the sky, and every gesture in which he wrings noise from his band is interestingly accentuated.

The other new roof garden is Oscar Hammerstein's Olympia, which blazes on Broadway.

[OSCAR'S MULTITUDE OF INJUNCTIONS.]

Oscar originally made a great reputation for getting out in-junctions. All court Judges in New York worked overtime when Oscar was in this business. He enjoined everybody in sight. He had a special machine made — "Drop a nickel in the Judge and get an injunction." Then he sent a man to Washington for $22,000 worth of nickels. In Harlem, where he then lived, it rained orders of the court every day at 12 o'clock. The street-cleaning commission was obliged to enlist a special force to deal with Oscar's injunctions. Citizens meeting on the street never said: "Good morning, how do you feel to-day?" They always said: "Good morning, have you been enjoined yet to-day?" When a man, perhaps, wished to enter a little game of draw, the universal form was changed, when he sent a note to his wife: "Dear Louise: I have received an order of the court restraining me from coming home to dinner to-night. Yours, George."

But Oscar changed. He smashed his machine, girded himself, and resolved to provide the public with amusement. And now we see this great mind applying itself to a roof garden with the same unflagging industry and boundless energy which had previously expressed itself in injunctions. The Olympia, his new roof garden, is a feat. It has an exuberance, which reminds one of the Union depot train shed of some Western city. The steel arches of the roof make a wide and splendid sweep, and over in a corner there are real swans swimming in real water. The whole structure glares like a conflagration with the countless electric lights. Oscar has caused the execution of decorative paintings upon the walls. If he had caused the execution of the decorative painters, he would have done better, but a man who has devoted the greater part of his life to the propagation of injunctions is not supposed to understand that wall decoration which appears to have been done with a nozzle is worse than none.

[A GAUDY AND DAZZLING SCENE.]

But if carpers say that Oscar failed in his landscapes none can say he failed in his measurements of the popular mind. The people come in swarms to the Olympia. Two elevators are busy at conveying them to where the cool and steady night wind insults the straw hat and the scene here during the popular part of the evening is perhaps more gaudy and dazzling than any other in New York.

The bicycle has attained an economic position of vast importance. The roof-garden ought to attain such a position, and it doubtless will as soon as we give it the opportunity it desires. The Arab or the Moor probably invented the roof-garden in some long-gone centuries, and they are at this day inveterate roof-gardeners. The American, surprisingly belated — for him — has but recently seized upon the idea, and its development here has been only partial. The possibilities of the roof-garden are still unknown.

Here is a vast city, in which thousands of people in summer half stifle, cry out continually for air, more air, fresher air. Just above their heads is what might be called a county of unoccupied land. It is not ridiculously small when compared with the area of New York County itself. But it is as lonely as a desert, this region of roofs. It is as untrodden as the corners of Arizona. Unless a man be a roof-gardener he knows practically nothing of this land.

Down in the slums necessity forces a solution of problems. It drives the pepole to the roofs. An evening upon a tenement roof, with the great golden march of the stars across the sky and Johnnie gone for a pail of beer, is not so bad if you have never seen the mountains nor heard, to your heart, the slow, sad song of the pines.

YELLOW UNDERSIZED DOG/BUT HE GIVES WARN-
INGS OF COMING/DYNAMITE BLASTS./BY STE-
PHEN CRANE.[*]

Harlem has always been famed for its geographical oblivion, being second only to Brooklyn in this branch, but lately it has become celebrated for a dog. The dog belongs to one of a gang of
laborers who are engaged in blasting out the mountainous abodes
of the goats to make room for gigantic apartment hotels.

"Mulligan," said the foreman, "yez bether sind yer dawg to
remain at home or some day he'll be going high wid th' rocks
whin th' blhastin' goes off."

But the blasting had some particular fascination for the dog.
He was of an observing and imaginative mind and the mystery
of this process took great hold upon him. Perched at a safe distance
he gave each detail his serious attention. He was yellow and undersized; not very intellectual in appearance; but he certainly mastered
the science of throwing rocks into the air.

For a long time one point baffled the dog. Previous to every
thunderous report a certain man in a red shirt walked out into the
lot and made strong signs and whooped. Then innumerable people
appeared, closing the windows of all the houses in the vicinity.
Now this yellow, undersized dog puzzled for hours as to why the
gesticulations and whoops of this man in the red shirt should create
such energy in the arms of all the servant girls of the neighborhood. The man in the red shirt was possessed of peculiar power.
This made him very impressive to the dog. The man never even
ate his dinner but what the little dog squatted in front of him and
watched with large, inquiring eyes.

---

[*] *Reprinted from Denver* Republican: *16 August 1896.*

*Dogs and horses fascinated Crane, as well as children — and
women. His earliest writings include sketches about dogs: "A
Boy and His Dog," "Black and White and Tan Hound," and
"Jack," which describes a black mastiff owned by Crane's
brother Edmund at Hartwood, New York. All these are fragments, portions existing only in manuscripts. Dogs figure, too,
in Crane's* Sullivan County Sketches, *as in "Black Dog: A Night
of Spectral Terror,"* New York Tribune: *24 July 1892. Poignant
is his sketch "Dark-Brown Dog" (see above), published post-
humously in* Cosmopolitan: *March 1901.*

Finally the dog's interest got so keen that when the man went on his trips of gesticulation and whoop he went too and contemplated the effect. Of course a knowledge of the meaning of gestures was always denied him, but he knew the significance of a whoop and very soon he took to whooping with the man in the red shirt. He got to know when a blast was ready, and when the man was to go whooping and invariably he accompanied him. The dog became a part of the force. He assumed responsibility and with it dignity. He exhibits great contempt now for even the swellest dogs of the locality. The presence of another dog on the lot makes him furious. The workmen think it is because he is afraid they will learn blasting and so become his rivals.

The dog is able to concentrate more thought upon his task than an average man or even a man who is above the average. He has only a little brain, perhaps, but at any rate he devotes it entirely to his business.

When the blast is preparing the little dog stands around in ill-concealed impatience. The moment it is in readiness he is off wildly excited. He howls at all the windows that should be closed and at others that are not important. He leaps frantically into the air, uttering at all times the most extraordinary cries. If you did not know the little dog was engaged in blasting you would think he was throwing fits.

All the servant girls know him and promptly close the windows. He will endure no carelessness; he is there to see that the windows are closed and he will submit to no quibble. The task of the man in the red shirt is now an easy one. He merely goes along and superintends the dog. But the dog does his work so thoroughly that even the office of superintendent is mainly an honorary position.

A peculiar result of the dog's occupation is the fact that his voice is developing in a marvelous way. He can now make more noise than eight ordinary dogs and when he is working it could easily be supposed that a general dog fight was in progress.

When the dog walks home at night with the workingmen many people take note of him. He is yellow, undersized; more than ordinarily insignificant in appearance, but his manner has undergone such a change that he could hardly fail to attract attention. He has none of that careless doggishness which may be said to stamp almost the entire canine race. He has, on the contrary, a demeanor of such sobriety and dignity that few people fail to gaze after him, as he paces thoughtfully along. Many of them say as did a man who stood on the corner the other evening: "There goes a dog with a good deal of business responsibility upon his shoulders."

IN THE TENDERLOIN/A DUEL BETWEEN AN ALARM CLOCK AND A SUICIDAL PURPOSE *

Everybody knows all about the Tenderloin district of New York.
There is no man that has the slightest claim to citizenship that does not know all there is to know concerning the Tenderloin. It is wonderful — this amount of truth which the world's clergy and police forces have collected concerning the Tenderloin. My friends from the stars obtain all this information, if possible, and then go into this wilderness and apply it. Upon observing you, certain spirits of the jungle will term you a wise guy, but there is no gentle humor in the Tenderloin, so you need not fear that this remark is anything but a tribute to your knowledge.

Once upon a time there was fought in the Tenderloin a duel between an Alarm Clock and a Suicidal Purpose. That such a duel was fought is a matter of no consequence, but it may be worth a telling, because it may be the single Tenderloin incident about which every man in the world has not exhaustive information.

It seems that Swift Doyer and his girl quarreled. Swift was jealous in the strange and devious way of his kind, and at midnight, his voice burdened with admonition, grief and deadly menace, roared through the little flat and conveyed news of the strife up the air-shaft and down the air-shaft.

"Lied to me, didn't you?" he cried. "Told me a lie and thought I wouldn't get unto you. Lied to me! There's where I get crazy. If you hadn't lied to me in one thing, and I hadn't collared you flat in it, I might believe all the rest, but now — how do I know you ever tell the truth? How do I know I ain't always getting a game? Hey? How do I know?"

To the indifferent people whose windows opened on the air-shaft there came the sound of a girl's low sobbing, while into it at times burst wildly the hoarse bitterness and rage of the man's tone. A grim thing is a Tenderloin air-shaft.

Swift arose and paused his harangue for a moment while he lit

* *Published in* Town Topics: *1 October 1896; reprinted in* Tales from Town Topics, *No. 33: September 1899.*

Bibliographer Charles Honce first made known this Crane sketch in The Papers of the Bibliographical Society of America *in 1941.*

a cigarette. He puffed at it vehemently and scowled, black as a storm-god, in the direction of the sobbing.

"Come! Get up out of that," he said, with ferocity. "Get up and look at me and let me see you lie!"

There was a flurry of white in the darkness, which was no more definite to the man than the ice-floes which your reeling ship passes in the night. Then, when the gas glared out suddenly, the girl stood before him. She was a wondrous white figure in her vestal-like robe. She resembled the priestess in paintings of long-gone Mediterranean religions. Her hair fell wildly on her shoulder. She threw out her arms and cried to Swift in a woe that seemed almost as real as the woe of good people.

"Oh, oh, my heart is broken! My heart is broken!"

But Swift knew as well as the rest of mankind that these girls have no hearts to be broken, and this acting filled him with a new rage. He grabbed an alarm clock from the dresser and banged her heroically on the head with it.

She fell and quivered for a moment. Then she arose, and, calm and dry-eyed, walked to the mirror. Swift thought she was taking an account of the bruises, but when he resumed his cyclonic tirade, she said: "I've taken morphine, Swift."

Swift leaped at a little red pill box. It was empty. Eight quarter-grain pills make two grains. The Suicidal Purpose was distinctly ahead of the Alarm Clock. With great presence of mind Swift now took the empty pill box and flung it through the window.

At this time a great battle was begun in the dining-room of the little flat. Swift dragged the girl to the sideboard, and in forcing her to drink whisky he almost stuffed the bottle down her throat. When the girl still sank to the depths of an infinite drowsiness, sliding limply in her chair like a cloth figure, he dealt her furious blows, and our decorous philosophy knows little of the love and despair that was in those caresses. With his voice he called the light into her eyes, called her from the sinister slumber which her senses welcomed, called her soul back from the verge.

He propped the girl in a chair and ran to the kitchen to make coffee. His fingers might have been from a dead man's hands, and his senses confused the coffee, the water, the coffee-pot, the gas stove, but by some fortune he managed to arrange them correctly. When he lifted the girlish figure and carried her to the kitchen, he was as wild, haggard, gibbering, as a man of midnight murders, and it is only because he was not engaged in the respectable and literary assassination of a royal duke that almost any sensible writer would be ashamed of this story. Let it suffice, then, that when the steel-blue dawn came and distant chimneys were

black against a rose sky, the girl sat at the dining-room table chattering insanely and gesturing. Swift, with his hands pressed to his
temples, watched her from the other side of the table, with all his
mind in his eyes, for each gesture was still a reminiscence, and
each tone of her voice a ballad to him. And yet he could not half
measure his misery. The tragedy was made of homeliest details.
He had to repeat to himself that he, worn-out, stupefied from his
struggle, was sitting there awaiting the moment when the unseen
hand should whirl this soul into the abyss, and that then he should
be alone.

The girl saw a fly alight on a picture. "Oh," she said, "there's
a little fly." She arose and thrust out her finger. "Hello, little fly,"
she said, and touched the fly. The insect was perhaps too cold to
be alert, for it fell at the touch of her finger. The girl gave a cry
of remorse, and, sinking to her knees, searched the floor, meanwhile uttering apologies.

At last she found the fly, and, taking it, [in] her palm went to
the gas-jet which still burned weirdly in the dawning. She held her
hand close to the flame. "Poor little fly," she said, "I didn't mean
to hurt you. I wouldn't hurt you for anything. There now — p'r'aps
when you get warm you can fly away again. Did I crush the poor
little bit of fly? I'm awful sorry — honest. I am. Poor little thing!
Why I wouldn't hurt you for the world, poor little fly — "

Swift was woefully pale and so nerve-weak that his whole
body felt a singular coolness. Strange things invariably come into
a man's head at the wrong time, and Swift was aware that this
scene was defying his preconceptions. His instruction had been
that people when dying behaved in a certain manner. Why did
this girl occupy herself with an accursed fly? Why in the name of
the gods of the drama did she not refer to her past? Why, by the
shelves of the saints of literature, did she not clutch her brow and
say: "Ah, once I was an innocent girl?" What was wrong with
this death scene? At one time he thought that his sense of propriety
was so scandalized that he was upon the point of interrupting the
girl's babble.

But here a new thought struck him. The girl was not going
to die. How could she under these circumstances? The form was
not correct.

All this was not relevant to the man's love and despair, but,
behold, my friend, at the tragic, the terrible point in life there
comes an irrelevancy to the human heart direct from the Wise
God. And this is why Swift Doyer thought those peculiar thoughts.

The girl chattered to the fly minute after minute, and Swift's
anxiety grew dim and more dim until his head fell forward on

the table and he slept as a man who has moved mountains, altered rivers, caused snow to come because he wished it to come, and done his duty.

For an hour the girl talked to the fly, the gas-jet, the walls, the distant chimneys. Finally she sat opposite the slumbering Swift and talked softly to herself.

When broad day came they were both asleep, and the girl's fingers had gone across the table until they had found the locks on the man's forehead. They were asleep, and this after all is a human action, which may safely be done by characters in the fiction of our time.

THE "TENDERLOIN" AS IT REALLY IS——BY STEPHEN CRANE./THE FIRST OF A SERIES OF STRIKING SKETCHES OF NEW YORK LIFE BY THE FAMOUS NOVELIST.*

Many requiems have been sung over the corpse of the Tenderloin. Dissipated gentlemen with convivial records burn candles to its memory each day at the corner of Twenty-eighth street and Broadway. On the great thoroughfare there are 4,000,000 men who at all times recite loud anecdotes of the luminous past.

They say: "Oh, if you had only come around when the old Haymarket was running!" They relate the wonders of this prehistoric time and fill the mind of youth with poignant regret. Everybody on earth must have attended regularly at this infernal Haymarket. The old gentlemen with convivial records do nothing but relate the glories of this place. To be sure, they tell of many other resorts, but the old gentlemen really do their conjuring with this one simple name — "the old Haymarket."

The Haymarket is really responsible for half the tales that are in the collections of these gay old boys of the silurian period. Some time a man will advertise "The Haymarket Restored," and

* *Reprinted from* New York *Journal: 25 October 1896.*
   Our discovery of this sketch was via a portion which appeared in the Literary Digest: *7 November 1896, as "A Picture of the Tenderloin." That portion is sheer Hemingway, beginning as it does, "Five men flung open the wicket doors of a brilliant cafe," and ending, "Let's have a drink." Here is an addition to the Crane canon.*

score a clamoring, popular success. The interest in a reincarnation of a vanished Athens must pale before the excitement caused by "The Haymarket Restored."

Let a thing become a tradition, and it becomes half a lie. These moss-grown columns that support the sky over Broadway street corners insist that life in this dim time was a full joy. Their descriptions are short, but graphic.

One of this type will cry: "Everything wide open, my boy; everything wide open! You should have seen it. No sneaking in side doors. Everything plain as day. Ah, those were the times! Reubs from the West used to have their bundles lifted every night before your eyes. Always somebody blowing champagne for the house. Great! Great! Diamonds, girls, lights, music. Well, maybe it wasn't smooth. Fights all over Sixth avenue. Wasn't room enough. Used to hold over-flow fights in the side streets. Say, it was great!"

Then the type heaves a sigh and murmurs: "But now? Dead — dead as a mackerel. The Tenderloin is a graveyard. Quiet as a tomb. Say, you ought to have been around here when the old Haymarket was running."

Perchance they miss in their definition of the Tenderloin. They describe it as a certain condition of affairs in a metropolitan district. But probably it is in truth something more dim, an essence, an emotion — something superior to the influences of politics or geographies, a thing unchangeable. It represents a certain wild impulse, and a wild impulse is yet more lasting than an old Haymarket. And so we come to reason that the Tenderloin is not dead at all and that the old croakers on the corners are men who have mistaken the departure of their own youth for the death of the Tenderloin, and that there still exists the spirit that flings beer bottles, jumps debts and makes havoc for the unwary; also sings in a hoarse voice at 3 a. m.

There is one mighty fact, however, that the croakers have clinched. In the old days there was a great deal of money and few dress clothes exhibited in the Tenderloin. Now it is all clothes and no money. The spirit is garish, for display, as are the flaming lights that advertise theatres and medicines. In those days long ago there might have been freedom and fraternity.

✿   ✿   ✿

Billie Maconnigle is probably one of the greatest society leaders that the world has produced. Seventh avenue is practically one voice in this matter.

He asked Flossie to dance with him, and Flossie did, seeming to enjoy the attentions of this celebrated cavalier. He asked her again, and she accepted again. Johnnie, her fellow, promptly interrupted the dance.

"Here!" he said, grabbing Maconnigle by the arm. "Dis is me own private snap! Youse gitaway f'm here an' leggo d' loidy!"

"A couple a nits," rejoined Maconnigle swinging his arm clear of his partner. "Youse go chase yerself. I'm spieling wit' dis loidy when I likes, an' if youse gits gay, I'll knock yer block off — an dat's no dream!"

"Youse'll knock nuttin' off."

"Won't I?"

"Nit. An' if yeh say much I'll make yeh look like a lobster, you fresh mug. Leggo me loidy!"

"A couple a nits."

"Won't?"

"Nit."

Blim! Blam! Crash!

The orchestra stopped playing and the musicians wheeled in their chairs, gazing with that semi-interest which only musicians in a dance hall can bring to bear upon such a scene. Several waiters ran forward, crying "Here, gents, quit dat!" A tall, healthy individual with no coat slid from behind the bar at the far end of the hall, and came with speed. Two well-dressed youths, drinking bottled beer at one end of the tables, nudged each other in ecstatic delight, and gazed with all their eyes at the fight. They were seeing life. They had come purposely to see it.

The waiters grabbed the fighters quickly. Maconnigle went through the door some three feet ahead of his hat, which came after him with a battered crown and a torn rim. A waiter with whom Johnnie had had a discussion over the change had instantly seized this opportunity to assert himself. He grappled Johnnie from the rear and flung him to the floor, and the tall, healthy person from behind the bar, rushing forward, kicked him in the head. Johnnie didn't say his prayers. He only wriggled and tried to shield his head with his arms, because every time that monstrous foot struck it made red lightning flash in his eyes.

But the tall, healthy man and his cohort of waiters had forgotten one element. They had forgotten Flossie. She could worry Johnnie; she could summon every art to make him wildly jealous; she could cruelly, wantonly harrow his soul with every device known to her kind, but she wouldn't stand by and see him hurt by gods nor men.

Blim! As the tall person drew back for his fourth kick, a beer mug landed him just back of his ear. Scratch! The waiter who had grabbed Johnnie from behind found that fingernails had made a ribbon of blood down his face as neatly as if a sign painter had put it there with a brush.

This cohort of waiters was, however, well drilled. Their leader was prone, but they rallied gallantly, and flung Johnnie and Flossie into the street, thinking no doubt that these representatives of the lower classes could get their harmless pleasure just as well outside.

The crowd at the door favored the vanquished. "Sherry!" said a voice. "Sherry! Here comes a cop!" Indeed a helmet and brass buttons shone brightly in the distance. Johnnie and Flossie sherried with all the promptitude allowed to a wounded man and a girl whose sole anxiety is the man. They ended their flight in a little dark alley.

Flossie was sobbing as if her heart was broken. She hung over her wounded hero, wailing and making moan to the sky, weeping with the deep and impressive grief of gravesides, when he swore because his head ached.

"Dat's all right," said Johnnie. "Nex' time youse needn't be so fresh wit' every guy what comes up."

"Well, I was only kiddin', Johnnie," she cried, forlornly.

"Well, yeh see what yeh done t' me wit'cher kiddin," replied Johnnie.

They came forth cautiously from their alley and journeyed homeward. Johnnie had had enough of harmless pleasure.

However, after a considerable period of reflective silence, he paused and said: "Say, Floss, youse couldn't a done a t'ing t' dat guy."

"I jest cracked 'im under d' ear," she explained. "An it laid 'im flat out, too."

A complacence for their victory here came upon them, and as they walked out of the glow of Seventh avenue into a side street it could have been seen that their self satisfaction was complete.

✿   ✿   ✿

Five men flung open the wicket doors of a brilliant cafe on Broadway and, entering, took seats at a table. They were in evening dress, and each man held his chin as if it did not belong to him.

"Well, fellows, what'll you drink?" said one. He found out, and after the ceremony there was a period of silence. Ultimately another man cried, "Let's have another drink." Following this outburst and its attendant ceremony there was another period of silence.

At last a man murmured: "Well, let's have another drink." Two members of the party discussed the state of the leather market. There was an exciting moment when a little newsboy slid into the place, crying a late extra, and was ejected by the waiter. The five men gave the incident their complete attention.

"Let's have a drink," said one afterward.

At an early hour of the morning one man yawned and said: "I'm going home. I've got to catch an early train, and" —

The four others awoke. "Oh, hold on, Tom. Hold on. Have another drink before you go. Don't go without a last drink."

He had it. Then there was a silence. Then he yawned again and said: "Let's have another drink."

They settled comfortably once more around the table. From time to time somebody said: "Let's have a drink."

*   *   *

Yes, the Tenderloin is more than a place. It is an emotion. And this spirit seems still to ring true for some people. But if one is ever obliged to make explanation to any of the old croakers, it is always possible to remark that the Tenderloin has grown too fine. Therein lies the cause of the change.

To the man who tries to know the true things there is something hollow and mocking about this Tenderloin of to-day, as far as its outward garb is concerned. The newer generation brought new clothes with them. The old Tenderloin is decked out. And wherever there are gorgeous lights, massive buildings, dress clothes and theatrical managers, there is very little nature, and it may be no wonder that the old spirit of the locality chooses to lurk in the darker places.

IN THE "TENDERLOIN," BY STEPHEN CRANE./THE SECOND OF A SERIES OF SKETCHES OF NEW YORK LIFE BY THE FAMOUS NOVELIST *

The waiters were very wise. Every man of them had worked at least three years in a Tenderloin restaurant, and this must be equal to seven centuries and an added two decades in Astoria. Even the man who opened oysters wore an air of accumulated information. Here the science of life was perfectly understood by all.

---

* Reprinted from New York Journal: 1 November 1896.

   This sketch is another addition to the Crane canon. The series began with the sketch of 25 October, "The 'Tenderloin' as It Really Is" (see above).

At 10 o'clock the place was peopled only by waiters and the man behind the long bar. The innumerable tables represented a vast white field, and the glaring electric lamps were not obstructed in their mission of shedding a furious orange radiance upon the cloths. An air of such peace and silence reigned that one might have heard the ticking of a clock. It was as quiet as a New England sitting room.

As 11 o'clock passed, however, and time marched toward 12, the place was suddenly filled with people. The process was hardly to be recognized. One surveyed at one moment a bare expanse of tables with groups of whispering waiters and at the next it was crowded with men and women attired gorgeously and plainly and splendidly and correctly. The electric glare swept over a region of expensive bonnets. Frequently the tall pride of a top hat — a real top hat — could be seen on its way down the long hall, and the envious said with sneers that the theatrical business was booming this year.

Without, the cable cars moved solemnly toward the mysteries of Harlem, and before the glowing and fascinating refrigerators displayed at the front of the restaurant a group of cabmen engaged in their singular diplomacy.

If there ever has been in a New York cafe an impulse from the really Bohemian religion of fraternity it has probably been frozen to death. A universal suspicion, a thing of so austere a cast that we mistake it for a social virtue, is the quality that generally oppresses us. But the hand of a bartender is a supple weapon of congeniality. In the small hours a man may forget the formulae which prehistoric fathers invented for him. Usually social form as practised by the stupid is not a law. It is a vital sensation. It is not temporary, emotional; it is fixed and, very likely, the power that makes the rain, the sunshine, the wind, now recognizes social form as an important element in the curious fashioning of the world. It is as solid, as palpable as a fort, and if you regard any landscape, you may see it in the foreground.

Therefore a certain process which moves in this restaurant is very instructive. It is a process which makes constantly toward the obliteration of the form. It never dangerously succeeds, but it is joyous and frank in the attempt.

＊　　　＊　　　＊

A man in race-track clothing turned in his chair and addressed a stranger at the next table. "I beg your pardon — will you tell me the time please?"

The stranger was in evening dress, very correct indeed. At

the question, he stared at the man for a moment, particularly including his tie in this look of sudden and subtle contempt. After a silence he drew forth his watch, looked at it, and returned it to his pocket. After another silence he drooped his eyes with peculiar significance, puffed his cigar and, of a sudden, remarked: "Why don't you look at the clock?"

The race-track man was a genial soul. He promptly but affably directed the kind gentleman to a place supposed to be located at the end of the Brooklyn trolley lines.

And yet at 4:30 a. m. the kind gentleman overheard the race-track man telling his experience in London in 1886, and as he had experiences similar in beauty, and as it was 4:30 a. m. and as he had completely forgotten the incident of the earlier part of the evening, he suddenly branched into the conversation, and thereafter it took ten strong men to hold him from buying a limitless ocean of wine.

❋   ❋   ❋

A curious fact of upper Broadway is the man who knows everybody, his origin, wealth, character and tailor. His knowledge is always from personal intercourse, too, and, without a doubt, he must have lived for ten thousand years to absorb all the anecdotes which he has at the tip of his tongue. If it were a woman, now, most of the stories would be weird resurrections of long-entombed scandals. The trenches for the dead on medieval battle fields would probably be clawed open to furnish evidence of various grim truths, or of untruths, still more grim. But if, according to a rigid definition, these men are gossips, it is in a kinder way than is usually denominated by the use of the word. Let a woman once take an interest in the shortcomings of her neighbors, and she immediately and naturally begins to magnify events in a preposterous fashion, until one can imagine that the law of proportion is merely a legend. There is one phrase which she uses eternally. "They say" — Herein is the peculiar terror of the curse. "They say" — It is so vague that the best spear in the world must fail to hit this shadow. The charm of it is that a woman seldom relates from personal experience. It is nearly always some revolving tale from a hundred tongues.

But it is evident in most cases that the cafe historians of upper Broadway speak from personal experience. The dove that brought the olive branch to Noah was one of their number. Another was in Hades at the time that Lucifer made his celebrated speech against the street-lighting system there. Another is an ex-member of the New Jersey Legislature. All modes, all experiences, all phases of existence are chronicled by these men. They are not obliged to fall back upon common report for their raw material. They possess it in the original form.

A cafe of the kind previously described is a great place for the concentration of the historians. Here they have great opportunities.

"See that fellow going there? That's young Jimmie Lode. Knew his father well. Denver people, you know. Old man had a strange custom of getting drunk on the first Friday after the first Thursday in June. Indian reservation near his house. Used to go out and fist-fight the Indians. Gave a twenty-dollar gold piece to every Indian he licked. Indians used to labor like thunder to get licked. Well, sir, one time the big chief of the whole push was trying to earn his money, and, by Jove, no matter what he did, he couldn't seem to fix it so the old man could lick him. So finally he laid down flat on the ground and the old man jumped on him and stove in his bulwarks. Indian said it was all right, but he thought forty dollars was a better figure for stove-in bulwarks. But the old man said he had agreed to pay twenty dollars, and he wouldn't give up another sou. So they had a fight — a real fight, you know — and the Indian killed him.

"Well, that's the son over there. Father left him a million and a half. Maybe Jack ain't spending it. Say! He just pours it out. He's crushed on Dollie Bangle, you know. She plays over here at the Palais de Glace. That's her now he's talking to. Ain't she a peach. Say? Am I right? Well, I should say so. She don't do a thing to his money. Burns it in an open grate. She's on the level with him, though. That's one thing. Well, I say she is. Of course, I'm sure of it."

In the meantime others pass before the historian's watchful vision, and he continues heroically to volley his traditions.

❈   ❈   ❈

The babble of voices grew louder and louder. The heavy smoke clouds eddied above the shining countenances. Into the street came the clear, cold blue of impending day-light, and over the cobbles roared a milk wagon.

A TENDERLOIN STORY, BY NOVELIST STEPHEN
CRANE./YEN-NOCK BILL/AND/HIS SWEETHEART.
/THE DISTINGUISHED AUTHOR OF "THE RED
BADGE OF COURAGE" WRITES A/CHARACTER
SKETCH OF A FAMOUS/TENDERLOIN CONFI-
DENCE MAN AND SHOPLIFTER, A MAN "WHO
NEVER DID/A CROOKED THING SINCE HE WAS
BORN." *

They called him Yen-Nock Bill. He had been a book agent, a confidence man, a member of a celebrated minstrel troupe, a shoplifter, a waiter in a Bowery restaurant and other things. But he
had never been guilty of a dishonest act in his life. He used to say
so, solemnly.

"No sir," he often remarked, "I've lived at a pretty hot gait
all my life, but I've always been on the level. Never did a crooked
thing since I was born. No, sir!"

He did not stick at an occupation because he was fond of a
certain delicate amusement of the Chinese. A most peculiar truth
of life is the fact that, when a man gets to be an opium smoker,
he has ill-fortune. Disaster comes upon his business schemes, and
his valuable friends slide unaccountably away from him. And so
it happened that, when Bill fell deadly ill with pneumonia, there
was nobody to come to him and bid him a good journey through the
skyland.

On the contrary, his dragon of a landlady paced the halls and
wondered who was going to provide the $4 Bill owed for lodging.
She was a woman with business principles, and she wanted her $4.
She did not give three hurrahs in Hades whether Bill lived or
died, so long as he did not put her to pecuniary loss. She was a
just woman; her life had been a hard struggle for daily bread, and

---

* Reprinted from New York Journal: 29 November 1896.
   This sketch relates to Crane's unsigned "Opium's Varied
Dreams" (see above) and to "Diamonds and Diamonds" (see
below). Crane locates his play "The Blood of the Martyr"
(1898) in China and cites "The City of Yen-Nock."

when anybody owed her $4, it was no more than fair that she should be paid.

Bill was a small man. He had a way of pulling the sheet up to his throat with one thin hand, and then coughing until his whole body jumped and writhed. When he was not coughing, he simply lay and rolled his eyes. In the days of his prosperity, when his particular confidence game was paying him a great deal of money, Bill had a sweetheart, and it becomes a most painful obligation to introduce her into this story.

When Julie heard of Bill's plight, she went there post haste. She flung herself down at the bedside and cried: "Oh, Billie!"

Bill raised himself and scanned her with a cold eye. "Why th'ell didn't you come before?" he demanded. "You're a nice one, you are. Leaving me here to die — leaving me here to die all alone — all alone — without a friend in the world." He shed tears.

Julie soothed him and flattered the man in the manner of woman, even in the face of his arrant injustice, and by the way the irritation in his voice was of a quality worse than knife blades.

"I'll take you right to the flat, dear," cried Julie, sobbing. "There I can take care of you and 'tend you until you get well; poor, poor boy!"

But when she put out her hand to smooth his brow, he brushed her away savagely. "Oh, you make me tired, you fool! Tell me how I'm going to get around there, will you? You are an ass."

Thereupon Julie pleaded with him. "I'll call a cab, dear, and have it right here at the door, and the coachman can help you downstairs. I'll go around now and borrow Swift Doyer's winter overcoat, and then I'll go home and have Mary fix everything ready for you. And then I'll have the doctor come right over. Won't you come, dear? Won't you?"

Bill turned his stern face toward the wall. "No," he answered. To one who had no interest in the proceedings it would have been plain that Bill lied, but since this woman loved this man, she could never tell when he lied to her. So she continued to beseech him. Always he answered: "No."

At last she went into the hall to beg the landlady to use her influence, but the door was no sooner closed behind her than Bill cried out, in a wild spasm of sick man's rage: "Julie, Julie!"

Julie returned in a flurry. "What, dear? What is it?"

"Why don't you order the cab?" he cried, shrilly. "Get a gait on you, will you! Think I want to lie here forever?"

"All right, Billie — all right," answered Julie. She kissed him and hurried away. Bill scowled at the wall and muttered sullenly to himself. Suddenly he had seemed possessed of some great grievance.

Julie returned, out of breath, and with Swift Doyer's winter overcoat over her arm. "It's all right!" she cried. "The cab's at the door, and everything is all fixed."

But here the landlady appeared as a factor. Previously she had been concerned chiefly about her four dollars, but now her ideas of respectability were concerned. She evidently had concluded that it would be better for Bill to die alone in the hall bedroom. "He shan't be taken from my house until I know where he is going," she said, coldly and significantly to Julie.

The girl flashed upon her one of those tearful glances into which a woman can put scorn, rage and at the same time entreaty. Julie hesitated a moment, and the landlady never knew how near she came to a time of fire and the sword, whirlwind and sudden death. Better ask a ravenous wolf to sleep under your pillow than to stand between a woman who loves so completely and a man.

But Julie went calmly away with no word. Later a four-wheeler drew up before the house, and Swift Doyer and Jimmie the Mole emerged from it. "We want that sick man," said Swift to the landlady. "I'm his friend, and I'm going to take him home."

The landlady gracefully accepted four dollars from Swift, and led the way to the hall bedroom.

"Let 'er go easy, boys," said Bill, with a wan smile, as they carried him around the curve of the stairs. In daylight Bill was a sad figure. Two weeks' growth of red beard [covered?] his leaden face, and his eyes swung and turned in a way that was at once childish and insane. But when they bundled him into the cab, Julie put her arms about his neck and cooed and murmured.

The instant they were alone in Julie's flat he began to howl at her. Swift Doyer was a good fellow, but he used to remark that Bill's voice made him wish that he was a horse, so that he could spring upon the bed and trample him to death. And for many days thereafter Bill bullied and abused, ranted and raged at the girl, until people whose windows opened on the air-shaft often remarked: "Say, why don't she kill him!"

Julie arrived at a point where she threw out her hands and said: "Oh, be good to me; won't you, Billie, dear?"

"No! Why should I?"

DIAMONDS AND DIAMONDS

Jimmie the Mole derived his name from a certain way he would look at you when you lied to him. Lie to Jimmie in those days and he would shrug down his shoulders and squint at you most horribly and steadfastly until you grew nervous, probably, and went away. But when he was lying to you, he was a polished and courtly gentleman with no shadow of facial deformity about him.

Once Jimmie was smitten with a financial famine. He was about to take a trip to Boston, too, where some confiding man had offered him work in a concert hall as a sweet singer of ballads. Jimmie had a Tenderloin voice. This means a tenor well-suited to the air: "She has fallen by the way-side." Sometimes he went forth into the great wide-world and made money with this voice.

Jimmie being penniless and anxious to go to Boston, went to see the Flasher. "You better go over to Nellie Doyer's and borrow enough money for my ticket to Boston and then let me take your ring along with me. I'll see if I can't cop out a small bundle." The obedient Flasher borrowed money for the ticket and the obedient Flasher gave her ring to Jimmie.

Jimmie went to Boston and for two weeks made glad the rafters with his Tenderloin voice.

While standing in a corner saloon one morning, he espied a large fat personage in black clothing and with a large diamond stuck in a shirt emphatically soiled. This man seemed to strike Jimmie with considerable interest. He hung near and furtively watched this fat person drink whiskey.

Once he found himself at the bar elbow to elbow with this man. As has been said, Jimmie was often a courtly and polished gentleman. "I beg your pardon," he said, "but would you like to buy a ring?"

The fat person had not been a Boston alderman for nothing. He turned sharply and said: "No."

---

* First published from the typescript in the Barrett Crane Collection (University of Virginia) in R. W. Stallman, "Stephen Crane: Some New Stories," Bulletin of the New York Public Library: October 1956. This is an addition to the Crane canon.

As Jimmie the Mole figures in this Tenderloin story and in "Yen-Nock Bill and His Sweetheart," New York Journal: 29 November 1896, it was probably written at the same time.

"I'm in hard luck just now and I need a hundred bad or I wouldn't think of selling it. If you happen to know of anybody who might like a nice diamond, I hope you won't mind telling me."

The fat person relented at this point because Jimmie's voice was obviously that of a courtly and polished gentleman. "Well, no, I don't remember anybody just now. Let's look at the ring."

Jimmie held forth a graceful hand.

"Fine stone," said the ex-alderman.

"Yes," replied Jimmie. "A present from my girl in Chicago. She'll be crazy when she finds out that I've blown it in. Can't help it though. Hard luck is hard luck. I came here looking for a theatrical job — that's my business — but I don't get a thing but a frost from every manager I strike. Hard luck is hard luck."

"Sure," said the fat person. "How much do you want for the ring?"

"Well, I'll take a hundred," answered Jimmie candidly, "and the ring is worth that to anybody. It'll stand me a hundred in any pawn-shop but I don't want to get up against the pawn-shops anymore and when I've got anything to sell I'd rather have it go outright to some good fellow."

The fat person again gazed down at the ring. "Let me see it off your finger, will you?"

"Sure," said Jimmie.

The other looked at the ring close and for inside and outside. "Looks like a good ring."

"It is a good ring. I'd like to see a man prove there was anything fake about that ring."

"Dan," called the fat person to the bartender. "How's that for a gig-lamp?" He pushed the trinket over the bar.

"Gee," cried the bartender, holding it high. "Say, that's a peach."

The fat person said to Jimmie: "Young feller, I'm almost coming around to giving up a hundred for it myself."

Jimmie shrugged his shoulders. "A hundred and it's yours."

The other again examined the ring. Finally he said: "Well — you bring it around to a jeweler's with me and if he says it's worth the money you say it is, why, I'll throw down a hundred for it." Whereupon he cast a keen eye at Jimmie.

But Jimmie promptly cried: "Certainly. Come ahead."

When they walked into the street, the fat person rather shied away from Jimmie and with singular intentness he kept his eyes straight to the front. "You say" — he observed. "You say your girl in Chicago gave you this ring?"

"Oh, that's on the level all right," answered the Mole. "But" — he added and he looked squarely at the fat person, "I've heard people say that they saw it on the finger of a ranchman from Montana just a little while before he came to Chicago on a skate."

"Um," said the fat person with a quick sidelong glance. He whistled indifferently.

When they had entered the jeweler's shop, the fat person crowded his great form against the show-case and said: "My friend, would you mind telling us what this ring is worth?"

When the jeweler appeared he seemed bored. Evidently he was bored because he thought somebody was going to be swindled, but why this should bore him more than it should enrage him or make him weep, none can tell.

"Let's see it." Jimmie gave him the ring and he went away. When he returned, he drummed on the counter and stared at the ceiling. "It's worth about two hundred dollars."

"It is, is it?" said the fat person.

"Yes."

"Would you give two hundred for it?"

"If I was buying diamonds for myself I might. But as a dealer, I might give a hundred. Or maybe a hundred and fifty."

"You would, would you?" said the fat person. Jimmie took the ring again and the two marched away.

The fat person led swiftly some distance down the sidewalk. When he stopped he said: "Well, I'll take the ring at a hundred."

"All right," said the Mole.

"I'll keep to my bargain although it seems as if I might have struck higher."

"A hundred dollars is a good deal of money," said the fat person. "The Montana — "

"Take the ring," said Jimmie.

The other counted out the hundred in bills. "Here's your money — gimme the ring." At this point they eyed each other warily but the transfer was made in safety. This ornament of politics had the ring and the polished and courtly gentleman had the bills.

"Well, good-bye, old boy," cried the fat person.

"Good luck to you," rejoined Jimmie. "I'd come and break a cold bottle with you only I might light out for Chicago to see my girl. Say," he said facing around again, "I almost wish I hadn't" —

But the fat person waved his hand gaily and walked rapidly away. "Ta-ta, old boy," he cried. Jimmie the Mole gazed after him wistfully.

The next morning Jimmie was in New York. When he arrived

at Flasher's flat she was at breakfast. He took from his pocket one hundred dollars in bills and from his finger he took her ring. He laid them on the table before her.

"There," he said with a tired sigh.

"Same old game, Jimmie?"

"Same old game."

"You always were so smooth, Jimmie," murmured Flasher.

This money would have endured some time if the Mole had not fallen in love with his luck and gone to the races. In consequence he was again obliged to borrow the two hundred dollar diamond from Flasher.

The next day he appeared in a jewelry shop in a remote Eastside street. "Fred," he said to the proprietor, "I want you to make me a ringer for this again." He handed the man the diamond ring. "And, look here, I won't pay more than three dollars either. A guy in Boston the other day charged me four dollars and a half for the same fake you make."

If you are a politician and you allow a man to substitute a ring of paste and gold-plate for a two-hundred-dollar diamond ring and sell it to you for a hundred dollars merely because you have had a jeweler appraise the real diamond — if you are this kind of an ass and dwell in a live ward, let your idiocy be known. It will make you friends. People will laugh and vote for you out of a sense of humor. If you don't believe it, look at the returns and see who was elected last year to the board of aldermen from the 204th ward of the city of Boston.

A DETAIL*

The tiny old lady in the black dress and curious little black bonnet had at first seemed alarmed at the sound made by her feet upon the stone pavements. But later she forgot about it, for she suddenly came into the tempest of the Sixth Avenue shopping district, where from the streams of people and vehicles went up a roar like that from headlong mountain torrents.

---

* *Reprinted from* The Open Boat and Other Stories (*London, 1898*). *The sketch was first published in* Pocket Magazine: *November 1896.*

   This Sixth Avenue sketch links with "The Duel That Was Not Fought" and with Crane's unpublished script "Sixth Avenue" (see above).

She seemed then like a chip that catches, recoils, turns and wheels, a reluctant thing in the clutch of the impetuous river. She hesitated, faltered, debated with herself. Frequently she seemed about to address people; then of a sudden she would evidently lose her courage. Meanwhile the torrent jostled her, swung her this and that way.

At last, however, she saw two young women gazing in at a shop-window. They were well-dressed girls; they wore gowns with enormous sleeves that made them look like full-rigged ships with all sails set. They seemed to have plenty of time; they leisurely scanned the goods in the window. Other people had made the tiny old woman much afraid because obviously they were speeding to keep such tremendously important engagements. She went close to the girls and peered in at the same window. She watched them furtively for a time. Then finally she said —

"Excuse me!"

The girls looked down at this old face with its two large eyes turned towards them.

"Excuse me, can you tell me where I can get any work?"

For an instant the two girls stared. Then they seemed about to exchange a smile, but, at the last moment, they checked it. The tiny old lady's eyes were upon them. She was quaintly serious, silently expectant. She made one marvel that in that face the wrinkles showed no trace of experience, knowledge; they were simply little, soft, innocent creases. As for her glance, it had the trustfulness of ignorance and the candour of babyhood.

"I want to get something to do, because I need the money," she continued since, in their astonishment, they had not replied to her first question. "Of course I'm not strong and I couldn't do very much, but I can sew well; and in a house where there was a good many men folks, I could do all the mending. Do you know any place where they would like me to come?"

The young women did then exchange a smile, but it was a subtle tender smile, the edge of personal grief.

"Well, no, madame," hesitatingly said one of them at last; "I don't think I know any one."

A shade passed over the tiny old lady's face, a shadow of the wing of disappointment.

"Don't you?" she said, with a little struggle to be brave, in her voice.

Then the girl hastily continued — "But if you will give me your address, I may find some one, and if I do, I will surely let you know of it."

The tiny old lady dictated her address, bending over to watch the girl write on a visiting card with a little silver pencil. Then she said —

"I thank you very much." She bowed to them, smiling, and went on down the avenue.

As for the two girls, they walked to the curb and watched this aged figure, small and frail, in its black gown and curious black bonnet. At last, the crowd, the innumerable wagons, intermingling and changing with uproar and riot, suddenly engulfed it.

STEPHEN CRANE IN MINETTA LANE,/ONE OF GOTHAM'S MOST NOTORIOUS THOROUGHFARES. /THE NOVELIST TELLS WHAT HE SAW AND HEARD ON A STREET WHERE THE INHABITANTS HAVE/BEEN FAMOUS FOR EVIL DEEDS. WHERE THE BURGLAR AND THE SHOPLIFTER, AND/THE MURDERER LIVE SIDE BY SIDE. THE NOVEL RE-SORT OF/MAMMY ROSS AND OTHERS OF HER KIND.*

Minetta Lane is a small and becobbled valley between hills of dingy brick. At night the street lamps, burning dimly, cause the shadows to be important, and in the gloom one sees groups of quietly conversant negroes with occasionally the gleam of a passing growler. Everything is vaguely outlined and of uncertain identity unless indeed it be the flashing buttons and shield of the policeman on post. The Sixth Avenue horse cars jingle past one end of the Lane and, a block eastward, the little thoroughfare ends in the darkness of MacDougal Street.

One wonders how such an insignificant alley could get such an absurdly large reputation, but, as a matter of fact, Minetta

---

* *Reprinted here for the first time from Philadelphia* Press: *20 December 1896. The sketch appeared in* Last Words *(1902) as "Minetta Lane." It also appeared in some other newspaper in 1896, since the press clipping in Crane's Scrapbook in the Columbia University Crane Collection is not from the Philadelphia* Press.

Lane, and Minetta Street, which leads from it southward to Bleecker Street, MacDougal Street and nearly all the streets thereabouts were most unmistakably bad, but when the Minettas started out the other streets went away and hid. To gain a reputation in Minetta Lane, in those days, a man was obliged to commit a number of furious crimes, and no celebrity was more important than the man who had a good honest killing to his credit. The inhabitants, for the most part, were negroes, and they represented the very worst elements of their race. The razor habit clung to them with the tenacity of an epidemic, and every night the uneven cobbles felt blood. Minetta Lane was not a public thoroughfare at this period. It was a street set apart, a refuge for criminals. Thieves came here preferably with their gains, and almost any day peculiar sentences passed among the inhabitants. "Big Jim turned a thousand last night." "No-Toe's made another haul." And the worshipful citizens would make haste to be present at the consequent revel.

[NOT THEN A THOROUGHFARE.]

As has been said, Minetta Lane was then no thoroughfare. A peaceable citizen chose to make a circuit rather than venture through this place, that swarmed with the most dangerous people in the city. Indeed, the thieves of the district used to say: "Once get in the Lane and you're all right." Even a policeman in chase of a criminal would probably shy away instead of pursuing him into the lane. The odds were too great against a lone officer.

Sailors, and many men who might appear to have money about them, were welcomed with all proper ceremony at the terrible dens of the Lane. At departure, they were fortunate if they still retained their teeth. It was the custom to leave very little else to them. There was every facility for the capture of coin, from trap-doors to plain ordinary knockout drops.

And yet Minetta Lane is built on the grave of Minetta Brook, where, in olden times, lovers walked under the willows of the bank, and Minetta Lane, in later times, was the home of many of the best families of the town.

A negro named Bloodthirsty was perhaps the most luminous figure of Minetta Lane's aggregation of desperadoes. Bloodthirsty, supposedly, is alive now, but he has vanished from the Lane. The police want him for murder. Bloodthirsty is a large negro and very hideous. He has a rolling eye that shows white at the wrong time and his neck, under the jaw, is dreadfully scarred and pitted.

Bloodthirsty was particularly eloquent when drunk, and in the wildness of a spree he would rave so graphically about gore, that even the habituated wool of old timers would stand straight.

Bloodthirsty meant most of it, too. That is why his orations were impressive. His remarks were usually followed by the wide lightning sweep of his razor. None cared to exchange epithets with Bloodthirsty. A man in a boiler iron suit would walk down to City Hall and look at the clock before he would ask the time of day from single minded and ingenuous Bloodthirsty.

[NO TOE CHARLEY.]

After Bloodthirsty, in combative importance, came No Toe Charley. Singularly enough Charley was called No Toe solely because he did not have a toe to his feet. Charley was a small negro and his manner of amusement was not Bloodthirsty's simple ways. As befitting a smaller man, Charley was more wise, more sly, more roundabout than the other man. The path of his crimes was like a corkscrew, in architecture, and his method led him to make many tunnels. With all his cleverness, however, No Toe was finally induced to pay a visit to the gentlemen in the grim gray building up the river.

Black-Cat was another famous bandit who made the Lane his home. Black-Cat is dead. It is within some months that Jube Tyler has been sent to prison, and after mentioning the recent disappearance of Old Man Spriggs, it may be said that the Lane is now destitute of the men who once crowned it with a glory of crime. It is hardly essential to mention Guinea Johnson. Guinea is not a great figure. Guinea is just an ordinary little crook. Sometimes Guinea pays a visit to his friends, the other little crooks who make homes in the Lane, but he himself does not live there, and with him out of it, there is now no one whose industry in unlawfulness has yet earned him the dignity of a nickname. Indeed, it is difficult to find people now who remember the old gorgeous days, although it is but two years since the Lane shone with sin like a new headlight. But after a search the reporter found three.

Mammy Ross is one of the last relics of the days of slaughter still living there. Her weird history also reaches back to the blossoming of the first members of the Whyo gang in the old Sixth Ward, and her mind is stored with bloody memories. She at one time kept a sailor's boarding house near the Tombs Prison, and accounts of all the festive crimes of that neighborhood in ancient years roll easily from her tongue. They killed a sailor man every day, and the pedestrians went about the streets wearing stoves for fear of the handy knives. At the present day the route to Mammy's home is up a flight of grimy stairs that is pasted on the outside of an old and tottering frame house. Then there is a hall blacker than a wolf's throat, and this hall leads to a little kitchen where Mammy usually sits groaning by the fire. She is, of course, very old, and she is also very fat. She seems always to be in great pain. She says she is suffering from "de very las' dregs of de yaller fever."

[A PICTURE OF SUFFERING.]

During the first part of a reporter's recent visit old Mammy seemed most dolefully oppressed by her various diseases. Her great body shook and her teeth clicked spasmodically during her long and painful respirations. From time to time she reached her trembling hand and drew a shawl closer about her shoulders. She presented as true a picture of a person undergoing steady, unchangeable, chronic pain as a patent medicine firm could wish to discover for miraculous purposes. She breathed like a fish thrown out on the bank, and her old head continually quivered in the nervous tremors of the extremely aged and debilitated person. Meanwhile her daughter hung over the stove and placidly cooked sausages.

Appeals were made to the old woman's memory. Various personnages who had been sublime figures of crime in the long-gone days were mentioned to her, and presently her eyes began to brighten. Her head no longer quivered. She seemed to lose for a period her sense of pain in the gentle excitement caused by the invocation of the spirits of her memory.

It appears that she had had a historic quarrel with Apple Mag. She first recited the prowess of Apple Mag; how this emphatic lady used to argue with paving stones, carving knives and bricks. Then she told of the quarrel; what Mag said; what she said; what Mag said; what she said: It seems that they cited each other as spectacles of sin and corruption in more fully explanatory terms than are commonly known to be possible. But it was one of Mammy's most gorgeous recollections, and, as she told it, a smile widened over her face.

Finally she explained her celebrated retort to one of the most illustrious thugs that had blessed the city in bygone days. "Ah says to 'im, Ah says: 'You — you'll die in yer boots like Gallopin' Thompson — dat's what you'll do.' [Slug missing from newsprint here.] one chile an' he ain't nuthin' but er cripple, but le'me tel' you, man, dat boy'll live t' pick de feathers f'm de goose dat'll eat de grass dat grows over your grave, man! Dat's what I tol' 'm. But — lan's sake — how I know dat in less'n three day, dat man be lying in de gutter wif a knife stickin' out'n his back. Lawd, no, I sholy never s'pected nothing like dat."

[MEMORIES OF THE PAST.]

These reminiscences, at once maimed and reconstructed, have been treasured by old Mammy as carefully, as tenderly, as if they were the various little tokens of an early love. She applies the same back-handed sentiment to them, and, as she sits groaning by the fire, it is plainly to be seen that there is only one food for her ancient brain, and that is the recollection of the beautiful fights and murders of the past.

On the other side of the Lane, but near Mammy's house, Pop Babcock keeps a restaurant. Pop says it is a restaurant, and so it must be one, but you could pass there ninety times each day and never know that you were passing a restaurant. There is one obscure little window in the basement and if you went close and peered in, you might, after a time, be able to make out a small, dusty sign, lying amid jars on a shelf. This sign reads: "Oysters in every style." If you are of a gambling turn of mind, you will probably stand out in the street and bet yourself black in the face that there isn't an oyster within a hundred yards. But Pop Babcock made that sign and Pop Babcock could not tell an untruth. Pop is a model of all the virtues which an inventive fate has made for us. He says so.

As far as goes the management of Pop's restaurant, it differs from Sherry's. In the first place the door is always kept locked. The wardmen of the Fifteenth Precinct have a way of prowling through the restaurant almost every night, and Pop keeps the door locked in order to keep out the objectionable people that cause the wardmen's visits. He says so. The cooking stove is located in the main room of the restaurant, and it is placed in such a strategic manner that it occupies about all the space that is not already occupied by a table, a bench and two chairs. The table will, on a pinch, furnish room for the plates of two people if they are willing to crowd. Pop says he is the best cook in the world.

["POP'S" VIEW OF IT.]

When questioned concerning the present condition of the Lane, Pope said: "Quiet? Quiet? Lo'd save us, maybe it ain't! Quiet? Quiet?" His emphasis was arranged crescendo, until the last word was really a vocal explosion. "Why, disher' Lane ain't nohow like what it useter be — no indeed, it ain't. No, sir! 'Deed it ain't! Why, I kin remember dey was a-cuttin' an' a'slashin' 'long yere all night. 'Deed dey was! My — my, dem times was different! Dat dar Kent, he kep' de place at Green Gate Cou't — down yer ol' Mammy's — an' he was a hard baby — 'deed, he was — an' ol' Black-Cat an' ol'

Bloodthirsty, dey was a-roamin' round yere a-cuttin' an' a-slashin'. Didn't dar' say boo to a goose in dose days, dat you didn't, less'n you lookin' fer a scrap. No, sir!" Then he gave information concerning his own prowess at that time. Pop is about as tall as a picket on an undersized fence. "But dey didn't have nothin' ter say to me! No, sir! 'Deed, dey didn't! I wouldn't lay down fer none of 'em. No, sir! Dey knew my gait, 'deed, dey did! Man, man, many's de time I buck up agin 'em. Yes, sir!"

At this time Pop had three customers in his place, one asleep on the bench, one asleep on the two chairs, and one asleep on the floor behind the stove.

But there is one man who lends dignity of the real bevel-edged type to Minetta Lane, and that man is Hank Anderson. Hank, of course, does not live in the Lane, but the shadow of his social perfections falls upon it as refreshingly as a morning dew. Hank gives a dance twice in each week, at a hall hard by in MacDougal Street, and the dusky aristocracy of the neighborhood know their guiding beacon. Moreover, Hank holds an annual ball in Forty-fourth Street. Also he gives a picnic each year to the Montezuma Club, when he again appears as a guiding beacon. This picnic is usually held on a barge and the occasion is a very joyous one. Some years ago it required the entire reserve squad of an up-town police precinct to properly control the enthusiasm of the gay picnickers, but that was an exceptional exuberance and no measure of Hank's ability for management.

He is really a great manager. He was Boss Tweed's body-servant in the days when Tweed was a political prince, and any-one who saw Bill Tweed through a spyglass learned the science of leading, pulling, driving and hauling men in a way to keep men ignorant of it. Hank imbibed from this fount of knowledge and he applied his information in Thompson Street. Thompson Street salaamed. Presently he bore a proud title: "The Mayor of Thompson Street." Dignities from the principal political organization of the city adorned his brow and he speedily became illustrious.

[KEEPING IN TOUCH.]

Hank knew the Lane well in its direful days. As for the in-habitants, he kept clear of them and yet in touch with them according to a method that he might have learned in the Sixth Ward. The Sixth Ward was a good place in which to learn that trick. An-derson can tell many strange tales and good of the Lane, and he tells them in the graphic way of his class. "Why, they could steal your shirt without moving a wrinkle on it."

The killing of Joe Carey was the last murder that happened

in the Minettas. Carey had what might be called a mixed ale difference with a man named Kenny. They went out to the middle of Minetta Street to affably fight it out and determine the justice of the question. In the scrimmage Kenny drew a knife, thrust quickly and Carey fell. Kenny had not gone a hundred feet before he ran into the arms of a policeman.

There is probably no street in New York where the police keep closer watch than they do in Minetta Lane. There was a time when the inhabitants had a profound and reasonable contempt for the public guardians, but they have it no longer apparently. Any citizen can walk through there at any time in perfect safety unless, perhaps, he should happen to get too frivolous. To be strictly accurate, the change began under the reign of Police Captain Chapman. Under Captain Groo, the present commander of the Fifteenth Precinct, the Lane has donned a complete new garb. Its denizens brag now of its peace precisely as they once bragged of its war. It is no more a bloody lane. The song of the razor is seldom heard. There are still toughs and semi-toughs galore in it, but they can't get a chance with the copper looking the other way. Groo has got the poor old Lane by the throat. If a man should insist on becoming a victim of the badger game he could probably succeed upon search in Minetta Lane, as indeed, he could on any of the great avenues; but then Minetta Lane is not supposed to be a pearly street in Paradise.

In the meantime the Italians have begun to dispute possession of the Lane with the negroes. Green Gate Court is filled with them now, and a row of houses near the MacDougal Street corner is occupied entirely by Italian families. None of them seems to be overfond of the old Mulberry Bend fashion of life, and there are no cutting affrays among them worth mentioning. It is the original negro element that makes the trouble when there is trouble.

But they are happy in this condition, are these people. The most extraordinary quality of the negro is his enormous capacity for happiness under most adverse circumstances. Minetta Lane is a place of poverty and sin, but these influences cannot destroy the broad smile of the negro, a vain and simple child but happy. They all smile here, the most evil as well as the poorest. Knowing the negro, one always expects laughter from him, be he ever so poor, but it was a new experience to see a broad grin on the face of the devil. Even old Pop Babcock had a laugh as fine and mellow as would be the sound of falling glass, broken saints from high windows, in the silence of some great cathedral's hollow.

IN THE BROADWAY CARS: PANORAMA OF A DAY FROM THE DOWN-TOWN RUSH OF THE MORNING TO THE UNINTERRUPTED WHIRR OF THE CABLE AT NIGHT—THE MAN, AND THE WOMAN, AND THE CONDUCTOR.*

The cable cars come down Broadway as the waters come down at Lodore. Years ago Father Knickerbocker had convulsions when it was proposed to lay impious rails on his sacred thoroughfare. At the present day the cars, by force of column and numbers, almost dominate the great street, and the eye of even an old New Yorker is held by these long yellow monsters which prowl intently up and down, up and down, in a mystic search.

In the grey of the morning they come out of the up-town, bearing janitors, porters, all that class which carries the keys to set alive the great downtown. Later, they shower clerks. Later still, they shower more clerks. And the thermometer which is attached to a conductor's temper is steadily rising, rising, and the blissful time arrives when everybody hangs to a strap and stands on his neighbour's toes. Ten o'clock comes, and the Broadway cars, as well as elevated cars, horse cars, and ferryboats innumerable, heave sighs of relief. They have filled lower New York with a vast army of men who will chase to and fro and amuse themselves until almost nightfall.

The cable car's pulse drops to normal. But the conductor's pulse begins now to beat in split seconds. He has come to the crisis in his day's agony. He is now to be overwhelmed with feminine shoppers. They all are going to give him two-dollar bills to change. They all are going to threaten to report him. He passes his hand across his brow and curses his beard from black to grey and from grey to black.

Men and women have different ways of hailing a car. A man —

* Reprinted from Last Words (London, 1902).

We have preserved English spellings where our text utilizes English editions; hence, "neighbour," "waggon," "splendour," and so on. "In the Broadway Cars" and the following seven sketches form, more or less, a subsection which might be called "Undated New York City Sketches."

if he is not an old choleric gentleman, who owns not this road
but some other road — throws up a timid finger, and appears to believe that the King of Abyssinia is careering past on his war-
chariot, and only his opinion of other people's Americanism keeps
him from deep salaams. The gripman usually jerks his thumb over
his shoulder and indicates the next car, which is three miles away.
Then the man catches the last platform, goes into the car, climbs
upon some one's toes, opens his morning paper, and is happy.

When a woman hails a car there is no question of its being the
King of Abyssinia's war-chariot. She has bought the car for three
dollars and ninety-eight cents. The conductor owes his position to
her, and the gripman's mother does her laundry. No captain in the
Royal Horse Artillery ever stops his battery from going through a
stone house in a way to equal her manner of bringing that car
back on its haunches. Then she walks leisurely forward, and after
scanning the step to see if there is any mud upon it, and opening
her pocket-book to make sure of a two-dollar bill, she says: "Do you
give transfers down Twenty-eighth Street?"

Some time the conductor breaks the bell strap when he pulls it
under these conditions. Then, as the car goes on, he goes and
bullies some person who had nothing to do with the affair.

The car sweeps on its diagonal path through the Tenderloin
with its hotels, its theatres, its flower shops, its 10,000,000 actors
who played with Booth and Barret. It passes Madison Square and
enters the gorge made by the towering walls of great shops. It
sweeps around the double curve at Union Square and Fourteenth
Street, and a life insurance agent falls in a fit as the car dashes over
the crossing, narrowly missing three old ladies, two old gentlemen,
a newly-married couple, a sandwich man, a newsboy, and a dog.
At Grace Church the conductor has an altercation with a brave and
reckless passenger who beards him in his own car, and at Canal
Street he takes dire vengeance by tumbling a drunken man on to
the pavement. Meanwhile, the gripman has become involved with
countless truck drivers, and inch by inch, foot by foot, he fights
his way to City Hall Park. On past the Post Office the car goes, with
the gripman getting advice, admonition, personal comment, an invitation to fight from the drivers, until Battery Park appears at
the foot of the slope, and as the car goes sedately around the curve
the burnished shield of the bay shines through the trees.

It is a great ride, full of exciting actions. Those inexperienced
persons who have been merely chased by Indians know little of the
dramatic quality which life may hold for them. These jungles of
men and vehicles, these cañons of streets, these lofty mountains of
iron and cut stone — a ride through them affords plenty of excite-

ment. And no lone panther's howl is more serious in intention than
the howl of the truck driver when the cable car bumps one of his
rear wheels.

Owing to a strange humour of the gods that make our comfort,
sailor hats with wide brims come into vogue whenever we are all
engaged in hanging to cable-car straps. There is only one more
serious combination known to science, but a trial of it is at this day
impossible. If a troup of Elizabethan courtiers in large ruffs should
board a cable car, the complication would be a very awesome one,
and the profanity would be in old English, but very inspiring.
However, the combination of wide-brimmed hats and crowded
cable cars is tremendous in its power to cause misery to the patient
New York public.

Suppose you are in a cable car, clutching for life and family
a creaking strap from overhead. At your shoulder is a little dude in
a very wide-brimmed straw hat with a red band. If you were in
your senses you would recognise this flaming band as an omen of
blood. But you are not in your senses; you are in a Broadway cable
car. You are not supposed to have any senses. From the forward
end you hear the gripman uttering shrill whoops and running over
citizens. Suddenly the car comes to a curve. Making a swift running start, it turns three hand-springs, throws a cart wheel for luck,
bounds into the air, hurls six passengers over the nearest building,
and comes down a-straddle of the track. That is the way in which
we turn curves in New York.

Meanwhile, during the car's gamboling, the corrugated rim
of the dude's hat has swept naturally across your neck, and has left
nothing for your head to do but to quit your shoulders. As the car
roars your head falls into the waiting arms of the proper authorities.
The dude is dead; everything is dead. The interior of the car
resembles the scene of the battle of Wounded Knee, but this gives
you small satisfaction.

There was once a person possessing a fund of uncanny humour
who greatly desired to import from past ages a corps of knights in
full armour. He then purposed to pack the warriors into a cable car
and send them around a curve. He thought that he could gain much
pleasure by standing near and listening to the wild clash of steel
upon steel — the tumult of mailed heads striking together, the bitter grind of armoured legs bending the wrong way. He thought that
this would teach them that war is grim.

Towards evening, when the tides of travel set northward, it is
curious to see how the gripman and conductor reverse their tem-
pers. Their dispositions flop over like patent signals. During the
down-trip they had in mind always the advantages of being at

Battery Park. A perpetual picture of the blessings of Battery Park was before them, and every delay made them fume — made this picture all the more alluring. Now the delights of up-town appear to them. They have reversed the signs on the cars; they have reversed their aspiration. Battery Park has been gained and forgotten. There is a new goal. Here is a perpetual illustration which the philosophers of New York may use.

In the Tenderloin, the place of theatres, and of the restaurant where gayer New York does her dining, the cable cars in the evening carry a stratum of society which looks like a new one, but it is of the familiar strata in other clothes. It is just as good as a new stratum, however, for in evening dress the average man feels that he has gone up three pegs in the social scale, and there is considerable evening dress about a Broadway car in the evening. A car with its electric lamp resembles a brilliantly-lighted salon, and the atmosphere grows just a trifle strained. People sit more rigidly, and glance sidewise, perhaps, as if each was positive of possessing social value, but was doubtful of all others. The conductor says: "Ah, gwan. Git off th' earth." But this is to a man at Canal Street. That shows his versatility. He stands on the platform and beams in a modest and polite manner into the car. He notes a lifted finger and grabs swiftly for the bell strap. He reaches down to help a woman aboard. Perhaps his demeanour is a reflection of the manner of the people in the car. No one is in a mad New York hurry; no one is fretting and muttering; no one is perched upon his neighbour's toes. Moreover, the Tenderloin is a glory at night. Broadway of late years has fallen heir to countless signs illuminated with red, blue, green, and gold electric lamps, and the people certainly fly to these as the moths go to a candle. And perhaps the gods have allowed this opportunity to observe and study the best-dressed crowds in the world to operate upon the conductor until his mood is to treat us with care and mildness.

Late at night, after the diners and theatre-goers have been lost in Harlem, various inebriate persons may perchance emerge from the darker regions of Sixth Avenue and swing their arms solemnly at the gripman. If the Broadway cars run for the next 7000 years this will be the only time when one New Yorker will address another in public without an excuse sent direct from heaven. In these cars late at night it is not impossible that some fearless drunkard will attempt to inaugurate a general conversation. He is quite willing to devote his ability to the affair. He tells of the fun he thinks he has had; describes his feelings; recounts stories of his dim past. None reply, although all listen with every ear. The rake probably ends by borrowing a match, lighting a cigar, and entering into a wrangle with the conductor with an *abandon*, a ferocity, and a courage that do not come to us when we are sober.

In the meantime the figures on the street grow fewer and fewer. Strolling policemen test the locks of the great dark-fronted stores. Nighthawk cabs whirl by the cars on their mysterious errands. Finally the cars themselves depart in the way of the citizen, and for the few hours before dawn a new sound comes into the still thoroughfare — the cable whirring in its channel underground.

A DESERTION.*

The yellow gas-light that came with an effect of difficulty through the dust-stained windows on either side of the door, gave strange hues to the faces and forms of the three women who stood gabbling in the hall-way of the tenement. They made rapid gestures, and in the background their enormous shadows mingled in terrific conflict.

"Aye, she ain't so good as he thinks she is, I'll bet. He can watch over 'er an' take care of 'er all he pleases, but when she wants t' fool 'im, she'll fool 'im. An' how does he know she ain't foolin' 'im now?"

"Oh, he thinks he's keepin' 'er from goin' t' th' bad, he does. Oh, yes. He ses she's too purty t' let run round alone. Too purty! Huh! My Sadie — "

"Well, he keeps a clost watch on 'er, you bet. O'ny las' week, she met my boy Tim on th' stairs, an' Tim hadn't said two words to 'er b'fore th' ol' man begin to holler. 'Dorter, dorter, come here; come here!' "

At this moment a young girl entered from the street, and it was evident from the injured expression suddenly assumed by the three gossipers that she had been the object of their discussion.

---

* *Reprinted from* Last Words *(London, 1902). This sketch was first published in* Harper's Magazine: *November 1900.*

A portion of this sketch appears in Crane's "Pocket Notebook" which he carried with him in Park Row during 1892–1894. Crane jotted down impressions and notes for future sketches while sitting in some Park Row restaurant or Bowery saloon or while cooling his heels in S. S. McClure's outer office. "If you have any work for Mr. Crane," wrote Hamlin Garland to McClure, 2 January 1894, "talk things over with him and for mercy's sake! don't keep him standing for an hour as he did before out in your pen for culprits."

She passed them with a slight nod, and they swung about into a row to stare after her.

On her way up the long flights the girl unfastened her veil. One could then clearly see the beauty of her eyes, but there was in them a certain furtiveness that came near to marring the effect. It was a peculiar fixture of gaze, brought from the street, as of one who there saw a succession of passing dangers, with menaces aligned at every corner.

On the top floor, she pushed open a door and then paused on the threshold, confronting an interior that appeared black and flat like a curtain. Perhaps some girlish idea of hobgoblins assailed her then, for she called in a little breathless voice, "Daddie!"

There was no reply. The fire in the cooking-stove in the room crackled at spasmodic intervals. One lid was misplaced, and the girl could now see that this fact created a little flushed crescent upon the ceiling. Also, a series of tiny windows in the stove caused patches of red upon the floor. Otherwise, the room was heavily draped with shadows.

The girl called again, "Daddie!"

Yet there was no reply.

"Oh, Daddie!"

Presently she laughed as one familiar with the humours of an old man. "Oh, I guess yer cussin' mad about yer supper, dad," she said, and she almost entered the room, but suddenly faltered, overcome by a feminine instinct to fly from this black interior, peopled with imagined dangers.

Again she called, "Daddie!" Her voice had an accent of appeal. It was as if she knew she was foolish but yet felt obliged to insist upon being reassured. "Oh, Daddie!"

Of a sudden a cry of relief, a feminine announcement that the stars still hung, burst from her. For, according to some mystic process, the smouldering coals of the fire went aflame with sudden, fierce brilliance, splashing parts of the walls, the floor, the crude furniture, with a hue of blood-red. And in the light of this dramatic outburst of light, the girl saw her father seated at a table with his back turned toward her.

She entered the room, then, with an aggrieved air, her logic evidently concluding that somebody was to blame for her nervous fright. "Oh, yer on'y sulkin' 'bout yer supper. I thought mebbe ye'd gone somewheres."

Her father made no reply. She went over to a shelf in the corner, and, taking a little lamp, she lit it and put it where it would give her light as she took off her hat and jacket in front of the tiny mirror. Presently, she began to bustle among the cooking utensils

that were crowded into the sink, and as she worked she rattled talk
at her father, apparently disdaining his mood.

"I'd 'a come home earlier t'night, Dad, o'ny that fly foreman,
he kep' me in th' shop 'til half-past six. What a fool. He came t' me,
yeh know, an' he ses, 'Nell, I wanta give yeh some brotherly advice.'
Oh, I know him an' his brotherly advice. 'I wanta give yeh some
brotherly advice. Yer too purty, Nell,' he ses, 't' be workin' in this
shop an' paradin' through the streets alone, without somebody t'
give yeh good brotherly advice, an' I wanta warn yeh, Nell. I'm a
bad man, but I ain't as bad as some, an' I wanta warn yeh.' 'Oh,
g'long 'bout yer business,' I ses. I know 'im. He's like all of 'em, o'ny
he's a little slyer. I know 'im. 'You g'long 'bout yer business,' I ses.
Well, he ses after a while that he guessed some evenin' he'd come
up an' see me. 'Oh, yeh will,' I ses, 'yeh will? Well, you jest let my
ol' man ketch yeh comin' foolin' 'round our place. Yeh'll wish yeh
went t' some other girl t' give brotherly advice.' 'What th' 'ell do I
care fer yer father?' he ses. 'What's he t' me?' 'If he throws yeh
down stairs, yeh'll care for 'im,' I ses. 'Well,' he ses, 'I'll come when
'e ain't in, b' Gawd, I'll come when 'e ain't in.' 'Oh, he's allus in
when it means takin' care 'a me,' I ses. 'Don't yeh fergit it either.
When it comes t' takin' care 'a his dorter, he's right on deck every
single possible time.'"

After a time, she turned and addressed cheery words to the
old man. "Hurry up th' fire, Daddie! We'll have supper pretty soon."

But still her father was silent, and his form in its sullen posture
was motionless.

At this, the girl seemed to see the need of the inauguration of
a feminine war against a man out of temper. She approached him
breathing soft, coaxing syllables.

"Daddie! Oh, Daddie! O — o — oh, Daddie!"

It was apparent from a subtle quality of valour in her tones
that this manner of onslaught upon his moods had usually been
successful, but to-night it had no quick effect. The words, coming
from her lips, were like the refrain of an old ballad, but the man
remained stolid.

"Daddie! My Daddie! Oh, Daddie are yeh mad at me, really —
truly mad at me!"

She touched him lightly upon the arm. Should he have turned
then he would have seen the fresh, laughing face, with dew-
sparkling eyes, close to his own.

"Oh, Daddie! My Daddie! Pretty Daddie!"

She stole her arm about his neck, and then slowly bended her
face toward his. It was the action of a queen who knows that she
reigns notwithstanding irritations, trials, tempests.

But suddenly, from this position, she leaped backward with the mad energy of a frightened colt. Her face was in this instant turned to a grey, featureless thing of horror. A yell, wild and hoarse as a brute-cry, burst from her. "Daddie!" She flung herself to a place near the door, where she remained, crouching, her eyes staring at the motionless figure, spattered by the quivering flashes from the fire. Her arms extended, and her frantic fingers at once besought and repelled. There was in them an expression of eagerness to caress and an expression of the most intense loathing. And the girl's hair that had been a splendour, was in these moments changed to a disordered mass that hung and swayed in witchlike fashion.

Again, a terrible cry burst from her. It was more than the shriek of agony — it was directed, personal, addressed to him in the chair, the first word of a tragic conversation with the dead.

It seemed that when she had put her arm about its neck, she had jostled the corpse in such a way, that now she and it were face to face. The attitude expressed an intention of arising from the table. The eyes, fixed upon hers, were filled with an unspeakable hatred.

The cries of the girl aroused thunders in the tenement. There was a loud slamming of doors, and presently there was a roar of feet upon the boards of the stairway. Voices rang out sharply.

"What is it?"

"What's th' matter?"

"He's killin' her!"

"Slug 'im with anythin' yeh kin lay hold of, Jack."

But over all this came the shrill shrewish tones of a woman. "Ah, th' damned ol' fool, he's drivin' 'er inteh th' street — that's what he's doin'. He's drivin' 'er inteh th' street."

THE AUCTION *

Some said that Ferguson gave up sailoring because he was tired of the sea. Some said it was because he loved a woman. In truth it was because he was tired of the sea and because he loved a woman.

He saw the woman once, and immediately she became for him the symbol of all things unconnected with the sea. He did not trouble to look again at the grey old goddess, the muttering

* Reprinted from The Open Boat and Other Stories (London, 1898), where it first appeared.

slave of the moon. Her splendours, her treacheries, her smiles, her rages, her vanities, were no longer on his mind. He took heels after a little human being, and the woman made his thought spin at all times like a top; whereas the ocean had only made him think when he was on watch.

He developed a grin for the power of the sea, and, in derision, he wanted to sell the red and green parrot which had sailed four voyages with him. The woman, however, had a sentiment concerning the bird's plumage, and she commanded Ferguson to keep it in order, as it happened, that she might forget to put food in its cage.

The parrot did not attend the wedding. It stayed at home and blasphemed at a stock of furniture, bought on the instalment plan, and arrayed for the reception of the bride and groom.

As a sailor, Ferguson had suffered the acute hankering for port; and being now always in port, he tried to force life to become an endless picnic. He was not an example of diligent and peaceful citizenship. Ablution became difficult in the little apartment, because Ferguson kept the wash-basin filled with ice and bottles of beer: and so, finally, the dealer in second-hand furniture agreed to auction the household goods on commission. Owing to an exceedingly liberal definition of a term, the parrot and cage were included. "On the level?" cried the parrot, "On the level? On the level? On the level?"

On the way to the sale, Ferguson's wife spoke hopefully. "You can't tell, Jim," she said. "Perhaps some of 'em will get to biddin', and we might get almost as much as we paid for the things."

The auction room was in a cellar. It was crowded with people and with house furniture; so that as the auctioneer's assistant moved from one piece to another he caused a great shuffling. There was an astonishing number of old women in curious bonnets. The rickety stairway was thronged with men who wished to smoke and be free from the old women. Two lamps made all the faces appear yellow as parchment. Incidentally they could impart a lustre of value to very poor furniture.

The auctioneer was a fat, shrewd-looking individual, who seemed also to be a great bully. The assistant was the most imperturbable of beings, moving with the dignity of an image on rollers. As the Fergusons forced their way down the stair-way, the assistant roared: "Number twenty-one!"

"Number twenty-one!" cried the auctioneer. "Number twenty-one! A fine new handsome bureau! Two dollars? Two dollars is bid! Two and a half! Two and a half! Three? Three is bid. Four! Four dollars! A fine new handsome bureau at four dollars! Four dollars! Four dollars! F-o-u-r d-o-l-l-a-r-s! Sold at four dollars."

"On the level?" cried the parrot, muffled somewhere among furniture and carpets. "On the level? On the level?" Every one tittered.

Mrs. Ferguson had turned pale, and gripped her husband's arm. "Jim! Did you hear? The bureau — four dollars — "

Ferguson glowered at her with the swift brutality of a man afraid of a scene. "Shut up, can't you!"

Mrs. Ferguson took a seat upon the steps; and hidden there by the thick ranks of men, she began to softly sob. Through her tears appeared the yellowish mist of the lamplight, streaming about the monstrous shadows of the spectators. From time to time these latter whispered eagerly: "See, that went cheap!" In fact when anything was bought at a particularly low price, a murmur of admiration arose for the successful bidder.

The bedstead was sold for two dollars, the mattresses and springs for one dollar and sixty cents. This figure seemed to go through the woman's heart. There was derision in the sound of it. She bowed her head in her hands. "Oh, God, a dollar-sixty! Oh, God, a dollar-sixty!"

The parrot was evidently under heaps of carpet, but the dauntless bird still raised the cry, "On the level?"

Some of the men near Mrs. Ferguson moved timidly away upon hearing her low sobs. They perfectly understood that a woman in tears is formidable.

The shrill voice went like a hammer, beat and beat, upon the woman's heart. An odour of varnish, of the dust of old carpets, assailed her and seemed to possess a sinister meaning. The golden haze from the two lamps was an atmosphere of shame, sorrow, greed. But it was when the parrot called that a terror of the place and of the eyes of the people arose in her so strongly that she could not have lifted her head any more than if her neck had been of iron.

At last came the parrot's turn. The assistant fumbled until he found the ring of the cage, and the bird was drawn into view. It adjusted its feathers calmly and cast a rolling wicked eye over the crowd.

> "Oh, the good ship Sarah sailed the seas,
> And the wind it blew all day — "

This was the part of a ballad which Ferguson had tried to teach it. With a singular audacity and scorn, the parrot bawled these lines at the auctioneer as if it considered them to bear some particular insult.

The throng in the cellar burst into laughter. The auctioneer attempted to start the bidding, and the parrot interrupted with a repetition of the lines. It swaggered to and fro on its perch, and gazed at the faces of the crowd, with so much rowdy understanding and derision that even the auctioneer could not confront it. The auction was brought to a halt; a wild hilarity developed, and every one gave jeering advice.

Ferguson looked down at his wife and groaned. She had cowered against the wall, hiding her face. He touched her shoulder and she arose. They sneaked softly up the stairs with heads bowed.

Out in the street, Ferguson gripped his fists and said: "Oh, but wouldn't I like to strangle it!"

His wife cried in a voice of wild grief: "It — it m — made us a laughing-stock in — in front of all that crowd!"

For the auctioning of their household goods, the sale of their home — this financial calamity lost its power in the presence of the social shame contained in a crowd's laughter.

A POKER GAME.*

Usually a poker game is a picture of peace. There is no drama so low-voiced and serene and monotonous. If an amateur loser does not softly curse, there is no orchestral support. Here is one of the most exciting and absorbing occupations known to intelligent American manhood; here a year's reflection is compressed into a moment of thought; here the nerves may stand on end and scream to themselves, but a tranquillity as from heaven is only interrupted by the click of chips. The higher the stakes the more quiet the scene; this is a law that applies everywhere save on the stage.

And yet sometimes in a poker game things happen. Everybody remembers the celebrated corner on bay rum that was triumphantly consummated by Robert F. Cinch, of Chicago, assisted by the United States Courts and whatever other federal power he needed. Robert F. Cinch enjoyed his victory four months. Then he died, and young Bobbie Cinch came to New York in order to more clearly demonstrate that there was a good deal of fun in twenty-two million dollars.

Old Henry Spuytendyvil owns all the real estate in New York save that previously appropriated by the hospitals and Central

---

* *Reprinted from* Last Words (*London, 1902*).
    Crane was a poor poker player, and what Archie Bracketts says to young Bob in this sketch applied to Crane.

Park. He had been a friend of Bob's father. When Bob appeared in New York, Spuytendyvil entertained him correctly. It came to pass that they just naturally played poker.

One night they were having a small game in an up-town hotel. There were five of them, including two lawyers and a politician. The stakes depended on the ability of the individual fortune.

Bobbie Cinch had won rather heavily. He was as generous as sunshine, and when luck chases a generous man it chases him hard, even though he cannot bet with all the skill of his opponents.

Old Spuytendyvil had lost a considerable amount. One of the lawyers from time to time smiled quietly, because he knew Spuytendyvil well, and he knew that anything with the name of loss attached to it sliced the old man's heart into sections.

At midnight Archie Bracketts, the actor, came into the room. "How you holding 'em, Bob?" said he.

"Pretty well," said Bob.

"Having any luck, Mr. Spuytendyvil?"

"Blooming bad," grunted the old man.

Bracketts laughed and put his foot on the round of Spuytendyvil's chair. "There," said he, "I'll queer your luck for you." Spuytendyvil sat at the end of the table. "Bobbie," said the actor, presently, as young Cinch won another pot, "I guess I better knock your luck." So he took his foot from the old man's chair and placed it on Bob's chair. The lad grinned good-naturedly and said he didn't care.

Bracketts was in a position to scan both of the hands. It was Bob's ante, and old Spuytendyvil threw in a red chip. Everybody passed out up to Bobbie. He filled in the pot and drew a card.

Spuytendyvil drew a card. Bracketts, looking over his shoulder, saw him holding the ten, nine, eight, and seven of diamonds. Theatrically speaking, straight flushes are as frequent as berries on a juniper tree, but as a matter of truth the reason that straight flushes are so admired is because they are not as common as berries on a juniper tree. Bracketts stared; drew a cigar slowly from his pocket, and placing it between his teeth forgot its existence.

Bobbie was the only other stayer. Bracketts flashed an eye for the lad's hand and saw the nine, eight, six, and five of hearts. Now, there are but six hundred and forty-five emotions possible to the human mind, and Bracketts immediately had them all. Under the impression that he had finished his cigar, he took it from his mouth and tossed it toward the grate without turning his eyes to follow its flight.

There happened to be a complete silence around the green-clothed table. Spuytendyvil was studying his hand with a kind of contemptuous smile, but in his eyes there perhaps was to be seen a cold, stern light expressing something sinister and relentless.

Young Bob sat as he had sat. As the pause grew longer, he looked up once inquiringly at Spuytendyvil.

The old man reached for a white chip. "Well, mine are worth about that much," said he, tossing it into the pot. Thereupon he leaned back comfortably in his chair and renewed his stare at the five straight diamonds. Young Bob extended his hand leisurely toward his stack. It occurred to Bracketts that he was smoking, but he found no cigar in his mouth.

The lad fingered his chips and looked pensively at his hand. The silence of those moments oppressed Bracketts like the smoke from a conflagration.

Bobbie Cinch continued for some moments to coolly observe his cards. At last he breathed a little sigh and said, "Well, Mr. Spuytendyvil, I can't play a sure thing against you." He threw in a white chip. "I'll just call you. I've got a straight flush." He faced down his cards.

Old Spuytendyvil's fear, horror, and rage could only be equalled in volume to a small explosion of gasolene. He dashed his cards upon the table. "There!" he shouted, glaring frightfully at Bobbie. "I've got a straight flush, too! And mine is Jack high!"

Bobbie was at first paralysed with amazement, but in a moment he recovered, and apparently observing something amusing in the situation he grinned.

Archie Bracketts, having burst his bond of silence, yelled for joy and relief. He smote Bobbie on the shoulder. "Bob, my boy," he cried exuberantly, "you're no gambler, but you're a mighty good fellow, and if you hadn't been you would be losing a good many dollars this minute."

Old Spuytendyvil glowered at Bracketts. "Stop making such an infernal din, will you, Archie," he said morosely. His throat seemed filled with pounded glass. "Pass the whisky."

A MAN BY THE NAME OF MUD.*

Deep in a leather chair, the Kid sat looking out at where the rain slanted before the dull brown houses and hammered swiftly upon an occasional lonely cab. The happy crackle from the great and

Reprinted from Last Words (London, 1902).

glittering fireplace behind him had evidently no meaning of content for him. He appeared morose and unapproachable, and when a man appears mororse and unapproachable it is a fine chance for his intimate friends. Three or four of them discovered his mood, and so hastened to be obnoxious.

"What's wrong, Kid? Lost your thirst?"

"He can never be happy again. He has lost his thirst."

"That's right, Kid. When you quarrel with a man who can whip you, resort to sarcastic reflection and distance."

They cackled away persistently, but the Kid was mute and continued to stare gloomily at the street.

Once a man who had been writing letters looked up and said, "I saw your friend at the Comique the other night." He waited a moment and then added, "In back."

The Kid wheeled about in his chair at this information, and all the others saw then that it was important. One man said with deep intelligence, "Ho, ho, a woman, hey? A woman's come between the two Kids. A woman. Great, eh?" The Kid launched a glare of scorn across the room, and then turned again to a contemplation of the rain. His friends continued to do all in their power to worry him, but they fell ultimately before his impregnable silence.

As it happened, he had not been brooding upon his friend's mysterious absence at all. He had been concerned with himself. Once in a while he seemed to perceive certain futilities and lapsed them immediately into a state of voiceless dejection. These moods were not frequent.

An unexplained thing in his mind, however, was greatly enlightened by the words of the gossip. He turned then from his harrowing scrutiny of the amount of pleasure he achieved from living, and settled into a comfortable reflection upon the state of his comrade, the other Kid.

Perhaps it could be indicated in this fashion: "Went to Comique, I suppose. Saw girl. Secondary part, probably. Thought her rather natural. Went to Comique again. Went again. One time happened to meet omnipotent and good-natured friend. Broached subject to him with great caution. Friend said — 'Why, certainly, my boy, come round to-night, and I'll take you in back. Remember, it's against all rules, but I think that in your case, etc.' Kid went. Chorus girls winked same old wink. 'Here's another dude on the prowl.' Kid aware of this, swearing under his breath and looking very stiff. Meets girl. Knew beforehand that the footlights might have sold him, but finds her very charming. Does not say single thing to her which she naturally expected to hear. Makes no reference to her beauty nor her voice — if she has any. Perhaps takes it for granted that she knows. Girl don't exactly love this attitude, but then feels admiration, because after all she can't tell whether he thinks her nice or whether he don't. New scheme this. Worked by occasional guys in Rome and Egypt, but still, new scheme. Kid goes away. Girl thinks. Later, nails omnipotent and good-natured friend. 'Who was that you brought back?' 'Oh, him? Why, he — ' Describes the Kid's wealth, feats, and virtue — virtues of disposition. Girl propounds clever question — 'Why did he wish to meet me?' Omnipotent person says, 'Damned if I know.' "

Later, Kid asks girl to supper. Not wildly anxious, but very evident that he asks her because he likes her. Girl accepts; goes to supper. Kid very good comrade and kind. Girl begins to think that here at last is a man who understands her. Details ambitions — long, wonderful ambitions. Explains her points of superiority over the other girls of stage. Says their lives disgust her. She wants to work and study and make something of herself. Kid smokes vast number of cigarettes. Displays and feels deep sympathy. Recalls, but faintly, that he has heard it on previous occasions. They have an awfully good time. Part at last in front of apartment house. "Good-night, old chap." "Good-night." Squeeze hands hard. Kid has no information at all about kissing her good-night, but don't even try. Noble youth. Wise youth. Kid goes home and smokes. Feels strong desire to kill people who say intolerable things of the girl in rows. "Narrow, mean, stupid, ignorant, damnable people." Contemplates the broad, fine liberality of his experienced mind.

Kid and girl become very chummy. Kid like a brother. Listens to her troubles. Takes her out to supper regularly and regularly. Chorus girls now tacitly recognise him as the main guy. Sometimes, may be, girl's mother sick. Can't go to supper. Kid always very noble. Understands perfectly the probabilities of there being others. Lays for 'em, but makes no discoveries. Begins to wonder whether he is a winner or whether she is a girl of marvellous cleverness. Can't tell. Maintains himself with dignity, however. Only occasionally inveighs against the men who prey upon the girls of the stage. Still noble.

Time goes on. Kid grows less noble. Perhaps decides not to be noble at all, or as little as he can. Still inveighs against the men who prey upon the girls of the stage. Thinks the girl stunning. Wants to be dead sure there are no others. Once suspects it, and immediately makes the colossal mistake of his life. Takes the girl to task. Girl won't stand it for a minute. Harangues him. Kid surrenders and pleads with her — pleads with her. Kid's name is mud.

A SELF-MADE MAN. AN EXAMPLE OF SUCCESS
THAT ANY ONE CAN FOLLOW.*

Tom had a hole in his shoe. It was very round and very uncomfortable, particularly when he went on wet pavements. Rainy days made him feel that he was walking on frozen dollars, although he had only to think for a moment to discover he was not.

He used up almost two packs of playing cards by means of putting four cards at a time inside his shoe as a sort of temporary sole, which usually lasted about half a day. Once he put in four aces for luck. He went down town that morning and got refused work. He thought it wasn't a very extraordinary performance for a young man of ability, and he was not sorry that night to find his packs were entirely out of aces.

One day Tom was strolling down Broadway. He was in pursuit of work, although his pace was slow. He had found that he must take the matter coolly. So he puffed tenderly at a cigarette and walked as if he owned stock. He imitated success so successfully, that if it wasn't for the constant reminder (king, queen, deuce, and trey) in his shoe, he would have gone into a store and bought something.

He had borrowed five cents that morning off his landlady, for his mouth craved tobacco. Although he owed her much for board, she had unlimited confidence in him, because his stock of self-assurance was very large indeed. And as it increased in a proper ratio with the amount of his bills, his relations with her seemed on a firm basis. So he strolled along and smoked with his confidence in fortune in nowise impaired by his financial condition.

Of a sudden he perceived an old man seated upon a railing and smoking a clay pipe.

He stopped to look, because he wasn't in a hurry, and because it was an unusual thing on Broadway to see old men seated upon railings and smoking clay pipes.

And to his surprise the old man regarded him very intently in

---

* *Reprinted from* Last Words (*London, 1902*). *The sketch was first published in* Cornhill *Magazine: March 1899.*

Crane wrote this piece in Ravensbrook — before moving to Brede Place, Sussex — in early 1899 upon his return from Havana and the Spanish-American War.

return. He stared, with a wistful expression, into Tom's face, and he clasped his hands in trembling excitement.

Tom was filled with astonishment at the old man's strange demeanour. He stood puffing at his cigarette, and tried to understand matters. Failing, he threw his cigarette away, took a fresh one from his pocket, and approached the old man.

"Got a match?" he inquired, pleasantly.

The old man, much agitated, nearly fell from the railing as he leaned dangerously forward.

"Sonny, can you read?" he demanded in a quavering voice.

"Certainly, I can," said Tom, encouragingly. He waived the affair of the match.

The old man fumbled in his pocket. "You look honest, sonny. I've been looking for an honest feller fur a'most a week. I've set on this railing fur six days," he cried, plaintively.

He drew forth a letter and handed it to Tom. "Read it fur me, sonny, read it," he said, coaxingly.

Tom took the letter and leaned back against the railings. As he opened it and prepared to read, the old man wriggled like a child at a forbidden feast.

Thundering trucks made frequent interruptions, and seven men in a hurry jogged Tom's elbow, but he succeeded in reading what follows: —

> *Office of Ketchum R. Jones, Attorney-at-Law,*
> *Tin Can, Nevada, May 19, 18 — .*

Rufus Wilkins, Esq.

Dear Sir, — I have as yet received no acknowledgment of the draft from the sale of the north section lots, which I forwarded to you on 25th June. I would request an immediate reply concerning it.

Since my last I have sold the three corner lots at five thousand each. The city grew so rapidly in that direction that they were surrounded by brick stores almost before you would know it. I have also sold for four thousand dollars the ten acres of out-laying sage bush, which you once foolishly tried to give away. Mr. Simpson, of Boston, bought the tract. He is very shrewd, no doubt, but he hasn't been in the west long. Still, I think if he holds it for about a thousand years, he may come out all right.

I worked him with the projected-horse-car-line gag.

Inform me of the address of your New York attorneys, and I will send on the papers. Pray do not neglect to write me concerning the draft sent on 25th June.

In conclusion, I might say that if you have any eastern friends who are after good western investments inform them of the glorious future of Tin Can. We now have three railroads, a bank, an electric light plant a projected horse-car line, and an art society. Also, a saw manufactory, a patent car-wheel mill, and a Methodist Church. Tin Can is marching forward to take her proud stand as the metropolis of the west. The rose-hued future holds no glories to which Tin Can does not —

Tom stopped abruptly. "I guess the important part of the letter came first," he said.

"Yes," cried the old man, "I've heard enough. It is just as I thought. George has robbed his dad."

The old man's frail body quivered with grief. Two tears trickled slowly down the furrows of his face.

"Come, come, now," said Tom, patting him tenderly on the back. "Brace up, old feller. What you want to do is to get a lawyer and go put the screws on George."

"Is it really?" asked the old man, eagerly.

"Certainly, it is," said Tom.

"All right," cried the old man, with enthusiasm. "Tell me where to get one." He slid down from the railing and prepared to start off.

Tom reflected. "Well," he said, finally, "I might do for one myself."

"What," shouted the old man in a voice of admiration, "are you a lawyer as well as a reader?"

"Well," said Tom again, "I might appear to advantage as one. All you need is a big front," he added, slowly. He was a profane young man.

The old man seized him by the arm. "Come on, then," he cried, "and we'll go put the screws on George."

Tom permitted himself to be dragged by the weak arms of his companion around a corner and along a side street. As they proceeded, he was internally bracing himself for a struggle, and putting large bales of self-assurance around where they would be likely to obstruct the advance of discovery and defeat.

By the time they reached a brown-stone house, hidden away in a street of shops and warehouses, his mental balance was so admirable that he seemed to be in possession of enough information and brains to ruin half of the city, and he was no more concerned about the king, queen, deuce, and trey than if they had been discards that didn't fit his draw. He infused so much confidence and courage into his companion, that the old man went along the street, breathing war, like a decrepit hound on the scent of new blood.

He ambled up the steps of the brown-stone house as if he were charging earthworks. He unlocked the door and they passed along a dark hallway. In a rear room they found a man seated at table engaged with a very late breakfast. He had a diamond in his shirt front and a bit of egg on his cuff.

"George," said the old man in a fierce voice that came from his aged throat with a sound like the crackle of burning twigs, "here's my lawyer, Mr. er — ah — Smith, and we want to know what you did with the draft that was sent on 25th June."

The old man delivered the words as if each one was a musket shot. George's coffee spilled softly upon the tablecover, and his fingers worked convulsively upon a slice of bread. He turned a white, astonished face toward the old man and the intrepid Thomas.

The latter, straight and tall, with a highly legal air, stood at the old man's side. His glowing eyes were fixed upon the face of the man at the table. They seemed like two little detective cameras taking pictures of the other man's thoughts.

"Father, what d — do you mean," faltered George, totally unable to withstand the two cameras and the highly legal air.

"What do I mean?" said the old man with a feeble roar as from an ancient lion. "I mean that draft — that's what I mean. Give it up or we'll — we'll" — he paused to gain courage by a glance at the formidable figure at his side — "we'll put the screws on you."

"Well, I was — I was only borrowin' it for 'bout a month," said George.

"Ah," said Tom.

George started, glared at Tom, and then began to shiver like an animal with a broken back. There were a few moments of silence. The old man was fumbling about in his mind for more imprecations. George was wilting and turning limp before the glittering orbs of the valiant attorney. The latter, content with the exalted advantage he had gained by the use of the expression "Ah," spoke no more, but continued to stare.

"Well," said George, finally, in a weak voice, "I s'pose I can give you a cheque for it, 'though I was only borrowin' it for 'bout a month. I don't think you have treated me fairly, father, with your lawyers and your threats, and all that. But I'll give you the cheque."

The old man turned to his attorney. "Well?" he asked.

Tom looked at the son and held an impressive debate with himself. "I think we may accept the cheque," he said coldly after a time.

George arose and tottered across the room. He drew a cheque that made the attorney's heart come privately into his mouth. As he and his client passed triumphantly out, he turned a last highly legal glare upon George that reduced that individual to a mere paste.

On the side-walk the old man went into a spasm of delight and called his attorney all the admiring and endearing names there were to be had.

"Lord, how you settled him," he cried ecstatically.

They walked slowly back toward Broadway. "The scoundrel," murmured the old man. "I'll never see 'im again. I'll desert 'im. I'll find a nice quiet boarding-place and — "

"That's all right," said Tom. "I know one. I'll take you right up," which he did.

He came near being happy ever after. The old man lived at advanced rates in the front room at Tom's boarding-house. And the latter basked in the proprietress' smiles, which had a commercial value, and were a great improvement on many we see.

The old man, with his quantities of sage bush, thought Thomas owned all the virtues mentioned in high-class literature, and his opinion, too, was of commercial value. Also, he knew a man who knew another man who received an impetus which made him engage Thomas on terms that were highly satisfactory. Then it was that the latter learned he had not succeeded sooner because he did not know a man who knew another man.

So it came to pass that Tom grew to be Thomas G. Somebody. He achieved that position in life from which he could hold out for good wines when he went to poor restaurants. His name became entangled with the name of Wilkins in the ownership of vast and valuable tracts of sage bush in Tin Can, Nevada.

At the present day he is so great that he lunches frugally at high prices. His fame has spread through the land as a man who carved his way to fortune with no help but his undaunted pluck, his tireless energy, and his sterling integrity.

Newspapers apply to him now, and he writes long signed articles to struggling young men, in which he gives the best possible advice as to how to become wealthy. In these articles, he, in a burst of glorification, cites the king, queen, deuce, and trey, the four aces, and all that. He alludes tenderly to the nickel he borrowed and spent for cigarettes as the foundation of his fortune.

"To succeed in life," he writes, "the youth of America have only to see an old man seated upon a railing and smoking a clay pipe. Then go up and ask him for a match."

MANACLED*

In the First Act there had been a farm scene, wherein real horses had drunk real water out of real buckets, afterward dragging a real waggon off stage L. The audience was consumed with admiration of this play, and the great Theatre Nouveau rang to its roof with the crowd's plaudits.

The Second Act was now well advanced. The hero, cruelly victimised by his enemies, stood in prison garb, panting with rage, while two brutal warders fastened real handcuffs on his wrists and real anklets on his ankles. And the hovering villain sneered.

"'Tis well, Aubrey Pettingill," said the prisoner. "You have so far succeeded; but, mark you, there will come a time —— "

The villain retorted with a cutting allusion to the young lady whom the hero loved.

"Curse you," cried the hero, and he made as if to spring upon this demon; but, as the pitying audience saw, he could only take steps four inches long.

Drowning the mocking laughter of the villain came cries from both the audience and the people back of the wings. "Fire! Fire! Fire!" Throughout the great house resounded the roaring crashes of a throng of human beings moving in terror, and even above this noise could be heard the screams of women more shrill than whistles. The building hummed and shook; it was like a glade which holds some bellowing cataract of the mountains. Most of the people who were killed on the stairs still clutched their play-bills in their hands as if they had resolved to save them at all costs.

The Theatre Nouveau fronted upon a street which was not of the first importance, especially at night, when it only aroused when the people came to the theatre, and aroused again when they came out to go home. On the night of the fire, at the time of the scene between the enchained hero and his tormentor, the thoroughfare echoed with only the scraping shovels of some street-cleaners, who were loading carts with blackened snow and mud. The gleam of

---

* Reprinted from the London edition of The Monster and Other Stories (Harper & Brothers, 1901); not in the New York edition (Harper & Brothers, 1899). The sketch was first published in Argosy: August 1900.

Crane recreates a dream he had one summer night in 1899 at Brede Place.

lights made the shadowed pavement deeply blue, save where lay some yellow plum-like reflection.

Suddenly a policeman came running frantically along the street. He charged upon the fire-box on a corner. Its red light touched with flame each of his brass buttons and the municipal shield. He pressed a lever. He had been standing in the entrance of the theatre chatting to the lonely man in the box-office. To send an alarm was a matter of seconds.

Out of the theatre poured the first hundreds of fortunate ones, and some were not altogether fortunate. Women, their bonnets flying, cried out tender names; men, white as death, scratched and bleeding, looked wildly from face to face. There were displays of horrible blind brutality by the strong. Weaker men clutched and clawed like cats. From the theatre itself came the howl of a gale.

The policeman's fingers had flashed into instant life and action the most perfect counter-attack to the fire. He listened for some seconds, and presently he heard the thunder of a charging engine. She swept around a corner, her three shining enthrilled horses leaping. Her consort, the hose-cart, roared behind her. There were the loud clicks of the steel-shod hoofs, hoarse shouts, men running, the flash of lights, while the crevice-like streets resounded with the charges of other engines.

At the first cry of fire, the two brutal warders had dropped the arms of the hero and run off the stage with the villain. The hero cried after them angrily —

"Where are you going? Here, Pete — Tom — you've left me chained up, damn you!"

The body of the theatre now resembled a mad surf amid rocks, but the hero did not look at it. He was filled with fury at the stupidity of the two brutal warders, in forgetting that they were leaving him manacled. Calling loudly, he hobbled off stage L, taking steps four inches long.

Behind the scenes he heard the hum of flames. Smoke, filled with sparks sweeping on spiral courses, rolled thickly upon him. Suddenly his face turned chalk-colour beneath his skin of manly bronze for the stage. His voice shrieked —

"Pete — Tom — damn you — come back — you've left me chained up."

He had played in this theatre for seven years, and he could find his way without light through the intricate passages which mazed out behind the stage. He knew that it was a long way to the street door.

The heat was intense. From time to time masses of flaming wood sunk down from above him. He began to jump. Each jump advanced him about three feet, but the effort soon became heart-breaking. Once he fell, and it took time to get upon his feet again.

There were stairs to descend. From the top of this flight he tried to fall feet first. He precipitated himself in a way that would have broken his hip under common conditions. But every step seemed covered with glue, and on almost every one he stuck for a moment. He could not even succeed in falling downstairs. Ultimately he reached the bottom, windless from the struggle.

There were stairs to climb. At the foot of the flight he lay for an instant with his mouth close to the floor trying to breathe. Then he tried to scale this frightful precipice up the face of which many an actress had gone at a canter.

Each succeeding step arose eight inches from its fellow. The hero dropped to a seat on the third step, and pulled his feet to the second step. From this position he lifted himself to a seat on the fourth step. He had not gone far in this manner before his frenzy caused him to lose his balance, and he rolled to the foot of the flight. After all, he could fall downstairs.

He lay there whispering. "They all got out but I. All but I." Beautiful flames flashed above him, some were crimson, some were orange, and here and there were tongues of purple, blue, green.

A curiously calm thought came into his head. "What a fool I was not to foresee this! I shall have Rogers furnish manacles of *papier-mâché* to-morrow."

The thunder of the fire-lions made the theatre have a palsy.

Suddenly the hero beat his handcuffs against the wall, cursing them in a loud wail. Blood started from under his finger-nails. Soon he began to bite the hot steel, and blood fell from his blistered mouth. He raved like a wolf.

Peace came to him again. There were charming effects amid the flames. . . . He felt very cool, delightfully cool. . . . "They've left me chained up."

THE MAN FROM DULUTH/BY/STEPHEN/CRANE/ THE LAST STORY OF/NEW YORK LIFE BY/THE AUTHOR OF * */"THE RED BADGE/OF COUR- AGE," * */"SECRET SERVICE,"/ETC. * * * * *

The man from Duluth reproached his companions. "I don't see as we're having much fun," he said. "This is about the dreamiest time I ever run up against."

One of the New York men waved his hand mournfully. "Well, you see, it is Sunday night, for one thing; and besides that, the town is about dead now, anyhow."

"That's what it is," said the others. They began plaintively to deplore the ravages of reform. Their voices filled with pathos, they spoke of the days that had been. It was the wail of the Tenderloin, the lamentation of the "rounders" who have seen their idols of men and places taken from them.

"Why, I can remember when — "

But the man from Duluth interrupted these tales. "Oh, I've no doubt it was all very great," said he, "but what are we going to do now? That's the point."

The five men stood on a street corner and reflected. Occasion- ally the visitor from the West prodded the others with accounts of the splendors of life in his country, and poked at them comments upon their slumbrous environment.

"It's dead slow," he told them, "dead slow. I'll never come East again expecting to play horse. I'll do my flying in Chicago. You fellows have all been turned down. You're buried. Come out and see me in Chicago and I'll show you real dives with electric lights out in front, and whole neighborhoods that get drunk by half-past three in the afternoon."

The others were eager to explain. "Well, you see, we — "

"Oh, I know you can still have fun in New York if you are a nervy spender," interrupted the man from Duluth; "but I guess you could do that in Mecca or Jerusalem, too. That's no sign of a red- hot town. It's the sign of a dead-slow town."

---

* *Reprinted from* Metropolitan Magazine: *February 1901. Here Crane's* Active Service *is mistakenly called "Secret Service."* Crampton's Magazine: *May 1901, reprinted this sketch but without the illustrations.*

He stared severely at the New York men. They cast down their eyes and pondered in mournful silence.

At last one man suddenly spoke. He wore an air of having arrived at the only real golden suggestion. "Well, let's go and get a drink, anyhow." It was said with great vigor.

The party aroused at this. "All right, come ahead." "Where'll we go?" "Oh, anywhere; what's the matter with the little French concert hall?" "All right, come ahead."

Led by one, they paraded down the avenue. They were presently among the criss-cross streets of Greenwich. The river was in sight before they halted. Once the silence of their tongues had been broken by the voice of the man from Duluth: "This is a derned long ways to go for a drink."

The man who was in advance conducted the party up the steps of a private house. He rang the bell, and the door presently was opened a little way. A woman's head was thrust out warily. She exclaimed in French when she discovered the size of the band of invaders. She was about to slam the door, but two or three of the men burst forth in very bad but voluble French.

There was a rapid parley. The man from Duluth edged forward. If it came to the worst, he could put his foot where it would prevent the door from closing.

The conductor of the party was a painter who had studied in France. He volleyed prayers and entreaties in a way that he learned in that country. Presently the woman let them in quickly and then banged the door upon the form of some stranger who had tried to insinuate himself inside.

They passed down a mutilated hallway. In the rear of the house, where no doubt had once been kitchens and dining room, there was now a little hall. A gallery occupied one end; at the other there was a tiny stage. There was a scenic arrangement in the form of papier-maché rocks and boulders. They looked indescribably dusty.

The ceiling was high; in it some little transoms were turned to let in the night air. At the tables that filled the floor space sat two-score people babbling French. The polish of the surface of these tables had been worn away in spots by the contact of countless beer and wine glasses. There was an air of dilapidation in the room that imparted itself even to the waiters and to the youth over in the corner who thrummed the piano.

But with it all there was in the atmosphere, enwrapped, it may be, in thick clouds of cigarette smoke that hung and hovered overhead, the irresistible spirit of French carelessness. It was an angel that had flown over seas. There was the presence of a memory of

Paris. Everything remained local save the thoughts; these were fleeting, reminiscent. There was something retrospective in the very way the men pounded tables with their glasses, the while humming in chorus with the clattering piano. It was a gayety that was inherited, and it recalled in a way that was meagre and sad the mother of it — Paris.

And one then could instantly see that little did it matter here if there were dust and suggestions of cobwebs, nor if the linen generally of the company was soiled, nor if the waiter who brought the wine had stains on his apron and only one eye. In blessed security from these things dwelt this assemblage. The environment was made rose-hued by the laughter of girls; the color of wine was a weapon with which to defy cobwebs and dust stains and spots; whole legions of one-eyed waiters would fail to dampen the ardor of these existences.

Three men sat near the youth who played on the piano. At intervals one of them would arise, vanish for a moment in the bosom of the paper mountains, and then suddenly appear upon the little stage. They relieved each other with the regularity of sentries, and sang from the inexhaustible store of French comic songs. One was wretched, one was fair, and one was an artist. Even the man from Duluth, who comprehended less of French than he did of Sanscrit, enjoyed this latter performer. It is not always necessary to understand a language; sometimes one can be glad that he does not. But the man from Duluth revelled in the songs of him who was an artist. There were eloquent gestures and glances of the eyes that were full symbols. The man from Duluth was ignorant of details; that at which he grinned and giggled was the universal part. Good art of this kind cannot be confined to a language; there is something absorbingly intelligent to the thinking Zulu in the exhibition of a master of it.

One could wonder what he of the eloquent hands was paid. Probably he received the merest trifle. Some French customs are transported in completeness to certain portions of New York, and perhaps in France emotions are cheap. It is usually in the colder countries that publics pay fabulous prices for good emotions.

But the man from Duluth was not always satisfied with the universal part of art. When the audience would suddenly laugh he would lean forward and demand translation from the painter who had studied in France. The latter politely struggled with the difficulties of the task, but usually he failed.

"Say, what was that — what did he say then?" demanded once the man from Duluth.

"Oh — er — well," the painter replied. "Er — well — you see —

he was going along the street with three chickens in a basket — and then — er — he, you know — he looked up at a window — and there was a girl in the window, you know — and he looked up at her and kissed his hand, and he said, 'Good-day, sweetheart' — and then he — he was walking backward when he said that — 'Good-day, sweetheart' — and then, you know, he didn't see where he was going — and he — he fell down and the chickens got away — and flew up to this girl's window, you know — and he began to — to yell at her, 'Oh, I say, sweetheart, return to me my chickens' — and she laughed at him, and then he said — he said — oh, I don't know what he said. It's funny in French, but it don't sound funny in English — I couldn't make you understand."

The man from Duluth seemed strangely puzzled.

Also, later in the evening, he began to grow weary of even the artistic performer. "Say," he demanded, "don't they ever have girls here that sing?" Every one hastened to explain to him: "Well, you know, it's Sunday night — "

However, at frequent intervals after this time he would burst forth: "Say, this is pretty slow, ain't it?" "Ain't this slow, hey?" "Good Gawd, this is slow!"

"They always have a dance afterward — perhaps you will like that better," somebody said, to comfort him.

Presently, indeed, the performers ceased to pop out from behind the paper rocks. The one-eyed waiter and his fellows made a clear space by dragging away chairs and tables and stacking them in an end of the room. Then the young man at the piano suddenly attacked his instrument, and the ball began. Couples emerged from all portions of the hall to go whirling about in reckless fashion. There was nothing uniform or sedate. It was all emotional. Each couple danced according to moods. Some went solemnly, some affectionately, and at all times; a man would swirl his partner about the floor with a mad speed that would threaten to send her head flying. They were having lots of fun; almost every one was laughing.

"It's dead slow," said the man from Duluth.

Then, suddenly, in the middle of the floor there was a fight. The music stopped with a shrill crash; the dancers scurried out of the way. The atmosphere of the place became instantly tense, ominous, battleful. A woman shrieked; another threw her hand up to her throat, as if feeling an agony of strangulation. The man from Duluth stood on a chair.

Two furious men had dropped from the ceiling, or come up through the floor or from somewhere. They appeared suddenly, like apparitions, in the very centre of the hall. It was all as quick as an explosion. There had been peace and jollity; in a flash it was changed to lurid war. Violent, red-faced, swift of motion, they were hammering at each other with their fists, and lunging with their feet in the manner of French infantry soldiers. Their eyes flashed tragic hatred. There was prodigal expenditure of the most vast and extraordinary emotions. The blows were delivered with the energy of mad murder. In that instant of silence that followed the first shrieks and exclamations of the women one could hear their breaths come quick and harsh from between their clenched teeth.

But the men were about eight feet apart from each other. Their savage fists cut harmlessly through the air; the terrific deadly lunges of their feet were mere demonstrations of some kind. The man from Duluth climbed down from his chair. "They're a pair of birds," he said with supreme contempt. He regarded them with eyes of reproach. Apparently he considered that they had swindled him out of something, and he was much injured.

The vivid picture was blurred in a few seconds. Everybody had been frozen for a minute; then all rushed forward. Friends of both parties took flying leaps to avert a dreadful tragedy. The floor became a surge of men, tussling, tugging, and gesticulating in tremendous excitement. The principals in the affair were dragged this way and that way. There arose a wild clamor of explanation, condemnation, and reiteration.

The women, left without escorts, stood trying to look in other directions. Some shuddered with fear; some incessantly tapped the floor with the tips of their boots. They turned to each other with little nervous remarks. And over at a table directly opposite the battle sat the man from Duluth and his friends, silent, motionless, absorbed, grinning with wild, strange glee.

It was impossible to look upon the jumble of men, emotions, and swift French oaths without expecting some sort of a deadly riot. There was an impending horror. Men, frenzied with rage, gestured in each other's faces, the quivering fingers threatened eyes. The lightning-blooded spirit of battle hovered over the swaying crowd. The man from Duluth and his friends were carven with interest. There was a great fight coming, and they were on the spot.

But the crowd finally finished their explanations, their condemnations, and their reiterations. Their fury expended itself in the air; the flaming words and gestures had absorbed the energy for war. Generally the men went back to their female friends. Their collars were wilted, from the grandeur of their emotions perhaps, but they had expressed themselves, and they were satisfied. Only a little mob of five or six people was left upon the scene. They still gestured and roared at each other.

"Oh, what a fake!" said the disgusted man from Duluth. "A

great big fight in which nobody hits anybody else. It gives me a pain." He leaned back in his chair and stretched out his legs. He thrust his hands into his pockets and stared calmly, contemptuously, and with incredible insolence at the agitated group before him. "What a husky lot of willies!" Gradually he assumed a demeanor of the greatest importance and prowess. He sneered boldly and obviously at the wrangle. "Holy smoke! I could whip about eight hundred pounds of 'em." He was getting just a little bit drunk.

Downstairs from the gallery at that moment came a little, fat, tipsy Frenchman who was fated to play a great part. Evidently he was aware that there had been a difficulty, and he decided, of course, that with his peculiarly lucid intellect he could go over and straighten the whole thing. So he tootered uncertainly to the crowd, and, wedging his fat body among the gesticulators, he began to argue and explain in a slow, aimless, drunken fashion. No one paid attention to him at first, but it was not long before he had inaugurated an entirely new turmoil. He got one of the principals by the lapel and began another slow, distant harangue. This impassioned individual jerked away and swore in intense French.

Then came again the red apparition of war. There were renewed jostlings, gestures, oaths. Another tragedy impended, perhaps, but the man from Duluth stretched himself and said, "Oh, Gawd," in a tone from the profound and absolute depth of scorn.

Suddenly a woman came toward the crowd. Her hands were outstretched like the claws of an eagle. There was an unspeakable rage in her face, but her high and quavering voice held a burden of tears. "Ah, I kin lick you meself," she cried, with an accent that was from the street. She made a furious dive at the little, fat, tipsy Frenchman.

It seemed that this other man, a principal in the previous affair, was something to her. She had waited back there and trembled long enough. Now she was coming forward like a chieftainess of savages. That little, fat, tipsy Frenchman was the final exasperation; he had renewed the peril to her lover. She sprang at him. At last, at last there was war — real, red war. The man from Duluth climbed swiftly to an erect position upon his chair and cheered with valiant enthusiasm.

The little, fat, tipsy Frenchman was like a porpoise caught in a mighty human net. His face wore an expression of utter drunken woe and astonishment. There was one long crimson mark down his cheek. A dozen men held him and hauled him and berated him and fought at him. A half-dozen more beseeched the woman, holding her arms. Her shrill scream rose above the hoarse babble.

Then from an inner room came a large waiter. He was pushed

on by the proprietress of the place, a dingy woman in a brown dress. She was giving him hurried directions, and he was nodding his head, "Yes, yes."

He made a violent charge and seized the little Frenchman, who was casting despairing glances at the ceiling, praying for succor or at least explanation of this phenomenon. The large waiter grappled his coat collar. He gave a prodigious jerk. The little Frenchman's collar and necktie came off with a ripping sound. He was in the last agonies of bewilderment.

Two or three men were trying to pacify the woman. She was turning from them always to shriek at the little Frenchman, who was being noisily dragged out by the large waiter.

She replied in screams to her friends who intercepted her: "Well, no man dare call me a name like that, not any man here. I dare any johnnie in this room to call me a name like that."

"Hurrah!" shouted the man from Duluth from on top of his chair. "Hurrah! hurrah for America and the star spangled banner! No man here dare call the lady anything."

"What's that?" said the woman. She came ominously toward him. Her face was red and fierce. Her hands were held in the same peculiar clawlike manner. "What's that yeh say?"

"Madam," said the man from Duluth, suddenly sober and serious, "I didn't mean to reflect upon you in any way." His chair shook a little as he changed his weight from one leg to the other. His friends, down below at the table, were gazing solemnly at the ceiling. They were in deep thought.

"Well, yeh think yer jollyin' me, don't yeh?" burst out the woman with sudden violence. "I'll let yeh know — "

The man from Duluth looked down at his friends. He bowed swiftly, but with satirical ceremony. "This is too many for me, boys. I've got no further use for this place. Tra-la-loo! I'll see you next year." He made a flying leap and ran for the door. The woman made a grab at his coat-tails, but she missed him.

2 STEPHEN CRANE, DORA CLARK, AND THE POLICE

S. CRANE AND DORA CLARK./THE NOVELIST AP-
PEARS IN COURT/IN HER BEHALF./SHE WAS AR-
RESTED FOR STREET WALKING/AFTER BEING
WITH HIM IN A BROADWAY/RESORT – HE DE-
CLARES THAT SHE COULD NOT/HAVE BEEN
GUILTY, AND SHE IS DISCHARGED.*

Dora Clark, who gave her age as 21, and her address as 137
East Eighty-first street, was charged in Jefferson Market Court
yesterday with soliciting on the street. The complainant against
the woman was Ward Man Becker of the West Thirtieth street
station. When the case was called, Becker said that while standing in the entrance to the Grand Hotel, about 2 o'clock yesterday morning, he saw the woman come out of a café on the west
side of Broadway, between Thirty-first and Thirty-second streets,
and walk south. Near Thirty-first street, Becker said that the
woman solicited two men, and afterward joined a man and woman
who were standing on the corner. After watching all the woman's
movements, Becker said he walked across the street, placed her
under arrest, and warned her companions not to associate with
her, as they would only compromise themselves and perhaps be
arrested.

"What have you got to say to this charge, young woman?"
asked Magistrate Cornell.

"All I have to say is that the charge is false," was the girl's
answer. "The charge is founded, not upon fact, but upon the
desire of this policeman to assist a couple of brother officers in
gratifying a spite they have against me."

The woman here broke down and wept bitterly. Presently
she continued her story:

"You may recall, sir, that this is not the first time I have
been a prisoner in this court. Three or four weeks ago I was
brought here by Policeman Rosenberg of the station to which
this officer is attached. When Rosenberg arrested me I was walking along a section of Broadway which was illy lighted. Rosenberg
came up and accosted me. I told him to go along about his business, adding that I wanted nothing to do with negroes. The man

---

* Reprinted here for the first time from New York Sun: 17
September 1896.

is very dark, and I really supposed him to be a negro. He arrested me, and then I recognized my mistake. When I explained matters to the Judge who was sitting here in the morning there was a titter in the court room, and Rosenberg became extremely angry. After I was discharged and left the court room, the man walked up to me and swore he would get even if he had to arrest me every night.

"He made good his threat two nights later, and got his side partner, Conway, to arrest me on a side street while I was on my way home. A short time before I had been warned by two cabmen in Twenty-third street that Rosenberg and his partner, Conway, were looking for me. I was fined $5 by the Judge who was then sitting here. I have been arrested twice since then on sight. This morning two friends, a man and woman, and myself came out of the Broadway Garden and walked to the corner of Thirty-first street. While the man was handing the other woman into a cable car I stood on the corner. I spoke to no one. In fact, I noticed no one until this policeman came up to me, took hold of my arm, and said:

" 'Aha! I've caught you at it again! You come along to the station house.' "

"But you do not deny that you frequent the Tenderloin, do you?" asked the Magistrate.

"There would be no use in making such a denial," was the answer.

"Well — "

"Just a word, your Honor!"

The interruption came from a slender young man of medium height, with very long, tawny hair, parted in the middle and falling in great masses over his temples. It was Mr. Stephen Crane, the writer. With the "red badge of courage" flaming on his breast, Mr. Crane stepped up to the bar and said:

"I was the man whom this woman spoke of as being with her and a companion when they came out of the Broadway Garden this morning. I am studying the life of the Tenderloin for the purpose of getting material for some sketches. I was in the resort mentioned and was introduced to this woman. So far as I know, I had never seen her before. I left the place with the prisoner and one other woman, walked with them to Thirty-first street, where I put one of them on a Broadway car, leaving this woman standing at the corner. I could see the prisoner all the while, and I am positive that she spoke to no one."

"Upon the testimony of this gentleman, whom I know, I will discharge you," said the Magistrate, "but you should guard against placing yourself in a position that will justify your arrest again."

"But, sir, I am almost sure to be arrested the very next time I appear in the precinct, no matter if I am simply walking along the street."

"I will look out for that," answered the Magistrate. Thus reassured the girl left the court room. Seen later, Mr. Crane said:

"This arrest was an outrage. There was absolutely no occasion for it. I was astounded when I saw the woman being lugged to the station house. Although I had never seen her before until last night, I made up my mind to find out what she was arrested for, and to see her through. The Sergeant at the desk in the West Thirteenth street station told me the woman was just an ordinary street walker, and that I had better not get mixed up in the case, adding that it might do me a deal of harm if I did. But what did I care for such talk? I'd do the same thing again, if I though it necessary. By Heaven, I'd do it, even if I lost any little reputation I may have and strived to get. It would be well if others would follow my example."

And the "red badge of courage" flamed with a new brightness as Mr. Crane walked away.

CRANE SAVED HER A FINE/THE NOVELIST TESTIFIES FOR/A WOMAN ACCUSED OF SOLICITING/ DORA CLARK, AGAIN ARRESTED, DECLARES/ THAT SHE IS THE VICTIM OF POLICE/PERSECUTION – STEPHEN CRANE MET/HER LAST NIGHT WHILE GATHERING/MATERIAL FOR PEN SKETCHES, AND/WAS NEAR AT THE TIME OF THE/ARREST – INVESTIGATION TO BE MADE *

Dora Clark, 21 years old, who said that she lived in East Eighty-first street, was arraigned in the Jefferson Market Police Court this morning on a charge of soliciting. She had several times be-

_____

* Reprinted here for the first time from an unidentified and undated newspaper clipping in the Columbia University Crane Collection.

A considerable number of the articles in New York City

fore been arraigned on the same charge, but always made a strong denial.

Detective Becker of the West Thirtieth street station was the complainant against the young woman this morning, and she again declared that she was the victim of police persecution. Stephen Crane, the novelist, testified in her behalf, and Magistrate Cornell discharged her and said that he would investigate the charge of persecution that she made.

Becker told the Magistrate that he was standing in the vestibule of the Grand Hotel this morning at 2 o'clock and saw the young woman leave the Broadway Garden and walk to the corner of Thirty-first street. He said that then she solicited two men and afterward joined a man and a woman on the corner. He walked up to her and told her that she was under arrest and also told the other man and woman that they had better not associate with her or they, too, would be arrested.

The young woman denied this story and wept as she told the Magistrate that she was being persecuted.

This is the story she told: "The police have been persecuting me ever since I was arrested about three weeks ago by Policeman Rosenberg of the same station as Detective Becker. On that occasion I was walking on Broadway, where it was rather dark, and Rosenberg approached me and spoke. I told him to go about his business, calling him a negro. Then he arrested me, and when I told the Magistrate when I was arraigned the following morning of the mistake I had made in supposing that Rosenberg was a negro the policeman became angry.

"He threatened to arrest me for spite. Two nights later I was talking with a friend at Twenty-third street, and I was warned by two hackmen that Rosenberg and Policeman Conway were looking for me. I waited until after I thought they had gone and then I started home through a side street. Conway was following me and he arrested me when there was no one about.

"The next morning I was fined. Since that time I have been arrested on sight by all of the precinct police in citizen clothes.

"I was in the Broadway Garden last night with a man and woman and we left the place together. Becker came across the street and, while the man was placing the other woman on the car, he took hold of my arm and placed me under arrest. I had spoken to no one."

---

newspapers concerning the Dora Clark affair exist in press clippings pasted into Crane's Scrapbook. He was a subscriber to Authors' Clipping Bureau of Boston. The Scrapbook is in CUCC.

Novelist Crane then told Magistrate Cornell that he wished to testify. He said that he was searching for material for sketches, and that last night he was introduced to the prisoner in the Broadway Garden. He said that he, the prisoner and two other women left the Broadway Garden together and walked to Thirty-first street, where he left the Clark woman for a moment while he escorted one of the other women to a Broadway cable car. The prisoner was never out of his sight for a minute, and he knew that she did not speak to any men.

"The testimony of this gentleman, whom I know," said Magistrate Cornell, "causes me to discharge you this time."

"But, your Honor," said the prisoner, "I will be arrested on sight the next time I show my face in the precinct."

"I will look out for that," said Magistrate Cornell.

The young woman hurried from the court. Mr. Crane afterward said that he had never seen her before last night and that all he knew about the matter was what he had seen.

Mr. Stephen Crane, when seen this afternoon, said: "I was never so astounded in my life as when I saw that fellow grabbing the woman whom I had left on the sidewalk while accompanying the third one to the cable car. You know, I had been with two women — chorus girls — in the Broadway Garden, and I wish it to be understood that I was not acquainted with the one who was arrested until she was introduced to me by the other two. They said at the station that they knew her perfectly well as a streetwalker, but that doesn't make the slightest difference to me. I don't care if she was fifty times a street-walker. The sergeant at the police station recommended me to keep out of the case in a very fatherly way, saying that it might do me a good deal of harm to be involved in it, and could not do me any good. But I was determined to see it out, and would do the same thing to-morrow or any day.

"I have frequented the Tenderloin for some years past, for I am interested in it, and am making a study of it for magazine stories. It may be against my interest to act as I did; but, by Heaven, I'd do it every time, though I have some little reputation, which I have starved myself to acquire, and though I should lose it by my action.

"I would do the same, and I wish every one would follow my example."

STEPHEN CRANE AS/BRAVE AS HIS HERO./
SHOWED THE "BADGE OF COUR-/AGE" IN A NEW
YORK/POLICE COURT./BOLDLY AVOWED HE HAD
BEEN/THE ESCORT OF A TENDER-/LOIN WOMAN./
SHE WAS UNDER ARREST, CHARGED WITH/AN
OFFENCE THAT MEANT THE/DEPRIVATION OF
HER LIBERTY./YOUNG NOVELIST TOLD THE
TRUTH./RISKED THE CENSURE OF THOUSANDS
WHO AD-/MIRE HIS BOOKS BY MANFULLY CHAM-/
PIONING A WOMAN OF WHOSE AN-/TECEDENTS
HE KNEW NOTHING.*

"Your Honor, I know this girl to be innocent."

It was a slender young man who spoke. He was pale and nervous, but his voice had a ring of vibrant strength. He was plainly dressed in a dark blue suit and blue striped shirt. Even the look of thoughtful intelligence on his face could hardly have prepared an observer for the news that he was Stephen Crane, the youngest, latest and most successful of American novelists. He had been on the bridge in Jefferson Market Police Court since the opening hour, and had been watching the tide of human misery flow past.

A very pretty girl, barely twenty years old, was led from the prisoners' box, sobbing violently. She was gruffly ordered to the bar. There she stood, flushed and downcast, ringed in by

---

Reprinted here for the first time from New York Journal: *17 September 1896. Approximately two-thirds of this story, under the headline "Crane Is Brave," was run in the Boston* Evening Record: *18 September 1896. The Editors have omitted three news stories on Dora Clark's arrest: New York* Times: *17 September, New York* Daily Tribune: *17 September, and Boston* Herald: *18 September.*

Other than a brief recapitulation of the hearing on 15–16 October, the Times *ignored the affair in favor of the Bryan-McKinley Presidential race.*

rows of pitiless eyes. She was charged with that most degrading of all offences, soliciting.

She had given her name as Dora Clark, of No. 137 East Eighty-first street. She felt the cruel gaze of the crowd, and the red flush in her cheeks deepened as the Magistrate formally stated the charge.

Policeman Charles Becker, who had made the arrest, gave his evidence. He said that while in citizen's clothes, on Broadway, early yesterday morning, he had seen the girl accost two men. He had then arrested her. His testimony was unhesitatingly positive and direct.

"Have you anything to say for yourself?" asked Magistrate Cornell, turning sternly to the girl. She raised her eyes and swept them, in a desperate glance, around the circle, and as she did this the faces of some who observed her grew softer.

"She is an old offender," said Becker airily. At that a flash of anger nerved the girl to speak. She grasped the rail with both of her small hands and looked straight up into the Judge's face.

"Yes, Judge, it's true," she said bitterly, "that I have been arrested before. But do you know why I was arrested before? It was because a policeman insultingly spoke to me and I repelled him. He arrested me then and swore a conviction upon me, and he told the other policemen that I was bad and had insulted him, and asked them to keep arresting me, too."

The Magistrate was annoyed, for he had often listened to baseless charges against policemen.

"It's the truth," she cried, "but what is a girl's word against a policeman's? And so he's right, Judge, when he says I've been arrested."

"Haven't you anything definite to say?" said the Magistrate, sharply.

"I have the truth to say," she replied, defiantly. "I was in Broadway Garden last night with a man and two women. I know it was late and I suppose I ought to have been in my own room alone — but I wonder if men can understand how deadly lonesome that is? I was out where there were people and lights and music. And we four left the Garden together and the man stepped to a car with one of the women and I was arrested."

The Magistrate hesitated. "Is there any doubt in this case, officer?" he said.

"None at all," said Becker. "She's an old hand and always lies about it."

"Young woman," said the Magistrate, "I have listened patiently because it is a terrible thing to judge a girl on such a charge unheard. But the officer's testimony and your past record" —

"Your Honor, I know the girl to be innocent. I am the man who was with her, and there is no truth in what the officer has charged!"

"And who are you?" exclaimed the Magistrate.

"I am Stephen Crane, the novelist," was the quiet reply.

"And you say you were with her?"

Crane held himself with an air that was curiously like that of the girl, for he, like her, knew that he was surrounded by condemnatory eyes. The girl, in uncomprehending wonder, gazed at him. She could hardly understand how it was that he dared defend her.

The novelist briefly said that he had been studying human nature in the Tenderloin of late for descriptive use in magazine stories. He said he had been with two chorus girls in the Garden, and that Dora Clark, who knew one of them, had joined them. They all left together, and he had walked to the middle of the street to put one of the girls on a car. In a few moments he stepped back again without having had the prisoner out of his sight for a moment. She was, he declared, entirely innocent of the policeman's charge.

"You are discharged," said the Magistrate to the girl. But the girl appeared neither exultant nor happy. "Thank Your Honor," she said, "but they'll only arrest me again."

"I'll see to that," said the Magistrate. Then the girl walked away.

At his home last evening Mr. Crane said: "As to the girl's character I know nothing. I only know that while with me she acted respectably, and that the policeman's charge was false. She certainly did not look dissipated, and she was very neatly and prettily dressed. I noticed, too, that she was still neat in court, even after the hours of imprisonment.

"The policeman roughly threatened to arrest me, when I told him that the girl had done no wrong. He arrested the other girl, too, but let her go when she went into hysterics at the police station. I was strongly advised by Sergeant McDermott not to try to help her, for I seemed a respectable sort of man, he said, and it would injure me. I well knew I was risking a reputation that I have worked hard to build. But," he added, "she was a woman and unjustly accused, and I did what was my duty as a man. I realized that if a man should stand tamely by, in such a case, our wives and sisters would be at the mercy of any ruffian who disgraces the uniform. The policeman flatly lied, and if the girl will have him prosecuted for perjury I will gladly support her."

"While waiting to speak in the court room, and to thus openly dare the censure of the public, did you not feel like your own hero in the 'Red Badge of Courage' before his first battle?" the novelist was asked.

He smiled. "Yes, I did. I was badly frightened, I admit, and would gladly have run away, could I have done so with honor."

"And now that it is over, I presume you are also like your hero, in being ready to face a sword ordeal without a tremor?"

"No, no!" Mr. Crane exclaimed. "I differ from my own hero, for I would be just as frightened the next time!"

"Just how would you describe the girl, Mr. Crane?"

"Why," he said, "she was really handsome, you know, and she had hair — red hair — dark red" —

"Yes" —

"And she was dressed, I am pretty sure, in some kind of shirt waist," he concluded, desperately.

At the Nineteenth Precinct Police Station it was learned last evening that the girl's fears of re-arrest were well founded.

"I only hope she'll be out to-night and be run in here!" said Sergeant Daly, chuckling gleefully at the thought.

Captain Chapman said he fully believed Becker's story.

"Does it make no difference that a man of world-wide reputation states that she committed no offense?" he was asked.

"Who is this Crane? An actor?"

"No. An author."

"Never heard of him before. Becker is a good man, and has been on the force four years. I know him well, and so do the police generally. And I believe him."

He admitted, however, that very recently Becker had made a similar arrest, and that a number of reporters had alleged that the girl in that case was innocent.

ADVENTURES OF A NOVELIST./BY STEPHEN CRANE./THE DISTINGUISHED AUTHOR'S NARRATIVE OF HOW HE SOUGHT/"MATERIAL" IN REAL LIFE IN THE "TENDERLOIN" AND/FOUND MORE THAN HE BARGAINED FOR.*

Last week the Journal arranged with Mr. Stephen Crane, the novelist whose "Red Badge of Courage" everybody has read, to write a series of studies of life in New York. He chose the police courts as his first subject.

Bright and early Monday morning Mr. Crane took a seat beside Magistrate Cornell at the Jefferson Market Police Court, and observed the machinery of justice in full operation. The novelist felt, however, that he had seen but a kaleidoscopic view of the characters who passed rapidly before the judicial gaze of the presiding Magistrate. He must know more of that throng of unfortunates; he must study the police court victims in their haunts.

With the scenes of the forenoon still flitting through his mind, the novelist sought out a Broadway resort that evening. He was soon deeply interested in the women who had gathered at his table — two chorus girls and a young woman of uncertain occupation. The novelist cared not who they were. It was enough that he had found the types of character that he was after.

Later in the evening the party separated, and the novelist courteously escorted one of the women to a Broadway car. While his back was turned for a moment a policeman seized one of the party — Dora Wilkins. Mr. Crane at once protested, and, following the officer to the station house, explained that a mistake had been made.

Bright and early next morning the novelist was once more at Jefferson Market Court. This time he was a witness. The novelist had sought a closer knowledge of the unfortunate creatures of the courts, and he found himself in the midst of them.

---

* *Reprinted from New York* Journal: *20 September 1896.*
   This is an addition to the Crane canon. The typed manuscript with autograph corrections — 6 folio leaves; leaf 5 wanting; leaves 1 and 3 mutilated — is in the Barrett Crane Collection.

This is a plain tale of two chorus girls, a woman of the streets and a reluctant laggard witness. The tale properly begins in a resort on Broadway, where the two chorus girls and the reluctant witness sat the entire evening. They were on the verge of departing their several ways when a young woman approached one of the chorus girls, with outstretched hand.

"Why, how do you do?" she said. "I haven't seen you for a long time."

The chorus girl recognized some acquaintance of the past, and the young woman then took a seat and joined the party. Finally they left the table in this resort, and the quartet walked down Broadway together. At the corner of Thirty-first street one of the chorus girls said that she wished to take a car immediately for home, and so the reluctant witness left one of the chorus girls and the young woman on the corner of Thirty-first street while he placed the other chorus girl aboard an uptown cable car. The two girls who waited on the corner were deep in conversation.

The reluctant witness was returning leisurely to them. In the semi-conscious manner in which people note details which do not appear at the time important, he saw two men passing along Broadway. They passed swiftly, like men who are going home. They paid attention to none, and none at the corner of Thirty-first street and Broadway paid attention to them.

The two girls were still deep in conversation. They were standing at the curb facing the street. The two men passed unseen — in all human probability — by the two girls. The reluctant witness continued his leisurely way. He was within four feet of these two girls when suddenly and silently a man appeared from nowhere in particular and grabbed them both.

The astonishment of the reluctant witness was so great for the ensuing seconds that he was hardly aware of what transpired during that time, save that both girls screamed. Then he heard this man, who was now evidently an officer, say to them: "Come to the station house. You are under arrest for soliciting two men."

With one voice the unknown woman, the chorus girl and the reluctant witness cried out: "What two men?"

The officer said: "Those two men who have just passed."

And here began the wildest and most hysterical sobbing of the two girls, accompanied by spasmodic attempts to pull their arms away from the grip of the policeman. The chorus girl seemed nearly insane with fright and fury. Finally she screamed:

"Well, he's my husband." And with her finger she indicated the reluctant witness. The witness at once replied to the swift, questioning glance of the officer, "Yes; I am."

If it was necessary to avow a marriage to save a girl who is not a prostitute from being arrested as a prostitute, it must be done, though the man suffer eternally. And then the officer forgot immediately — without a second's hesitation, he forgot that a moment previously he had arrested this girl for soliciting, and so, dropping her arm, released her.

"But," said he, "I have got this other one." He was as picturesque as a wolf.

"Why arrest her, either?" said the reluctant witness.

"For soliciting those two men."

"But she didn't solicit those two men."

"Say," said the officer, turning, "do you know this woman?"

The chorus girl had it in mind to lie then for the purpose of saving this woman easily and simply from the palpable wrong she seemed to be about to experience. "Yes; I know her" — "I have seen her two or three times" — "Yes; I have met her before" — But the reluctant witness said at once that he knew nothing whatever of the girl.

"Well," said the officer, "she's a common prostitute."

There was a short silence then, but the reluctant witness presently said: "Are you arresting her as a common prostitute? She has been perfectly respectable since she has been with us. She hasn't done anything wrong since she has been in our company."

"I am arresting her for soliciting those two men," answered the officer, "and if you people don't want to get pinched, too, you had better not be seen with her."

Then began a parade to the station house — the officer and his prisoner ahead and two simpletons following.

At the station house the officer said to the sergeant behind the desk that he had seen the woman come from the resort on Broadway alone, and on the way to the corner of Thirty-first street solicit two men, and that immediately afterward she had met a man and a woman — meaning the chorus girl and the reluctant witness — on the said corner, and was in conversation with them when he arrested her. He did not mention to the sergeant at this time the arrest and release of the chorus girl.

At the conclusion of the officer's story the sergeant said, shortly: "Take her back." This did not mean to take the woman back to the corner of Thirty-first street and Broadway. It meant to take her back to the cells, and she was accordingly led away.

The chorus girl had undoubtedly intended to be an intrepid champion; she had avowedly come to the station house for that purpose, but her entire time had been devoted to sobbing in the wildest form of hysteria. The reluctant witness was obliged to devote his entire time to an attempt to keep her from making an uproar of some kind. This paroxysm of terror, of indignation, and the extreme mental anguish caused by her unconventional and strange situation, was so violent that the reluctant witness could not take time from her to give any testimony to the sergeant.

After the woman was sent to the cell the reluctant witness reflected a moment in silence; then he said:

"Well, we might as well go."

On the way out of Thirtieth street the chorus girl continued to sob. "If you don't go to court and speak for that girl you are no man!" she cried. The arrested woman had, by the way, screamed out a request to appear in her behalf before the Magistrate.

"By George! I cannot," said the reluctant witness. "I can't afford to do that sort of thing. I — I —"

After he had left this girl safely, he continued to reflect: "Now this arrest I firmly believe to be wrong. This girl may be a courtesan, for anything that I know at all to the contrary. The sergeant at the station house seemed to know her as well as he knew the Madison square tower. She is then, in all probability, a courtesan. She is arrested, however, for soliciting those two men. If I have ever had a conviction in my life, I am convinced that she did not solicit those two men. Now, if these affairs occur from time to time, they must be witnessed occasionally by men of character. Do these reputable citizens interfere? No, they go home and thank God that they can still attend piously to their own affairs. Suppose I were a clerk and I interfered in this sort of a case. When it became known to my employers they would say to me: 'We are sorry, but we cannot have men in our employ who stay out until 2:30 in the morning in the company of chorus girls.'

"Suppose, for instance, I had a wife and seven children in Harlem. As soon as my wife read the papers she would say: 'Ha! You told me you had a business engagement! Half-past two in the morning with questionable company!'

"Suppose, for instance, I were engaged to the beautiful Countess of Kalamazoo. If she were to hear it, she could write: 'All is over between us. My future husband cannot rescue prostitutes at 2:30 in the morning.'

"These, then, must be three small general illustrations of why men of character say nothing if they happen to witness some possible affair of this sort, and perhaps these illustrations could be multiplied to infinity. I possess nothing so tangible as a clerkship, as a wife and seven children in Harlem, as an engagement to the beautiful Countess of Kalamazoo; but all that I value may be chanced in this affair. Shall I take this risk for the benefit of a girl of the streets?

"But this girl, be she prostitute or whatever, was at this time manifestly in my escort, and — Heaven save the blasphemous philosophy — a wrong done to a prostitute must be as purely a wrong as a wrong done to a queen," said the reluctant witness — this blockhead.

"Moreover, I believe that this officer has dishonored his obligation as a public servant. Have I a duty as a citizen, or do citizens have duty, as a citizen, or do citizens have no duties? Is it a mere myth that there was at one time a man who possessed a consciousness of civic responsibility, or has it become a distinction of our municipal civilization that men of this character shall be licensed to depredate in such a manner upon those who are completely at their mercy?"

He returned to the sergeant at the police station, and, after asking if he could send anything to the girl to make her more comfortable for the night, he told the sergeant the story of the arrest, as he knew it.

"Well," said the sergeant, "that may be all true. I don't defend the officer. I do not say that he was right, or that he was wrong, but it seems to me that I have seen you somewhere before and know you vaguely as a man of good repute; so why interfere in this thing? As for this girl, I know her to be a common prostitute. That's why I sent her back."

"But she was not arrested as a common prostitute. She was arrested for soliciting two men, and I know that she didn't solicit the two men."

"Well," said the sergeant, "that, too, may all be true, but I give you the plain advice of a man who has been behind this desk for years, and knows how these things go, and I advise you simply to stay home. If you monkey with this case, you are pretty sure to come out with mud all over you."

"I suppose so," said the reluctant witness. "I haven't a doubt of it. But don't see how I can, in honesty, stay away from court in the morning."

"Well, do it anyhow," said the sergeant.

"But I don't see how I can do it."

The sergeant was bored. "Oh, I tell you, the girl is nothing but a common prostitute," he said, wearily.

The reluctant witness on reaching his room set the alarm clock for the proper hour.

In the court at 8:30 he met a reporter acquaintance. "Go

home," said the reporter, when he had heard the story. "Go home; your own participation in the affair doesn't look very respectable. Go home."

"But it is a wrong," said the reluctant witness.

"Oh, it is only a temporary wrong," said the reporter. The definition of a temporary wrong did not appear at that time to the reluctant witness, but the reporter was too much in earnest to consider terms. "Go home," said he.

Thus — if the girl was wronged — it is to be seen that all circumstances, all forces, all opinions, all men were combined to militate against her. Apparently the united wisdom of the world declared that no man should do anything but throw his sense of justice to the winds in an affair of this description. "Let a man have a conscience for the daytime," said wisdom. "Let him have a conscience for the daytime, but it is idiocy for a man to have a conscience at 2:30 in the morning, in the case of an arrested prostitute."

NO REPLY FROM MR. CRANE *

Chief Conlin yesterday gave out copies of a letter which he sent to Stephen Crane, the novelist, in regard to the arrest of Dora Clark, for whom Mr. Crane testified when she was arraigned on a charge of soliciting. Mr. Crane alleged that Policeman Becker, who made the arrest, had not been justified in his action. The Chief asked Mr. Crane to call at his office and make a statement about the case, but so far the novelist has made no reply.

STEVIE CRANE †

Stevie Crane seems to have gotten into warm water by his valiant defence of a young woman in police court at New York. The chances are that the youthful literary prodigy was on a genuine "lark," and, when his companion was apprehended, invented the tale about searching for book material. That is simply the way it looks to a cold and unprejudiced world.

---

* *Reprinted here for the first time from New York* Tribune: *29 September 1896.*

---

† *Editorial reprinted here for the first time from Boston* Traveler: *2 October 1896. The Editors have supplied the title.*

DORA CLARK MAKES/STARTLING CHARGES./SHE
ALLEGES THAT POLICEMAN/BECKER KNOCKED
HER DOWN/IN THE STREET./CLAIMS TO HAVE
SEVERAL WITNESSES/TO PROVE THE TRUTH OF
HER/STATEMENT./SHE IS THE WOMAN IN WHOSE
BEHALF/STEPHEN CRANE GAVE/TESTIMONY./
BECKER TALKS OF PROVING AN ALIBI./SEVERAL
CABMEN ADMIT THAT THEY WITNESSED/THE
ASSAULT, AND MAY BE PRESENT/WHEN THE
HEARING COMES UP/THIS AFTERNOON.*

Dora Clark, the woman of the Tenderloin in whose defence Novelist Stephen Crane appeared in Jefferson Market Court three weeks ago, has not only preferred charges against Policeman Becker for her arrest at that time, but now charges him with having brutally assaulted her Sunday morning at 3 o'clock. She gives the names of several witnesses to the assault. Policeman Becker denies that he assaulted the woman, and declares that at the time she says the assault occurred he was in the station house.

Dora Clark, it will be remembered, made an effort to have Mr. Crane prefer charges against Becker for the arrest, but the novelist declined to do so. Last Friday the woman went to Chief Conlin herself and called for the policeman's arraignment.

In the meantime Becker had, with another officer, shot at a young burglar named O'Brien, whom they killed.[1] Both officers were placed under detention and ordered to merely report at

---

* Reprinted here for the first time from New York Journal:
8 October 1896.

1. The killing of John Fay, alias John O'Brien, occurred on 20 September at 35th Street and Seventh Avenue. Policeman Michael J. Carey, 19th precinct, did the actual shooting; however, both Becker and Carey were suspended from duty. The New York *Times* played up the shooting with a page one story on 21 September in which the police force was criticized as "brutal and reckless in the use of bludgeons and firearms." An investigation was undertaken but nothing seems to have come of it.

their station house and remain there during their hours of duty.

Dora Clark in her new charge says: "I was standing on the corner of Sixth avenue and Twenty-eighth street early last Sunday morning talking to a group of cabmen, when Becker came along dressed in citizen's clothes. He walked straight up to me and said: 'So you made charges against me did you?' at the same time using profane language.

" 'You're a loafer to talk that way,' I replied, whereupon he seized me by the throat, kicked me and knocked me down. I got up and he threw me down again. The bystanders then interfered and Becker went."

In support of these charges the woman offers as witnesses George Huntley, foreman of the Cornell Iron Works, who is now superintending the building of the Waldorf Annex; Timothy Newbold, driver for Dodd's Express, of No. 46 Avenue B, and several cabmen who were present.

Huntley and Newbold admit they saw the assault made upon the woman, but did not know the man. The cabmen say they recognized the girl's assailant as Becker.

Chief Conlin turned the case over to Inspector Harley, who set a hearing for Tuesday, then for yesterday, and yesterday again postponed it until this afternoon at 2 o'clock. Dora Clark has engaged as her attorney David Newburger,[2] of No. 291 Broadway.

---

2. The name is variously spelled throughout the press accounts. Properly, it is David M. Neuberger.

NOVELIST CRANE A/HARD MAN TO SCARE./
RUMORS OF POLICE MUDSLING-/ING CAN'T
FRIGHTEN HIM/FROM HIS DUTY./SAYS HE WILL
STICK BY UNFOR-/TUNATE DORA CLARK TO/THE
END./NEVER HAD ANY IDEA OF ABANDONING/
HIS SHARE IN THE PROSECUTION OF/DETECTIVE
BECKER./DENIES HAVING BEEN COERCED./CUR-
RENT TENDERLOIN GOSSIP WAS THAT THE PO-/
LICE HAD THREATENED TO SHOW HIM UP/AS A
FAST LIVER AND KEEPER OF/AN OPIUM JOINT.*

Rumors have been going about the Tenderloin that the police
have frightened Novelist Stephen Crane away from his determination to appear as a witness against Detective Becker, against
whom Dora Clark has preferred charges, based on the policeman's arrest of her on a charge of soliciting on the night of
Wednesday, September 17. It will be remembered that the girl
was discharged on Crane's evidence.

One rumor is that the police of the Thirtieth Street Station
have told the novelist they are prepared to swear that he led a
fast life among the women of the Tenderloin, and that he would
be prosecuted on a charge of maintaining an opium joint in his
rooms if he testified in Dora Clark's behalf against Becker. Another rumor was that Crane had left town in order to avoid
being subpoenaed in the case.

When Mr. Crane was told of these rumors by a Journal
reporter yesterday he said:

"There is not an atom of truth in any report that I shall
fail to appear against Becker. I have not tried to avoid subpoena
servers, and I have not left town. My address is with a lawyer,
who will notify me when the time arrives to appear. I have not
received any intimations from the police that I would be 'shown
up' if I appeared against Becker, either. It wouldn't make the
slightest difference to me if I had. I have never, since I testified in

---

* *Reprinted here for the first time from New York* Journal:
11 October 1896.

the police court, had any idea of refusing to proceed further in the case."

When asked about his opium joint, Crane laughed. "I have got an opium lay-out in my room," he said, "but it is tacked to a plaque hung on the wall.

"I consider it my duty," he said, "having witnessed an outrage such as Becker's arrest of this girl, to do my utmost to have him punished. The fact that I was in her company, and had just left what the detective called a resort for thieves, prostitutes and crooks, does not bear on the matter in the least. I had a perfect right to be there, or in any other public resort anywhere else in the city where I choose to go."

NOVELIST CRANE WAS TRUE BLUE./TESTIFIED BEFORE COMMISSIONERS FOR THE TENDER-LOIN/WOMAN, DORA CLARK./WAITED AT HEAD-QUARTERS FROM/THREE O'CLOCK UNTIL EARLY/ THIS MORNING./THE WOMAN WHOM HE HAD BE-FRIENDED/ACCUSED POLICEMAN OF PERSE-/CU-TING HER./LOST A DINNER ENGAGEMENT./IN-STEAD OF DINING WITH FRIENDS THE SELF/AP-POINTED KNIGHT PARTOOK OF A SAND-/WICH AND A GLASS OF/BEER.*

Stephen Crane waited at Police Headquarters from 3 o'clock yesterday afternoon until this morning, to testify on behalf of Dora Clark, who had brought charges before the Police Commissioners against Policeman Charles Becker, whom she accuses of illegally arresting her on the night of Wednesday, September 17, while she was in the young novelist's company.

Reprinted here for the first time from New York Journal: 16 October 1896.

Commissioner Grant, mentioned in the story, was Colonel Frederick D. Grant, son of the President and Civil War general. At this time (1896), Theodore Roosevelt was president of the Police Board of New York City, as well as one of the police commissioners.

Crane was on hand promptly at the hour designated in his subpoena, and for an hour he leaned against a window in the corridor, smoking a cigar, apparently oblivious of the scowls of the policemen who were awaiting trial for various offences and who had been told that the boyish looking young fellow was a famous writer bold enough to stand up for a woman of the street against a member of the force.

Commissioner Grant conducted the trials yesterday with his usual painstaking deliberation. There were five or six cases ahead of Dora Clark's, all of them long ones, involving the testimony of scores of witnesses. At 4 o'clock Mr. Crane was told that he would probably be called to the stand at 5:30; at 5:30 Clerk Kip thought the case would come up at 7; at 7 o'clock there was a prospect that it might be reached in another hour, and the young novelist who had a dinner engagement at 8 sent a telegram and dined on a ham sandwich and a glass of beer in a Mulberry street saloon.

[CASE CALLED AT LAST.]

It was 9 o'clock before the case in which Crane was interested was called, and then he, with the other witnesses, including policemen, waiters, and street walkers of the Tenderloin, were banished from the courtroom, in order that the testimony of each might be given without suggestions from the others.

That meant another tedious wait in the corridor for Crane, who did not care to mingle with the herd in the ante-room. He withstood the ordeal with much patience, however, strolling up and down the long hallway and smoking cigarettes incessantly.

Dora Clark had made charges against Officer Conway of the Nineteenth Precinct as well as against Becker, for "unlawfully arresting her and falsely accusing her of soliciting men." The case against Conway was called first. The girl testified that one rainy Sunday night about the middle of August, Conway had arrested her in Twenty-third street between 2 and 3 o'clock and used vile language to her, and then locked her up in the police station, she being discharged by Magistrate Council in the morning.

The girl declares that she is being persecuted by the police, and that Conway arrested her by request of his fellow officer, Rosenberg, who had declared in court that he would drive her out of the Tenderloin.

Conway swore that he had arrested Dora Clark because he had seen her solicit three men, and Rosenberg backed up the other policeman's statement. The girl swore, on the other hand,

that there was not a man on the block between Fifth and Sixth
avenues, on Twenty-third street, when she was arrested, and two
cabmen corroborated her story.

Another woman of the streets who had come to headquarters
to testify in Dora Clark's favor, but who had had some conversation with officers of the Nineteenth Precinct before the case
was called, swore in corroboration of the evidence of Conway and
Rosenberg when she was put on the stand.

Becker's case came on about 10 o'clock, and Dora Clark
told the story about her adventure in Stephen Crane's company, which he has already related to the readers of the Journal.

On the night of Wednesday, September 17, she was introduced to the young novelist in the Broadway Garden by two
young women of her acquaintance, who were with him there.

The four came out of the place together and Crane put one
of the women on a street car. While the other two were waiting
for him to return to the sidewalk they were arrested by Becker.

Crane and the three young women left the Broadway Garden
together and walked to the corner of 31st street. Here Crane
put one of the girls on a street car, leaving Dora Clark and
the other girl standing on the sidewalk. He had scarcely left them
a moment when Becker came up and arrested them both on a
charge of soliciting, although there was not a man within speaking distance on the street.

Both girls were taken to the Thirtieth Street Police Station,
and Dora Clark was locked up over night. She was released in
the morning on Crane's evidence that he had been in her company
and she had not spoken to any one aside from the party she was
with.

Policeman Becker had retained Lawyer Louis D. Grant, who
cross-examined Dora Clark, with the assistance of Captain Chapman of the Nineteenth Precinct, who seemed deeply interested
in the case. The fact was brought out that the girl had been arrested half a dozen times for soliciting and fined once, and that
each time she had been arrested it was by either Becker, Conway
or Rosenberg.

"What is your address?" asked Lawyer Grant.

"I'd prefer not to tell," said the girl. "I'll be put out if I do.
I've been put out of three places already because of this case."

The lawyer pressed the question, however, and the girl gave
the address. She testified that when the story of her arrest was
first published she was living at No. 40 West Twenty-ninth street,
and that she was put out because Captain Chapman threatened to
"pull the house" unless her landlady caused her to leave. Cap-

tain Chapman arose and requested Commissioner Grant to let him go on the stand and deny that statement, but the Commissioner did not consider it necessary at that juncture. From West Twenty-ninth street, the girl testified, she moved to the Wilton Hotel, in Twenty-seventh street, and as soon as her name was known she was compelled to leave that place.

Dora Clark's testimony was not concluded until 11 o'clock, and then Commissioner Grant refused to adjourn the case, but took a recess, for half an hour, promising to go on until it was concluded. As there are about twenty witnesses to be called, the case will probably go on until early this morning.

Policeman Becker said he was standing in the vestibule of the Grand Hotel, Broadway and Thirty-first street, on special duty, when he saw Miss Clark leave the Broadway Garden and walk to the corner.

A few minutes previous to this he had seen Mr. Crane and a party, in company with two women and another young man, leave the hotel, walk to the corner and wait in the gutter for a car. While they were waiting for a car in the gutter, Miss Clark spoke to two men who passed, then the policeman placed her under arrest. Mr. Crane turned around and interfered.

The policeman would not testify that the men spoken to were not acquaintances. Lawyer Newburger attempted to bring out evidence in the effect that the policeman had threatened four weeks ago to arrest Miss Clark outright, but this was excluded by the Commissioner.

Alphonse Falardeau, the head waiter in the Broadway Garden, testified that Miss Clark was a member of Mr. Crane's party, and that he had accompanied the group to the door, and saw them all walk down the street together.

Mr. Crane took the stand at 1:50 o'clock this morning. He said he was introduced to Miss Clark in the garden and that she was with his party. He said he left Miss Clark on the corner while he placed one of the women on a car. The novelist testified positively that the young woman did not accost any one, repeating the statements he has made before flatly contradicting the police.

CRANE LONG UNDER FIRE/POLICEMAN BECKER'S
TRIAL/LASTED TILL EARLY MORNING./CIRCUM-
STANCES OF THE ARREST OF DORA/CLARK, OR
YOUNG, AS SHE CALLS HER-/SELF, GONE INTO IN
DETAIL — ANOTHER/WOMAN ATTACKS JANITOR
O'CONNOR/IN THE STREET AFTER THE HEAR-
ING*

It was 2:38 o'clock this morning when Police Commissioner
Grant finally declared the hearing in the charge made by Dora
Clark, or Young, as she gave her name on the witness stand,
against Policeman Becker of the Thirtieth Precinct closed.

Stephen Crane, the writer, who was in the Clark woman's
company on the morning she was arrested, and who testified in
her behalf when she was arraigned in the police court, was called
to the stand in rebuttal at 1:42 o'clock. In reply to questions by
Lawyer Newburger, counsel for the Clark woman, the witness
said that he went to the Broadway Garden on the night when the
Clark woman was arrested in company with two women, and was
there introduced to the Clark woman. She left the Garden in
company with himself and the other two women. They walked
down to the corner of Thirty-first street and Broadway. He
there put one of the women on board a cable car, and as he came
back to the corner where he had left Dora Clark and the other
woman, he saw the arrest made by Policeman Becker. Dora
Clark, he said, did not speak to any man, except himself, while
they were walking from the Garden to the corner of Thirty-first
street.

Lawyer Louis J. Grant, counsel for the accused policeman,
put the witness, Crane, through a very severe cross-examination,
which was interrupted every two or three minutes by objections
or comments on the part of Lawyer Newburger. The witness
refused to answer many of the questions put to him on the ground
that an answer might tend to degrade or incriminate him.

* Reprinted here for the first time from New York Sun: 16
October 1896.

The witness testified that his name was Stephen Crane, that he was 24 years old and was living at 281 Sixth avenue. He was a writer for newspapers and magazines. On the night of the arrest of Dora Clark he met the other two women by appointment in the Turkish Smoking Parlors in West Twenty-ninth street, and went to the Broadway Garden about midnight.

When asked where he lived previous to his present residence at 281 Sixth Avenue, the witness replied that he lived at 114 East Twenty-second street. He lived there about a month. Previous to that he lived on West Twenty-second street, further west, between Seventh and Eighth avenues. He refused to give the number.

Last spring he lived at 165 East Twenty-third street. In the summer he visited a certain house in West Twenty-seventh street. He refused to say how many times he had visited the house, and also refused to say whether or not he was acquainted with Sadie or Amy Huntington. He denied that he had smoked opium in the house in question.

He said that while in the Broadway Garden on the night of the arrest the Clark woman came over to the table where he was sitting and spoke to one of the woman in his company. A question as to the name of this woman was ruled out. The Clark woman was accompanied by a man who remained with the party a short time.

Commissioner Grant also ruled out testimony as to the name of this man, but in replying to Lawyer Grant the witness said that he was the keeper of a cigar store. Crane spent an hour and a half in the Garden in the company of the three women. Three rounds of drinks were served. He drank beer. He could not say what the women drank.

They left the Garden about 2 o'clock in the morning. He stood for a few minutes outside the Garden talking with one of the waiters, who was giving him some information about two other women. When they started down Broadway toward Thirty-first street one of the women who accompanied him to the Garden walked on the right of him, next to the curb. The Clark woman and the other woman walked at his left. They walked four abreast, and the Clark woman did not address any man on the street.

Crane said that after he had put one of the women on the cable car he walked back to the corner where he had left the other two. When he got within eight or ten feet of them he saw Policeman Becker place them both under arrest. He told Becker that one of the women was his wife, and she was released by the policeman. The Clark woman was arrested. In speaking of her at this point the witness spoke of the complainant as "Miss Clark," but immediately corrected himself and said "Miss Young."

The case was then declared closed by Commissioner Grant, and every one was preparing to leave the room when Lawyer Grant said that there was a suggestion made to him by Capt. Chapman which he wished to bring out. The Commissioner resumed his seat and directed the counsel to call his witness.

A man who gave his name as James O'Connor and who had been identified by Crane as janitor of the flat house in West Twenty-seventh street, took the stand and said that Crane had lived in the house in question for six weeks last summer with a woman, whose name he gave. Lawyer Newburger objected strenuously to the admission of such evidence and Commissioner Grant excluded it.

Policemen, reporters, witnesses, and spectators trooped down stairs and out into Mulberry street. As Janitor O'Connor reached the street, a young woman who had been an interested spectator throughout the trial stepped up to him, and calling him a vile name struck him in the face, at the same time saying: "I'll teach you to call me a thief."

She called him more names and then made another effort to strike him, but was prevented by two policemen. She was not arrested, and the Clark woman advised her to keep cool and go home. In a few minutes she left in company with a friend.

CRANE RISKED ALL/TO SAVE A WOMAN./HIS BO-
HEMIAN LIFE IN NEW/YORK LAID BARE FOR
THE/SAKE OF DORA CLARK./FOR TEN LONG
HOURS HE WAITED,/DETERMINED TO TESTIFY
AGAINST/POLICEMAN BECKER./COLD AS ICICLES
THE   NOVELIST'S   ANSWERS/CAME,   SHORT,
SNAPPY, AND/TO THE POINT./WOMEN AND CAB-
BIES AS WITNESSES./THEY SWEAR, AS THE
POLICE OF THE TENDERLOIN/SWEAR – DORA
CLARK DIRECTLY ACCUSES/CAPTAIN CHAPMAN
AND HE/DEMANDS A HEARING.*

Here are a few hard facts:

Stephen Crane is twenty-four years old and unmarried. He
makes his living by his pen. He is Bohemian in the best sense. His
writings prove him a student of character. His "Red Badge of
Courage" was immensely successful. It opened before him a brilliant career.

Stephen Crane was introduced one night to Dora Clark. She
has no reputation. She declares herself abandoned. That night
he saw her arrested. He believes that arrest was an outrage. He
knew he risked his reputation. He knew if he was misunderstood
he might blight his career. He knew, in a word, he would array
against him the police, who, Dora Clark swears, are hounding
her. Knowing all this, Stephen Crane has told the truth, as he
believes it, of Dora Clark's arrest. And he has told it under the
most trying conditions, the most remarkable circumstances.

It was 3 o'clock yesterday morning when the longest trial
session ever held in Police Headquarters ended and Commissioner
Grant wearily arose from the judge's chair. Dora Clark had
charged Policemen Charles Becker and Martin Conway, of the
Tenderloin precinct, with persecuting her and with unwarrantably
arresting her.

_____

* Reprinted here for the first time from New York Journal:
17 October 1896.

Stephen Crane's subpoena as a witness called him to Head-quarters at 3 p.m. He waited. Commissioner Grant carefully conducted the trials of other policemen, then Becker and Conway. Crane waited. The witnesses for Becker went thronging up the corridor. Crane waited. The women with artificial manners and complexions sneered at him; the hack drivers winked at each other and pointed at Crane. He cancelled an engagement to dine, dined off a sandwich and a glass of beer — and waited for ten hours, lacking five minutes. Stephen Crane's determination to tell the truth as he saw it kept him in that corridor. The witnesses in the case that bound him there were excluded from the trial room until they had testified. Stephen Crane was the last but one. He sat fifty feet from the door of the trial room. It was impossible for him to hear a syllable of what was said on the other side of that door.

At 1:55 a.m. yesterday David F. Newberger opened the door, and beckoning to Mr. Crane, talked with him there. Lawyer Newberger had openly declared:

"This girl has been so hounded by the police that two charitable institutions employed me to defend her."

As Mr. Newberger stood there talking to Mr. Crane, a fellow who had not lost sight of Crane for ten hours, stepped by them into the trial room. He whispered to Louis J. Grant, who appeared for Becker and Conway. Up jumped Mr. Grant, intensely indignant.

"This is an outrage, unjust to all concerned," he cried. "This witness, Crane, has heard everything that has been said in this room, has been waiting outside within ear-shot."

Perhaps you will understand now the attitude of the police toward Mr. Crane; you will understand what was arrayed against him. In the room were women with yellow hair and white diamonds; hack drivers, who search for fares in the Tenderloin all night long; policemen, policemen, policemen. Becker was well supported. With him was Captain Chapman, of the Tenderloin, the especial protege of Commissioner Roosevelt and his wardmen, Cadell and Welsh. All these stood around Mr. Crane as he seated himself and was sworn, anxiously regarding the man with a fixed determination who cared nothing for them.

They saw a thin, pale, young man, with straight hair plastered down on a curiously shaped head, with a poorly nourished mustache, a large nose, prominent teeth; a young man who does not look brainy, but who has proved he has brains. This young man sat on the edge of the witness chair, bending far over, looking at the floor until it came to answering questions. Then he

would raise his head for a moment, look straight into the eyes of
his questioner, and snap out his answer like the crack of a whip.
"Yes." "No." "If you want it so."

Mr. Crane told once again of going with two women to the
Broadway Garden on Broadway, between Thirty-first and Thirty-
second streets, on the night of September 17 last. He went there
in search of types that he might weave them into the stories he
may write. This explanation always amuses the police immensely.
They seem to think a writer should seek types in a composing
room or a printing office.

Well, Crane related again how he and the two women and
Dora Clark left the Broadway Garden between 1 and 2 o'clock
that morning. They walked, two and two, to Thirty-first street
and Broadway and halted. Mr. Crane went to the east side of
Broadway with one of the women, that he might put her on a
cable car. When he crossed the street again, Becker had Dora
Clark with one hand and the woman who introduced Crane to
Dora Clark with the other hand.

"What's the meaning of this?" asked Mr. Crane.

"These women have been soliciting," said Becker.

"This is outrageous," Mr. Crane declared. "This woman is
my wife."

Then Becker released the other woman and took Dora Clark
to the station house. Crane went there and again declared that
Dora Clark's arrest was an outrage. He went to Jefferson Market
Court the next morning and told the facts as he knew them to
Magistrate Cornell, a reform Police Magistrate who discharged
Dora Clark.

[BELIEVED IN CRANE.]

"I do not approve of women being on the street late at night.
But I know Mr. Crane, and I believe him."

While relating all this to Mr. Newburger, he was perfectly
self-controlled; cold as ice.

Then arose Lawyer Grant, who proceeded to cross-examine
Mr. Crane. It seems to be the police theory that, to prove Dora
Clark's arrest was justifiable, they must prove Stephen Crane
an opium smoker. He owns an opium layout, part of the bric-a-
brac in his apartments. Lawyer Grant laid much stress on that
opium layout. Really, he made it seem probable to the policemen,
the women with diamonds and the hack drivers that Crane's
mind was stupefied by opium that night at the Broadway Garden;
that Dora Clark appeared to him an angel, and Becker some cre-
ation of a drugged mind who carried off Dora Clark.

"Dopey," said the policeman, the women and the hack drivers. But it came to the direct question:

"Do you smoke opium?"

Mr. Crane raised his head, as always, in answering, looked straight into Mr. Grant's eyes, smiled as if to say, "Really, really, I have a type before me," and snapped out: "No."

Mr. Grant questioned this young unmarried man, this Bohemian, whose home is in Hartwood, as to where he had lived in New York. The cross-examination proceeded like this:

Mr. Crane (freezingly) — Yes, I lived in a flat house on West Twenty-second street.

Mr. Grant (sneeringly) — With what woman did you live there?

Mr. Neuberger — As your adviser, Mr. Crane, I tell you not to answer that question. It has absolutely nothing to do with the case in hand here.

Mr. Crane (wearily) — I refuse to answer.

Mr. Grant (triumphantly) — On what ground?

Mr. Crane — Because it would tend to degrade me.

Mr. Grant — Perhaps you think to answer this will tend to disgrace you. With whom did you live at such and such a place?

[NOT HIS WIFE.]

So it went. Mr. Grant turned over and over the fact that Mr. Crane told Becker that one of the women he arrested was his wife.

"She is not your wife?"

"No."

"Why did you say she was?"

"Because I know she was guiltless. It was impossible that she solicited, because she was under my protection; because I felt bound to protect her."

The policemen smiled at each other. The women were puzzled. Being of the Tenderloin, it was utterly impossible for them to understand the motive Mr. Crane expressed. So, having finished the course he laid out for himself, Stephen Crane arose, bowed to Commissioner Grant, turned on his heel and left Headquarters.

Policeman Becker seemed to be very intelligent. His manner was not that of the bully. He swore Dora Clark left the Broadway Garden that night alone, and walked alone toward Thirty-first street. He saw her speak to three men before he crossed over from the shadow of the Grand Hotel and arrested her.

Yet it was necessary to make the point that Mr. Crane said the other woman was his wife. Becker had to say the other woman

was with Dora Clark, who, he said, too, was alone. His testimony
was contradictory. He gave one most surprising definition.

"What do you understand by soliciting?" Mr. Newberger
asked.

"Any woman who appears on the street alone late at night
and talks to a man is a prostitute," answered Becker.

["BIG CHICAGO MAY."]

All the women with diamonds and all the hackmen were absolutely certain that Dora Clark left the Broadway Garden
alone. They positively swore so. One woman, known in the Tenderloin as "Big Chicago May," went further. She is a huge blonde,
whose diamond earrings are as big as hickory nuts. Miss "Big
Chicago May" is as familiar on Sixth avenue and on Twenty-
third street after dark as is the Masonic Temple. Calmly she
swore that Dora Clark offered her $25 if she would swear falsely
against Becker.

"Dora Clark went to other women," swore Miss "Big Chicago
May". "She said, 'We must protect ourselves. Becker is persecuting us. We must break him. Then I'm going to Europe.' "

"What's your occupation?" Mr. Newburger asked this
woman, whose blushes are not visible.

"I'm a typewriter," she retorted.

"On what machine do you typewrite?"

She did not know.

"Name one typewriting machine."

She could not.

"Did you earn those diamonds with your wages as a typewriter?"

Dora Clark declares the police of the Tenderloin choose her
for persecution. It was perfectly plain in the trial room that the
women of the Tenderloin are her enemies. She was in strong contrast to them. She is a good-looking brunette and she has good
manners. She wore a large black hat adorned with black feathers.
She was veiled and gloved. She wore a dress of some black stuff,
trimmed with purple velvet. Her only jewelry was a diamond star
at her throat. Charitable, philanthropic people have already
interested themselves in her. In a word — although it's hard to
express — she seems to be above the level of her class.

For example, two sisters — think of that, two sisters — were
witnesses for Becker. They swore Dora Clark left the Garden
alone. They spoke of her as "that woman" until Mr. Newberger
interrupted them.

"In what does she differ from you?" he asked. "Why do you call her 'that woman?' What enmity have you against her?"

[THE HEAD WAITER CHATTED.]

An interesting question suggests itself: How long will Alphonse Falardeau be head waiter at the Broadway Garden? Like a good head waiter he opened the door when the two women, Dora Clark and Mr. Crane went out together. As the patrons of the Broadway Garden do not object to talking to head waiters, Mr. Falardeau stood in the doorway and chatted with his four departing guests. He swore so.

Dora Clark once more told the old story. But, encouraged by Mr. Newberger, she declared that Captain Chapman drove her from house to house by threatening to raid the houses if she was not turned out. He went to one house the day after she left it, she said. When he learned she had gone, he plaintively said to the landlady:

"Oh, why didn't you keep her three days longer? I wouldn't have done a thing to her."

Captain Chapman's face flushed, and he sprang to his feet.

"I demand a hearing. I demand to be heard," he exclaimed.

There was much excitement in the trial room.

The last witness of all in this most remarkable trial was James O'Connor, who is employed in a house in West Twenty-second street. A woman who wore a round hat with a red feather in it seemed much interested in him, and leaned forward to look at him as he seated himself.

O'Connor swore that when Mr. Crane lived in West Twenty-second street he got out of bed night after night to admit Mr. Crane and a woman.

Mr. Newberger objected to that evidence.

"Oh, I'll rule that out," said Commissioner Grant. "We all know Mr. Crane to be a respectable man."

"Respectable!" shouted O'Connor. "Do you call a man decent who lives off the shame of a woman?"

The police were much gratified. O'Connor walked out of headquarters between two of them. The woman with the round hat and red feather followed him. She struck him crying:

"You will try to ruin my reputation, will you!"

O'Connor turned around. She struck him again.

She shouted: "Arrest that man!"

He gallantly squared off at her. But the two policemen told the woman to go home and led O'Connor away.

Commissioner Grant reserved his decision as to Becker and Conway, whom Dora Clark charged with having unwarrantably arrested her on another occasion.

CRANE HAD/A GAY NIGHT./RACY STORY BROUGHT OUT IN/THE TRIAL OF BECKER/AND CONWAY./DORA CLARK'S CHAMPION/A JANITOR TESTIFIED THAT THE/NOVELIST LIVED WITH A/TENDERLOIN GIRL./AN OPIUM-SMOKING EPISODE./EFFIE WARD STRUCK THE JANITOR IN THE/FACE AND THEN PULLED A/WOMAN'S HAIR.*

Six young women in Gainsborough hats sat until 1 o'clock this morning at Police Headquarters and looked defiantly at the bluecoats gathered there.

It was the trial of Policemen Becker and Conway, accused by Dora Clark or Ruby Young, as she is better known, of twice arresting her on the false charge of soliciting.

"I'll sit here till this case is disposed of," said Col. Grant. Novelist Stephen Crane, who had befriended the complainant when she was arrested, smiled approvingly.

Both sides had scores of witnesses. Becker and Conway brought policemen and cabmen to swear that the woman was violating the law. The young women were there to swear that she wasn't.

[DORA CLARK TESTIFIES.]

In the course of her cross-examination the woman admitted her true character, and said that she had received money lately from a wealthy man who lives at the Waldorf.

Lawyer Grant asked for that man's name, but at the suggestion of the counsel for the woman he withdrew the question.

---

* *Reprinted here for the first time from New York* World: *16 October 1896.*

The Editors have omitted three news stories on the hearing: New York News: *16 October, New York* Sun: *17 October, and New York* Press: *17 October.*

In answer to Lawyer Grant, after considerable hesitation, the woman testified that her present address is 185 West Thirty-fifth street.

She said that as soon as that became known she would be turned out of that house, as she had been out of the Wilton, in Twenty-seventh street, near Sixth avenue, and at 40 West Twenty-ninth street, where she had lived within the last two weeks.

She said that her companions were not women of the street and that she knew none of them personally. On re-direct examination, the witness said that she was hounded by the police of the "Tenderloin."

Patrolman Becker was called in his own behalf as the first witness for the defense.

He denied the story told by the woman relative to her leaving the Broadway Garden on the night in question in company with Crane and two other women. He said that she left the Garden alone, but at about the same time that the other party left it, and that he saw her solicit two men within half a block. For that reason he arrested her. Other witnesses were called, but brought out no new facts.

It was nearly 2 o'clock when Stephen Crane took the stand as a witness for Dora Clark.

Lawyer Newberger steered him through his story.

"I was introduced to Miss Young by one of these women. There was another gentleman there, but he left before we did.

"After leaving the Garden we walked down Broadway to Thirty-first street, leaving Miss Young and another young woman who is an actress. I saw the other to a cable-car.

"When I returned I saw that my friends had gotten into trouble and that a policeman apparently had them under arrest.

"I know that the complainant had not been with any men save myself.

"I had been with her for two or three hours, and I know that after we left the Broadway Garden she had not spoken to any man from that time until she was arrested."

Many questions were put to him by the lawyer which he refused to answer on the ground that they would tend to degrade and incriminate him.

He admitted knowing Sadie and Amy Huntington, but denied

that he had made a habit of going to their apartment and smoking opium with them.

Lawyer Grant wanted to know if it was not a fact that Mr. Crane lived by money given to him by women of the Tenderloin.

Mr. Crane denied that such was the case, but said that he made money by writing for newspapers and magazines.

So thick and fast did Lawyer Grant fire the red-hot questions at the witness that he finally put his hands up to his face as if to prevent them from burning into his brain.

"Yes, my name is Stephen Crane," he replied to a question, "and I am twenty-four years old, and I live at 231 Sixth avenue, and am a writer for newspapers and magazines."

"I want to know where you first met these women," said Lawyer Grant.

"Well," drawled Crane, "I did meet them by appointment at a Turkish smoking parlor in West Twenty-ninth street."

But the witness refused to give the number.

"By the way," queried the cross-examiner, "where did you live prior to your present residence?"

"At 114 East Twenty-second street, and I lived there about a month. Before that I lived at another house in Twenty-second street, between Seventh and Eighth avenues, but I refuse to mention the number. Last Spring I lived at 165 East Twenty-eighth street."

Lawyer Grant then took another tack. He asked the witness whether he knew a woman named Sadie or Amy Huntington. It was presumed that Lawyer Grant had reference to Sadie Traphagen, who was the friend of Annie Goodwin, the cigarette girl, who was a victim of Dr. McConigal. It will be remembered, as the Goodwin case was widely published at the time, that the girl was a victim of malpractice.

Whether Amy Huntington was really Sadie Traphagen was not developed.

[OPIUM SMOKING EPISODE.]

"Did you ever smoke opium with this Sadie or Amy in a house at 121 West Twenty-seventh street?" asked Lawyer Grant.

"I deny that," said Mr. Crane.

"On the ground that it would tend to degrade or incriminate you?"

"Well — yes," hesitatingly.

Lawyer Grant succeeded in tangling Mr. Crane as to how he met Dora Clark that night.

In one portion of his story Mr. Crane said he had met her in a smoking-room on West Twenty-ninth street.

Lawyer Grant made him say that Dora Clark, while in the Broadway Garden, approached the table where the witness and his two women friends were sitting and spoke to one of the women.

"Now, what we want to find out," said Lawyer Grant, "is the identity of this woman."

[IDENTITY OF THE "WOMAN".]

"She is an actress," said Mr. Crane, "and I decline to give her name."

Lawyer Grant insisted, but Commissioner Grant went to Crane's rescue and said he need not answer the question.

The same proceedings were gone through with when the cross-examiner attempted to ascertain the identity of the alleged Hotel Waldorf man who was a member of that gay party that night.

Lawyer Grant carried the witness over the story of Dora Clark's arrest.

"The woman who was with Dora Clark was also arrested by Becker, was she not?"

"No."

"Well, she was released because you told the policeman that she was your wife. Is not that a fact?" asked Lawyer Grant.

"Yes, I said so."

Commissioner Grant announced here that the case was completed and that the decision was reserved. The lawyers were gathering up their papers when Capt. Chapman, who is Becker's and Conway's commander, suggested that James O'Connor be called as a witness.

O'Connor said he was janitor at 121 West Twenty-seventh street.

The janitor said that Stephen Crane had lived in the house where he was janitor six weeks, and that the writer lived with a woman in that house, lived with her as his wife.

Lawyer Newberger jumped up and down with rage while O'Connor was testifying, and declared that such outrageous statements should not be allowed in the case.

[JANITOR CAUSED TROUBLE.]

The janitor intimated that women had been known to attempt to live in the Twenty-seventh street house who were not above thieving. He had an opportunity perhaps to regret the statement before he left the court-room.

The janitor said that Effie Ward often took men into her flat for the purpose of robbing them and that she did rob them. The witnesses and principals in the case filed downstairs.

[BELLIGERENT EFFIE WARD.]

When the janitor reached the stone steps in front of the building Effie Ward sprang at him, and before she could be prevented she had planted her fist in his face with such force as to send him on the run down the stairs to the sidewalk.

Before the infuriated woman could reach him again she was pulled to one side by a number of policemen.

[PULLED HER HAIR.]

She was released again, and in an instant she was at a young woman who appeared in behalf of the policeman, tooth and nail. She had grabbed a handful of the young woman's hair and was twisting it out by the roots when she was again seized and hauled off.

She was taken away by a reporter and disappeared around the corner into Bleecker street.

MR. CRANE AND THE POLICE.*

Stephen Crane, poet and novelist, was tried yesterday by a New York police commissioner. The commissioners have no legal authority to try citizens. They meet once in a while to try policemen who have been charged with drunkenness, neglect of duty, blackmail, collusion with thieves, insubordination and brutality — the offenses that they commit most often. But in this case the victim

---

* *Editorial reprinted here for the first time from Brooklyn* Daily Eagle: *17 October 1896.*

As has been indicated, almost all of these newspaper accounts of the Dora Clark (Ruby Young)-Charles Becker-Stephen Crane incident are new to the Crane bibliography. (The Editors have omitted at least ten on the grounds of repetition.) This editorial, however, is listed in Ames W. Williams and Vincent Starrett, Stephen Crane: A Bibliography *(1948), p. 155, and as the authors remark, it presents an excellent summation. It also agrees, in outlook and tone, with two other editorials regarding the incident which appeared in New York City newspapers: "A Police Outrage on a Gallant Gentleman" and "Stephen Crane Not an Opium Fiend."*

of police censure was a man who had not violated any laws, though he may have disturbed the equanimity of some who would like to be his friends. He was walking in New York one evening with Dora Clark, when a policeman named Becker walked up to Miss Clark and arrested her. Mr. Crane protested, but that availed nothing and he courageously stuck it out when he went before Commissioner Grant to continue the protest. The trial began with an insult from the commissioner; he kept Mr. Crane waiting for ten hours without his dinner. Then, as soon as he was admitted to the presence, Becker's lawyer was allowed to insult him without a word of objection from the commissioner; he accused Mr. Crane of eavesdropping during the preliminary hearing.

The offending policeman was surrounded by officers from his precinct who may not have been there with any intention of terrorizing the young man, but whose presence in mass was not called for. Becker's lawyer was then allowed to ask Mr. Crane irrelevant questions concerning his life, past and present, instead of confining his attention to the case in hand, and the commissioner said never a word. The latitude allowed to lawyers to worry, confuse, bully and insult citizens in this land is one of the surest evidences that it is a free country, and it is when we read of that kind of a lawyer getting his head punched out of court by the person he has insulted that we are glad it is not less free. Mr. Crane collects bric-a-brac, and among the odds and ends in his flat are an opium pipe and lamp. From this circumstance the lawyer tried to prove that he was an opium smoker. It would not have had an atom of bearing on Becker's arrest of Miss Clark whether he had smoked opium, cigars, cigarettes or nothing. Other questions intended to cast discredit on Mr. Crane were permitted and an outsider was allowed to disclaim virtuously against the witness as a man who lived on the proceeds of a woman's shame — a statement that so angered and disgusted the woman that she struck the man in the presence of the police.

When it came to the real trial of the policeman, he declared in his own defense that any lone woman who is seen on the street at night talking to a man is a prostitute. If this belief is to guide the police in future then must all women who value their good names refrain from asking the way to a hotel or to the home of a relative if they arrive in New York after nightfall, or to a station or ferry if they have occasion to leave town in answer to a telegram, or if they ask some respectable man to defend them from the advances of a loafer or abuse of a cabdriver, or if they have to seek a physician in some domestic emergency; it imperils shop girls, actresses, women compositors, telephone girls; it

stigmatizes the woman who may be compelled to walk home from
a theater or a social gathering because she has lost her pocket-
book, or because her escort has failed to arrive; it may end a
bicycle ride in the prisoners' pen; it spots the name of any and
every woman who may find herself under the need of asking a
proper question of any proper man.

And the remarkable thing about it all is that before a board
that has the public welfare in its keeping, the reputation of private citizens is permitted to be assailed without comment or protest, while so much is done to shield one of a body of men that,
collectively, was lately shown to be one of the most corrupt,
brutal, incompetent organizations in the world.

A POLICE OUTRAGE ON A GALLANT GENTLE-
MAN.*

The action of the police authorities in the matter of the charges
of Dora Clark (or Ruby Young) against Patrolman Becker has
been simply outrageous. The theory upon which the case was
tried before the proper tribunal plainly was that the woman was
of the lower half world, and that therefore any accusation made
by her against a policeman must be discredited if possible. The
police felt that the woman's position in the community gave
them the whip hand, and they proceeded with the evident intention of driving her to the wall. Such a theory is false and per-
nicious in the results it produces in practice. It is a theory condemned by legal authorities, who hold that the habitual criminal
when a crime is committed against him, is entitled to the same
protection and redress as the honest man. The public will hardly
forget that when Holland came from Texas to "beat the green
goods game" and shot the notorious swindler "Bob" Davis, he
was indicted and tried for murder.

If Dora Clark was guilty of soliciting, Policeman Becker's
act was justifiable; if she was innocent, his act was an offence
against his uniform and deserved punishment. The testimony of
eye witnesses was required, and testimony to the effect that she
was innocent was offered by a reputable man, who in the pursuit
of his calling as a novelist was engaged in the study of life in

---

* Editorial reprinted here for the first time from New York
Journal: 18 October 1896.

New York's darkest centre, and was in the company of the woman for that purpose. Mr. Stephen Crane acted the part of a man in declining to abandon Dora Clark to the tender mercies of the police out of fear that his own reputation might be besmirched. He confessed that he expected to be assailed, and his expectation was well founded. Mr. Crane has been haled before a Police Commissioner and subjected to questioning which was an outrage without qualification, and which that Commissioner should never have permitted. The only point that was fairly open to dispute was the novelist's credibility as a witness, and no testimony whatever was submitted on that point. Whether Mr. Crane had previously known Dora Clark, whether he had ever been acquainted with other women of the "Tenderloin" district, had nothing to do with the case, because such acquaintance does not necessarily make a man a liar.

The assault upon Mr. Crane's private life was part of a deliberate and despicable scheme of police intimidation of which any voluntary witness in a trial for police outrage may become a victim. A man who sees a policeman intoxicated while on duty would probably be assailed in a similar manner if he came forward freely as a witness at the trial of such an officer. One who saw an act of brutal clubbing or an unjustifiable arrest for any cause, and who in the interest of the community went before the Police Commissioners to tell what he saw would have to take the same chance that Mr. Crane did.

What will be the unhappy result of a general knowledge of this fact? Simply that when a citizen sees a police outrage, instead of offering his testimony in order that a uniformed miscreant may be properly punished or the police force purified by his dismissal, he will turn his head the other way and stop his ears. For he will, with good reason, fear that if he goes to Police Headquarters to testify he will have to submit to insinuation in the guise of legal examination that he is not a decent person, and that his past life has not been of the highly moral pattern which meets with the holy approval of the police.

The community has got to depend largely upon the public spirit of its orderly citizens for the enforcement of its demand for the employment of decent methods by the police. Men must feel that they can testify in cases of police outrage without running the risk of official libel by the force, or any part of it. We repeat that Mr. Crane's private history was entitled to protection. Distortion of it was not necessary, was unpardonable and was an outrageous assault upon an honorable gentleman who had the courage to protect an unfortunate woman.

TRIED BY THE/POLICE COMMISSIONERS *

The trial of Officer Nightstick of the police force took place yesterday before Commissioners Guff and Stuff in the presence of an enormous audience, which had been attracted by the news that some spicy and interesting testimony was to be elicited from the witnesses.

The chief witness in the case was Mr. Benjamin Cherryble, a gentleman of advanced years and amiable countenance, who testified that while he was crossing Broadway at an early hour on Sunday morning he saw two men engaged in robbing an intoxicated young man, who was standing beside a lamp-post. There was no policeman in sight, but Mr. Cherryble, who has always lived in New York, darted into a corner saloon and requested Officer Nightstick, whom he found engaged in the game of pinochle, to come out and arrest the highwaymen. The officer came very reluctantly and arrived just in time to find the two men dividing the proceeds of their robbery. He refused to make an arrest, on the ground that he had not witnessed the crime, and to Mr. Cherryble's remonstrance exclaimed, "G'wan now!" in a threatening manner.

Mr. Cherryble, having testified in accordance with these facts, was questioned searchingly by Commissioner Stuff, who asked him to name all the places in which he had lived for twenty years past, and then asked him if he did not know it to be a fact that the house in West Steenth street in which he, the witness, had boarded in 1880, had since been occupied by a confirmed opium smoker. Mr. Cherryble replied in a very embarrassed manner that he had never before heard that fact stated, to which the Commissioner rejoined significantly that the fact was one well known to all trustworthy and honest citizens.

Commissioner Guff then took the witness in hand and asked him if it was true that his wife had an uncle named Henry Pilfer, who had once served a term in the Joliet Prison for grand larceny, and on receiving an affirmative reply, observed with quiet

---

* Reprinted here for the first time from New York Journal: 18 October 1896.

This parody, signed by James L. Ford, appeared on the same page of the Journal as the editorial, "A Police Outrage on a Gallant Gentleman." Ford was editor of the humor magazine Truth, in which four of Crane's New York City Sketches had appeared in 1893–1894.

sarcasm, "It seems to run in the family." This remark was received by people in the audience with many manifestations of approval.

Further cross-examination by Messrs. Guff and Stuff brought
to light a great many dark and mysterious episodes in Mr.
Cherryble's career. It was proved conclusively that his uncle William, whom he resembled strongly in features and temperament,
was a man of marked bacchanalian proclivities and was in the
habit of returning home after the meetings of his lodge in an up-
roarious condition, pausing from time to time to practice on the
sidewalk the steps of some new and intricate dance, or to serenade
families with whom he was slightly acquainted.

It was also proved that Mrs. Cherryble's sister had been,
prior to her marriage to a well-to-do hardware dealer, a typewriter in a large building in Wall street.

"And," exclaimed Commissioner Stuff, "every honest man,
every father who respects the honor of his wife and daughter, every
brother and every mother in this great and noble city knows perfectly well what it means to have been a typewriter in Wall
street. I have no wish to delve further into the past of this unhappy woman, or to degrade her further in popular estimation,
but I doubt if it would be a possible thing for a man to live in the
same family with this unfortunate creature and preserve his
integrity."

At these eloquent words a storm of applause, in which Officer
Nightstick and all his witnesses joined heartily, shook the building to its foundations and Mr. Cherryble slunk away, an object
of contempt and derision.

As he left the stand a gentleman came forward to testify to
Mr. Cherryble's character for integrity and sobriety, but was
interrupted by Counsellor Squirm, of the defence, who asked him
to give the name of the lady with whom he had visited Coney
Island on the first Sunday in August 1895. After considerable
argument this answer was excluded by the Commissioners, but
Counsellor Squirm, who is noted for his urbanity and courtesy to
the press, took pains to inform the reporters that the lady's name
was Mrs. Sadie Sealskin, a grass widow residing in West Forty-
ninth street.

The defence was very ably conducted by the counsellor, who
declared that never, in the ten years that had elapsed since he
first established his office on the fifth step of the Tombs, had such
an outrageous case claimed his attention. He then proceeded to
prove, through Messrs. Teak and Chestnut, who supply the Police
Department with clubs, that the accused was a man of the highest

character and had never been known to club anybody except his wife.

The lawyer also introduced an affidavit from the junior member of the firm of Felt & Visor, the well-known hat manufacturers, who supply the Department with hats, to the effect that Officer Nightstick would not have left a game of pinochle under any circumstances whatever.

The Commissioners were so much impressed with this testimony that they informed the counsellor that nothing further was needed to rehabilitate their client in the regard of the public and of his superior officers.

"Thank you very much," said the counsellor, with a deferential bow: "but I was about to show that my client has an uncle who is a distiller, a fact which has been disputed by certain malevolent parties, greatly to the detriment of this gallant and meritorious officer. I have also a most important witness in the person of the elevator boy, who does night duty in the Banjo apartment house, on West Forty-third street. This young man," exclaimed the lawyer earnestly, "is an honest and hardworking son of Ireland, whose words cannot be doubted for a single moment. If Your Honor will adjourn this hearing until tomorrow, I pledge my word that that young man will come here and testify that Mr. Cherryble's brother has been in the habit of calling at the Banjo flats at an hour of the night when all reputable and decent citizens should be in bed. And," he added significantly, "that is not all that this honest and incorruptible young son of Erin will have to tell you on this witness stand tomorrow."

The hearing was adjourned to this afternoon at 2 in accordance with the counsellor's request.

James L. Ford.

STEPHEN CRANE NOT AN OPIUM FIEND*

The attempt of sundry police guardians of the peace (may their tribe decrease!) to prove that Stephen Crane, the writer, and champion of Dora Clark, is an opium fiend, does not appear to have been crowned with the success that such a laudable endeavor deserves. Neither was it pertinent to the point at issue, which was

---

* *Editorial reprinted here for the first time from New York Press: 24 October 1896. The Editors have supplied the title.*

Dora Clark was back in court on 1 November when she and her companion, "Chicago May" Kane, were charged with disorderly conduct. Crane was not with her that time.

merely a question of veracity, for the police lawyer to impugn Mr. Crane's chastity. Everybody who knows the young novelist believes that he told the truth under circumstances where many a man of the world would have deemed it discretion to have slipped away from the scene and left the girl to her fate — since what does one arrest, more or less, matter to an exile of society? But Mr. Crane, well aware that the affair might bring him a large amount of unsavory advertisement, did not shrink from doing an act of justice to a pariah. The whole world loves justice and takes high delight in a man. It may be divided in its opinions about this author's literary value, but it has no doubt about the essential worth of his nature.

A BLACKGUARD AS A POLICE OFFICER *

Everyone who thinks is likely to know that the right of arrest is one of the most dangerous powers which organized society can give to the individual. It is a power so formidable in its reaches that there is rarely a situation confronting the people which calls for more acation.

A blackguard as a private citizen is lamentable; a blackguard as a police officer is an abomination. Theoretically the first result of government is to put control into the hands of honest men and nullify as far as may be the ambitions of criminals. When government places power in the hands of a criminal it of course violates this principle and becomes absurd.

* Published here for the the first time from the one-page folio holograph manuscript in the Columbia University Crane Collection. This is an addition to the Crane canon.

NOTES ABOUT PROSTITUTES *

Prostitutes walk the streets. Hence it is a distinction of our municipal civilization that blockheads shall be licensed to depredate upon the sensibilities of all who are out late at night.

* Published here for the first time from the two-page folio holograph manuscript in the Barrett Crane Collection.

Written on legal cap paper, it has on one side (recto) a portion of "A Girl Arrested for Stealing" and on the other side (verso) "Notes About Prostitutes." Crane wrote this during the court trial of Dora Clark.

"Imprison them. Hang them! Brain them! Burn them. Do anything but try to drive them into the air like toy balloons, because," said the philosopher, "you can't do it." He also said that a man who possessed a sense of justice was a dolt, a simpleton, and double-dyed idiot for finally his sense of justice would get him into a corner and, if he obeyed it, make him infamous. There is such a thing as a moral obligation arriving inopportunely. The inopportune arrival of a moral obligation can bring just as much personal humiliation as can a sudden impulse to steal or any of the other mental suggestions which we account calamitous. For instance, suppose a business man of New York has a wife and thirteen children. In the wee hours one morning he is on Broadway. He sees[1]

A DESERTION *

In a large hall that blazed with light, there were crowds of women at small polished tables. Large doors ceaselessly slammed letting in and out two interminable processions of men. A stout waiter with a straw-colored moustache was stowing some moping clothes, soaked with beer, in a handy crevice between the forelegs of a bronzed, crouching lion. The sounds from without of rattling traffic blended with the clanking melody from a hidden machine.

In a shaded corner a man and a woman were seated at a table. He was a well-dressed and young/[2] fellow. A cigarette was held daintily in his gloved hand. His round, well-fed face wore the marks of cheer and good-nature. Her face was painted.

She was chatting blithely, evidently telling him of incidents of preceding days. She spoke with womanish confidence as if sure of interest and sympathy.

---

* Published here for the first time from the two-page manuscript in the Syracuse University Crane Collection. This is an addition to the Crane canon.

    This fragment, an early Bowery sketch, has the same title as Crane's sketch in Harper's Magazine: November 1900. On the manuscript, Crane wrote above the title: "The door clanged behind him," which may have been the last line of another piece, now lost. On the verso of this first sheet he wrote: "a ghastly, ineffaceable smile sculptored by fingers of scorn."

1. The manuscript ends abruptly at this point.
2. A virgule (/) indicates the end of a holograph sheet.

He stared steadily at the remains of an amber-colored liquid in a round glass. He fingered his cigarette gently. He was apparently absorbed in thought. The stream of chatter from the woman opposite seemed to go in unheeding ears.

After a time, he seemed to make up his mind to something. He moved his hands nervously and shot uneasy glances at the woman.

AN ELOQUENCE OF GRIEF *

The windows were high and saintly, of the shape that is found in churches. From time to time a policeman at the door spoke sharply to some incoming person. "Take your hat off!" He displayed in his

* *Published in* The Open Boat and Other Stories (*London, 1898*); *reprinted in* Wilson Follett, ed., The Work of Stephen Crane, XI (*1926*)

Published below for the first time is Crane's first draft from the same holograph manuscript in the Barrett Crane Collection referred to in the footnote to "Notes About Prostitutes" (see above). "Notes About Prostitutes" appears on verso of the autograph manuscript, while recto contains part of a study of a girl arrested for stealing; it is Crane's first draft of "An Eloquence of Grief."

> *constantly. None seemed to notice the girl and there was no reason why she should be noticed if the curious, rearward, were not interested in the devastation which tears bring to some complexions. Her tears however seemed to burn like acid and they left fierce pink marks on her face.*
>
> *Occasionally this girl looked across the room where two well-dressed young women and a man stood waiting with the serenity of people who are not concerned as to the interior fittings of jails.*
>
> *The business of the court progressed and presently the girl, the policeman and the well-dressed party stood before the judge. Thereupon two lawyers engaged in some preliminary rockets and fire-wheels which were endured, generally, in silence. The girl, it appeared, was accused of stealing fifty dollar's worth of silk underwear from the room of one of the well-dressed woman. She had been a servant in the house.*
>
> *In a clear way and with none of the ferocity that a plaintiff often shows*

voice the horror of a priest when the sanctity of a chapel is defied or forgotten. The court-room was crowded with people who sloped back comfortably in their chairs, regarding with undeviating glances the procession and its attendant and guardian policemen that moved slowly inside the spear-topped railing. All persons connected with a case went close to the magistrate's desk before a word was spoken in the matter, and then their voices were toned to the ordinary talking strength. The crowd in the court-room could not hear a sentence; they could merely see shifting figures, men that gestured quietly, women that sometimes raised an eager eloquent arm. They could not always see the judge, although they were able to estimate his location by the tall stands surmounted by white globes that were at either hand of him. And so those who had come for curiosity's sweet sake wore an air of being in wait for a cry of anguish, some loud painful protestation that would bring the proper thrill to their jaded, world-weary nerves — wires that refused to vibrate for ordinary affairs.

Inside the railing the court officers shuffled the various groups with speed and skill; and behind the desk the magistrate patiently toiled his way through mazes of wonderful testimony.

In a corner of this space, devoted to those who had business before the judge, an officer in plain clothes stood with a girl that wept constantly. None seemed to notice the girl, and there was no reason why she should be noticed, if the curious in the body of the court-room were not interested in the devastation which tears bring upon some complexions. Her tears seemed to burn like acid, and they left fierce pink marks on her face. Occasionally the girl looked across the room, where two well-dressed young women and a man stood waiting with the serenity of people who are not concerned as to the interior fittings of a jail.

The business of the court progressed, and presently the girl, the officer, and the well-dressed contingent stood before the judge. Thereupon two lawyers engaged in some preliminary fire-wheels, which were endured generally in silence. The girl, it appeared, was accused of stealing fifty dollars' worth of silk clothing from the room of one of the well-dressed women. She had been a servant in the house.

In a clear way, and with none of the ferocity that an accuser often exhibits in a police-court, calmly and moderately, the two young women gave their testimony. Behind them stood their escort, always mute. His part, evidently, was to furnish the dignity, and he furnished it heavily, almost massively.

When they had finished, the girl told her part. She had full, almost Afric, lips, and they had turned quite white. The lawyer for the others asked some questions, which he did — be it said, in passing — with the air of a man throwing flower-pots at a stone house.

It was a short case and soon finished. At the end of it the judge said that, considering the evidence, he would have to commit the girl for trial. Instantly the quick-eyed court officer began to clear the way for the next case. The well-dressed women and their escort turned one way and the girl turned another, toward a door with an austere arch leading into a stone-paved passage. Then it was that a great cry rang through the court-room, the cry of this girl who believed that she was lost.

The loungers, many of them, underwent a spasmodic movement as if they had been knived. The court officers rallied quickly. The girl fell back opportunely for the arms of one of them, and her wild heels clicked twice on the floor. "I am innocent! Oh, I am innocent!"

People pity those who need none, and the guilty sob alone; but innocent or guilty, this girl's scream described such a profound depth of woe — it was so graphic of grief, that it slit with a dagger's sweep the curtain of common-place, and disclosed the gloom-shrouded spectre that sat in the young girl's heart so plainly, in so universal a tone of the mind, that a man heard expressed some far-off midnight terror of his own thought.

The cries died away down the stone-paved passage. A patrolman leaned one arm composedly on the railing, and down below him stood an aged, almost toothless wanderer, tottering and grinning.

"Plase, yer honer," said the old man as the time arrived for him to speak, "if ye'll lave me go this time, I've niver been dhrunk befoor, sir."

A court officer lifted his hand to hide a smile.

3   ON THE NEW JERSEY COAST

HOWELLS DISCUSSED AT AVON-BY-THE-SEA*

Avon-by-the-Sea, Aug. 17 (Special). — At the Seaside Assembly the morning lecture was delivered by Professor Hamlin Garland, of Boston, on W. D. Howells, the novelist. He said: "No man stands for a more vital principle than does Mr. Howells. He stands for modern-spirit, sympathy and truth. He believes in the progress of ideals, the relative in art. His definition of idealism cannot be improved upon, 'the truthful treatment of material.' He does not insist upon, any special material, but only that the novelist be true to himself and to things as he sees them. It is absurd to call him photographic. The photograph is false in perspective, in light and sound, the comparison will have some meaning, and then it will not be used as a reproach. Mr. Howells' work has deepened in insight and widened in sympathy from the first. His canvas has grown large, and has thickened with figures. Between 'Their Wedding Journey' and 'A Hazard of New Fortunes' there is an immense distance. 'A Modern Instance' is the greatest, most rigidly artistic novel ever written by an American, and ranks with the great novels of the world. 'A Hazard of New Fortunes' is the greatest, sanest, truest study of a city in fiction. The test of the value of Mr. Howells' work will come fifty years from now, when his sheaf of novels will form the most accurate, sympathetic and artistic study of American society yet made by an American. Howells is a many-sided man, a humorist of astonishing delicacy and imagination, and he has writ-

---

* Reprinted from New York Tribune: 18 August 1891. Unsigned.

   Crane reported "Howells Fears Realists Must Wait" (see above) in the New York Times: 28 October 1894. Howells praised Crane in "New York Low Life in Fiction," New York World: 26 July 1896, a shortened version of which comprises "An Appreciation" (see above) in the 1896 London edition of Maggie: A Child of the Streets.

ten of late some powerful poems in a full, free style. He is by all
odds the most American and vital of our literary men to-day. He
stands for all that is progressive and humanitarian in our fiction,
and his following increases each day. His success is very great, and
it will last."

JOYS OF SEASIDE LIFE/AMUSEMENTS, STATION-
ARY AND PERIPATETIC.*

Asbury Park, N.J., July 16. — This town is not overrun with seaside
"fakirs," yet there are many fearful and wonderful types in the collection of them here. The man with the green pea under all or none
of three walnut shells is not present, nor is any of his class. There
is no fierce cry of "Five, five, the lucky five!" nor the coaxing call
of "Come, now, gentlemen, make your bets. The red or the black
wins." These men cannot pass the gigantic barriers erected by a
wise government, which recognizes the fact that these things should
not be.

However, the men who merely have things to sell can come and
flourish. There are scores of them, and they do a big business. The
summer guests come here with money. They are legitimate prey.
The fakirs attack them enthusiastically.

Those who are the most persistently aggressive are the Hindoos, who sell Indian goods, from silk handkerchiefs to embroidered
petticoats. They are an aggregation of little brown fellows, with
twinkling bright eyes. They wear the most amazing trousers and
small black surtouts, or coats of some kind. Apparently they are, as
a race, universally bow-legged, and are all possessed of ancestors
who were given to waddling. The Hindoos have soft, wheedling
voices, and when they invade a crowded hotel-porch and unload
their little white packs of silk goods they are very apt to cause a
disturbance in the pocketbooks of the ladies present. They parade
the streets in twos and threes. They all use large umbrellas of the
rural pattern to protect their chocolate skins from the rays of the
sun. A camera fiend was the first to discover an astonishing superstition of fear which possesses these men. Once she perceived three
of them reclining in picturesque attitudes on a shady bank. Their
bundles and umbrellas reposed beside them and they were fanning
themselves with their caps. She approached them with an engaging

---

* Reprinted from New York Tribune: 17 July 1892. Unsigned.

smile and a camera levelled at their heads. Astonishment and terror swept over their faces. With one accord they gave a great shout and raising their umbrellas, interposed them as a bulwark against the little glass eye of the camera. The fiend had her finger on the trigger, and she pulled it before she was aware of the bewildering revolution in the appearance of the objects of her ambition. As a result the picture is the most valued one in all the fiend's collection. There is the grassy bank and a few trees. In the foreground appear the tops of three large umbrellas. Underneath dangle three pairs of legs with also three pairs of feet. The picture is a great success and is the admiration of all beholders.

Of course the frankfurter man is prevalent. He is too ordinary to need more than mere mention. With his series of quick motions, consisting of the grab at the roll, the stab at the sausage and the deft little dab of mustard, he appears at all hours. He parades the avenues swinging his furnace and howling.

There is a sleight-of-hand Italian, with a courageous mustache and a clever nose. He manoeuvres with a quarter of a dollar and a pack of playing cards. He comes around to the hotels and mystifies the indolent guests. Nobody cares much to ask: "How does he do it," so the mustache takes a vain curve and the exhibition continues.

Tintype galleries are numerous. They are all of course painted the inevitable blue, and trundle about the country on wheels. It is quite the thing to have one's features libelled in this manner. The occupants of the blue houses make handsome incomes. Babies and pug dogs furnish most of the victims for these people.

Down near the beach are a number of contrivances to tumble-bumble the soul and gain possession of nickels. There is a "razzle-dazzle," invented apparently by a man of experience and knowledge of the world. It is a sort of circular swing. One gets in at some expense and by climbing up a ladder. Then the machine goes around and around, with a sway and swirl, like the motion of a ship. Many people are supposed to enjoy this thing, for a reason which is not evident. Solemn circles of more or less sensible-looking people sit in it and "go 'round."

On the lake shore is an "observation wheel," which is the name of a gigantic upright wheel of wood and steel, which goes around carrying little cars filled with maniacs, up and down, over and over. Of course there are merry-go-rounds loaded with impossible giraffes and goats, on which ride crowds of joyous children, who clutch for brass rings. All these machines have appalling steam organs run in connection with them, which make weird music eternally. Humanity had no respite from these things until the police made their owners tone them down a great deal, so that now they play low music instead of grinding out with stentorian force such airs as "Annie," the famous, so that they could be heard squares away.

The camera obscura is in Ocean Grove. It really has some value as a scientfic curiosity. People enter a small wooden building and stand in a darkened room, gazing at the surface of a small round table, on which appear reflections made through a lens in the top of the tower of all that is happening in the vicinity at the time. One gets a miniature of everything that occurs in the streets, on the boardwalk or on the hotel porches. One can watch the bathers gambolling in the surf or peer at the deck of a passing ship. A man stands with his hand on a lever and changes the scene at will.

These are the regular ways in which Asbury Park amuses itself. There is, however, a steady stream of transient fakirs, who stay a week, an hour or perchance go at once away. This week an aggregation of five Italian mandolin and guitar players came to town. They are really very clever with their instruments, and have already made themselves popular with the hotel guests. One "Jesse Williams" is a favorite with everybody, too. He is very diminutive and very black. He has a disreputable silk-hat and a pair of nimble feet. He passes from house to house, and sings and dances. He accompanies both his dances and his songs on an old weather-beaten banjo. The entire populace adore him, because he sometimes discloses various qualities of the true comedian, and is never exactly idiotic. But the most terrific of all the fakirs, the most stupendous of all the exhibitions is that of the Greek dancer, or whatever it is. Two Italians, armed with a violin and a harp, recently descended upon the town. With them came a terrible creature in an impossible apparel, and with a tambourine. He, or she, wore a dress which would take a geometrical phenomenon to describe. He, or she, wore orange stockings, with a bunch of muscle in the calf. The rest of his, or her, apparel was a chromatic delirium of red, black, green, pink, blue, yellow, purple, white and other shades and colors not known. There were accumulations of jewelry on different portions of his, or her, person. Beneath were those grotesque legs; above, was a face. The grin of the successful midnight assassin and the smile of the coquette were commingled upon it. When he, or she, with his, or her, retinue of Italians, emerged upon the first hotel veranda, there was a panic. Brave men shrunk. Then he, or she, opened his, or her, mouth and began to sing in a hard, high, brazen voice, songs in an unknown tongue. Then he, or she, danced, with ballet airs and graces. The scowl of the assassin sat side by side with the simper and smirk of the country maiden who is not well-balanced mentally. The fantastic legs slid over the floor to the music of the violin and harp. And, finally, he, or she, passed the tambourine about among the crowd, with a villainously-lovable smile upon his, or her, features. Since then he, or she, has become a well-known figure on the streets. People are beginning to get used to it, and he, or she, is not mobbed, as one might expect him, or her, to be.

ON THE NEW-JERSEY COAST/SUMMER DWELLERS AT ASBURY PARK AND/THEIR DOINGS./THE WHEEL THAT GOES AROUND NO MORE—THE/ BICYCLE CHAMPION . . .*

The big "Observation Wheel" on Lake-ave. has got into a great deal of trouble, and it is feared that the awe-stricken visitor will be unable to see the "wheel go 'round" hereafter. Complaints were made by the hotel-owners in the neighborhood that the engine connected with the machine distributed ashes and sparks over their counterpanes. Also, residents of Ocean Grove came and said that the steam organ disturbed their pious meditations on the evils of the world. Thereupon the minions of the law violently suppressed the wheel and its attendants. The case comes before Chancellor McGill, of Jersey City.

Captain Minot, the popular proprietor of the Minot House on Third-ave., was, one evening this week, presented by his guests with a large Sevres plaque and two pitchers, on a table of carved oak.

Arthur Zimmerman, the famous American bicycle rider, who has been smashing English records, and who is, incidentally, the idol of Asbury Park wheelers, is to be here on August 5 and 6. He will race here on those days against some of the cracks of the country. It is certain that he will receive a tremendous ovation.

The thousands of summer visitors who have fled from the hot, stifling air of the cities to enjoy the cool sea breezes are not entirely forgetful of the unfortunates who have to stay in their crowded tenements. Jacob Riis, the author of "How the Other Half Lives," gave an illustrated lecture on the same subject in the Beach Auditorium on Wednesday evening. The proceeds were given to the tenement-house work of the King's Daughters. Over $300 was cleared, which, at $2 each, will give 150 children a two-weeks outing in the country.

---

* *Reprinted from New York Tribune: 24 July 1892. Unsigned.*

ON THE NEW JERSEY COAST./GUESTS CONTINUE TO ARRIVE IN LARGE NUMBERS./PARADES AND ENTERTAINMENTS—WELL-KNOWN/PEOPLE WHO ARE REGISTERED AT/THE VARIOUS HOTELS.*

ASBURY PARK, N.J., Aug. 20 (Special). — The parade of the Junior Order of United American Mechanics here on Wednesday afternoon was a deeply impressive one to some persons. There were hundreds of the members of the order, and they wound through the streets to the music of enough brass bands to make furious discords. It probably was the most awkward, ungainly, uncut and uncarved procession that ever raised clouds of dust on sun-beaten streets. Nevertheless, the spectacle of an Asbury Park crowd confronting such an aggregation was an interesting sight to a few people.

Asbury Park creates nothing. It does not make; it merely amuses. There is a factory where nightshirts are manufactured, but it is some miles from town. This is a resort of wealth and leisure, of women and considerable wine. The throng along the line of march was composed of summer gowns, lace parasols, tennis trousers, straw hats and indifferent smiles. The procession was composed of men, bronzed, slope-shouldered, uncouth and begrimed with dust. Their clothes fitted them illy, for the most part, and they had no ideas of marching. They merely plodded along, not seeming quite to understand, stolid, unconcerned and, in a certain sense, dignified — a pace and bearing emblematic of their lives. They smiled occasionally and from time to time greeted friends in the crowd on the sidewalk. Such an assemblage of the spraddle-legged men of the middle class, whose hands were bent and shoulders stooped from delving and constructing, had never appeared to an Asbury Park summer crowd, and the latter was vaguely amused.

---

* Published in New York Tribune: 21 August 1892. Unsigned. The sketch was reprinted in the Newark Sunday Call: 14 January 1931; in Charles Honce, The Public Papers of a Bibliomaniac (1942); and in R. W. Stallman, ed., Stephen Crane: An Omnibus (1952).

The article was discovered by B. J. R. Stolper. That Crane was dismissed by the Tribune for writing it is a point of considerable dispute, for he appeared in the paper as late as 11 September 1892 with "The Seaside Hotel Hop."

The bona fide Asbury Parker is a man to whom a dollar, when held close to his eye, often shuts out any impression he may have had that other people possess rights. He is apt to consider that men and women, especially city men and women, were created to be mulcted by him. Hence the tan-colored, sun-beaten honesty in the faces of the members of the Junior Order of United American Mechanics is expected to have a very staggering effect upon them. The visitors were men who possessed principles. . . .

SELECTIONS FROM THE MAIL./THE JUNIOR OR-
DER OF UNITED AMERICAN/MECHANICS.*

To the Editor of The Tribune.

Sir: I, as a member of the Junior Order of American Mechanics, take the liberty of writing to The Tribune in the name of all who belong to this patriotic American organization, in answer to the uncalled-for and un-American criticism published in The Tribune on Sunday, August 21, in regard to the annual outing of the order at Asbury Park, on Wednesday, August 17.

Personally I do not think The Tribune would publish such a slur on one of the largest bodies of American-born citizens if it knew the order, its objects, or its principles. In the strictest sense, we are a National political organization, but we do not recognize any party. Our main objects are to restrict immigration, and to protect the public schools of the United States and to prevent sectarian interference therein. We also demand that the Holy Bible be read in our public schools, not to teach sectarianism but to inculcate its teachings. We are bound together to promote Americans in business and shield them from the depressing effects of foreign competition. We are not a labor organization, nor are we a military company, drilled to parade in public and be applauded for our fine appearance and precision; but we were appreciated for our Americanism and we were applauded for it.

As a body we recognize no society, party or creed. We are brothers, one and all, bound together to honor and protect our country and to vow allegiance to the Stars and Stripes.

E. A. CANFIELD,
Clinton Council, No. 187, Jr. O. U. A. M.
New-York, Aug. 23, 1892.

---

* *Reprinted from New York* Tribune: *24 August 1892.*

(We regret deeply that a bit of random correspondence, passed inadvertently by the copy editor, should have put into our columns sentiments both foreign and repugnant to The Tribune. To those who know the principles and policy of this paper in both its earlier and later years, its devotion to American interests and its abhorrence of vain class distinctions, it can scarcely be necessary to say that we regard the Junior Order of United American Mechanics with high respect and hold its principles worthy of all emulation. The offence which has been unintentionally given by the correspondence referred to is as much deplored by The Tribune as it is resented by the members of the Order. — Ed.)

THE PACE OF YOUTH *

i

Stimson stood in a corner and glowered. He was a fierce man and had indomitable whiskers, albeit he was very small.

"That young tarrier," he whispered to himself. "He wants to quit makin' eyes at Lizzie. This is too much of a good thing. First thing you know, he'll get fired."

His brow creased in a frown, he strode over to the huge open doors and looked at a sign. "Stimson's Mammoth Merry-Go-Round," it read, and the glory of it was great. Stimson stood and contemplated the sign. It was an enormous affair; the letters were as large as men. The glow of it, the grandeur of it was very apparent to Stimson. At the end of his contemplation, he shook his head thoughtfully, determinedly. "No, no," he muttered. "This is too much of a good thing. First thing you know, he'll get fired."

A soft booming sound of surf, mingled with the cries of bathers, came from the beach. There was a vista of sand and sky and sea that drew to a mystic point far away in the northward. In the mighty angle, a girl in a red dress was crawling slowly like some kind of a spider on the fabric of nature. A few flags hung

---

* *Reprinted from* The Open Boat and Other Stories (*London,* 1898).

A tale of Asbury Park, New Jersey, it was included here by Crane as one of his Midnight Sketches. It was first published in New York Press: *19 January 1895. The sketch did not appear in the American edition of* The Open Boat and Other Tales of Adventure (*1898*).

lazily above where the bath-houses were marshalled in compact squares. Upon the edge of the sea stood a ship with its shadowy sails painted dimly upon the sky, and high overhead in the still, sun-shot air a great hawk swung and drifted slowly.

Within the Merry-Go-Round there was a whirling circle of ornamental lions, giraffes, camels, ponies, goats, glittering with varnish and metal that caught swift reflections from windows high above them. With stiff wooden legs, they swept on in a never-ending race, while a great orchestrion clamoured in wild speed. The summer sunlight sprinkled its gold upon the garnet canopies carried by the tireless racers and upon all the devices of decoration that made Stimson's machine magnificent and famous. A host of laughing children bestrode the animals, bending forward like charging cavalrymen, and shaking reins and whooping in glee. At intervals they leaned out perilously to clutch at iron rings that were tendered to them by a long wooden arm. At the intense moment before the swift grab for the rings one could see their little nervous bodies quiver with eagerness; the laughter rang shrill and excited. Down in the long rows of benches, crowds of people sat watching the game, while occasionally a father might arise and go near to shout encouragement, cautionary commands, or applause at his flying offspring. Frequently mothers called out: "Be careful, Georgie!" The orchestrion bellowed and thundered on its platform, filling the ears with its long monotonous song. Over in a corner, a man in a white apron and behind a counter roared above the tumult: "Pop corn! Pop corn!"

A young man stood upon a small, raised platform, erected in a manner of a pulpit, and just without the line of the circling figures. It was his duty to manipulate the wooden arm and affix the rings. When all were gone into the hands of the triumphant children, he held forth a basket, into which they returned all save the coveted brass one, which meant another ride free and made the holder very illustrious. The young man stood all day upon his narrow platform, affixing rings or holding forth the basket. He was a sort of general squire in these lists of childhood. He was very busy.

And yet Stimson, the astute, had noticed that the young man frequently found time to twist about on his platform and smile at a girl who shyly sold tickets behind a silvered netting. This, indeed, was the great reason of Stimson's glowering. The young man upon the raised platform had no manner of licence to smile at the girl behind the silvered netting. It was a most gigantic insolence. Stimson was amazed at it. "By Jiminy," he said to himself again, "that fellow is smiling at my daughter." Even in this tone of great wrath it could be discerned that Stimson was filled with wonder that any youth should dare smile at the daughter in the presence of the august father.

Often the dark-eyed girl peered between the shining wires, and, upon being detected by the young man, she usually turned her head away quickly to prove to him that she was not interested. At other times, however, her eyes semed filled with a tender fear lest he should fall from that exceedingly dangerous platform. As for the young man, it was plain that these glances filled him with valour, and he stood carelessly upon his perch, as if he deemed it of no consequence that he might fall from it. In all the complexities of his daily life and duties he found opportunity to gaze ardently at the vision behind the netting.

This silent courtship was conducted over the heads of the crowd who thronged about the bright machine. The swift eloquent glances of the young man went noiselessly and unseen with their message. There had finally become established between the two in this manner a subtle understanding and companionship. They communicated accurately all that they felt. The boy told his love, his reverence, his hope in the changes of the future. The girl told him that she loved him, that she did not love him, that she did not know if she loved him, that she loved him. Sometimes a little sign saying "cashier" in gold letters, and hanging upon the silvered netting, got directly in range and interfered with the tender message.

The love affair had not continued without anger, unhappiness, despair. The girl had once smiled brightly upon a youth who came to buy some tickets for his little sister, and the young man upon the platform observing this smile had been filled with gloomy rage. He stood like a dark statue of vengeance upon his pedestal and thrust out the basket to the children with a gesture that was full of scorn for their hollow happiness, for their insecure and temporary joy. For five hours he did not once look at the girl when she was looking at him. He was going to crush her with his indifference; he was going to demonstrate that he had never been serious. However, when he narrowly observed her in secret he discovered that she seemed more blythe than was usual with her. When he found that his apparent indifference had not crushed her he suffered greatly. She did not love him, he concluded. If she had loved him she would have been crushed. For two days he lived a miserable existence upon his high perch. He consoled himself by thinking of how unhappy he was, and by swift, furtive glances at the loved face. At any rate he was in her presence, and he could get a good view from his perch when there was no interference by the little sign: "Cashier."

But suddenly, swiftly, these clouds vanished, and under the imperial blue sky of the restored confidence they dwelt in peace, a peace that was satisfaction, a peace that, like a babe, put its trust in the treachery of the future. This confidence endured until the next day, when she, for an unknown cause, suddenly refused to look at him. Mechanically he continued his task, his brain dazed, a tortured victim of doubt, fear, suspicion. With his eyes he supplicated her to telegraph an explanation. She replied with a stony glance that froze his blood. There was a great difference in their respective reasons for becoming angry. His were always foolish, but apparent, plain as the moon. Hers were subtle, feminine, as incomprehensible as the stars, as mysterious as the shadows at night.

They fell and soared, and soared and fell in this manner until they knew that to live without each other would be a wandering in deserts. They had grown so intent upon the uncertainties, the variations, the guessings of their affair that the world had become but a huge immaterial background. In time of peace their smiles were soft and prayerful, caresses confided to the air. In time of war, their youthful hearts, capable of profound agony, were wrung by the intricate emotions of doubt. They were the victims of the dread angel of affectionate speculation that forces the brain endlessly on roads that lead nowhere.

At night, the problem of whether she loved him confronted the young man like a spectre, looming as high as a hill and telling him not to delude himself. Upon the following day, this battle of the night displayed itself in the renewed fervour of his glances and in their increased number. Whenever he thought he could detect that she too was suffering, he felt a thrill of joy.

But there came a time when the young man looked back upon these contortions with contempt. He believed then that he had imagined his pain. This came about when the redoubtable Stimson marched forward to participate.

"This has got to stop," Stimson had said to himself, as he stood and watched them. They had grown careless of the light world that clattered about them; they were become so engrossed in their personal drama that the language of their eyes was almost as obvious as gestures. And Stimson, through his keenness, his wonderful, infallible penetration, suddenly came into possession of these obvious facts. "Well, of all the nerves," he said, regarding with a new interest the young man upon the perch.

He was a resolute man. He never hesitated to grapple with a crisis. He decided to overturn everything at once, for, although small, he was very fierce and impetuous. He resolved to crush this dreaming.

He strode over to the silvered netting. "Say, you want to quit your everlasting grinning at that idiot," he said, grimly.

The girl cast down her eyes and made a little heap of quarters into a stack. She was unable to withstand the terrible scrutiny of her small and fierce father.

Stimson turned from his daughter and went to a spot beneath the platform. He fixed his eyes upon the young man and said —

"I've been speakin' to Lizzie. You better attend strictly to your own business or there'll be a new man here next week." It was as if he had blazed away with a shot-gun. The young man reeled upon his perch. At last he in a measure regained his composure and managed to stammer: "A — all right, sir." He knew that denials would be futile with the terrible Stimson. He agitatedly began to rattle the rings in the basket, and pretend that he was obliged to count them or inspect them in some way. He, too, was unable to face the great Stimson.

For a moment, Stimson stood in fine satisfaction and gloated over the effect of his threat.

"I've fixed them," he said complacently, and went out to smoke a cigar and revel in himself. Through his mind went the proud reflection that people who came in contact with his granite will usually ended in quick and abject submission.

ii

One evening, a week after Stimson had indulged in the proud reflection that people who came in contact with his granite will usually ended in quick and abject submission, a young feminine friend of the girl behind the silvered netting came to her there and asked her to walk on the beach after "Stimson's Mammoth Merry-Go-Round" was closed for the night. The girl assented with a nod.

The young man upon the perch holding the rings saw this nod and judged its meaning. Into his mind came an idea of defeating the watchfulness of the redoubtable Stimson.

When the Merry-Go-Round was closed and the two girls started for the beach, he wandered off aimlessly in another direction, but he kept them in view, and as soon as he was assured that he had escaped the vigilance of Stimson, he followed them.

The electric lights on the beach made a broad band of tremoring light, extending parallel to the sea, and upon the wide walk there slowly paraded a great crowd, intermingling, intertwining, sometimes colliding. In the darkness stretched the vast purple expanse of the ocean, and the deep indigo sky above was peopled with yellow stars. Occasionally out upon the water a whirling mass of froth suddenly flashed into view, like a great ghostly robe appearing, and then vanished, leaving the sea in its darkness, from whence came those bass tones of the water's unknown emotion. A wind, cool, reminiscent of the wave wastes, made the women hold their wraps about their throats, and caused the men to grip the rims of their straw hats. It carried the noise of the band in the pavilion in gusts. Sometimes people unable to hear the music, glanced up at the pavilion and were reassured upon beholding the distant leader still gesticulating and bobbing, and the other members of the band with their lips glued to their instruments. High in the sky soared an unassuming moon, faintly silver.

For a time the young man was afraid to approach the two girls; he followed them at a distance and called himself a coward. At last, however, he saw them stop on the outer edge of the crowd and stand silently listening to the voices of the sea. When he came to where they stood, he was trembling in his agitation. They had not seem him.

"Lizzie," he began. "I — "

The girl wheeled instantly and put her hand to her throat.

"Oh, Frank, how you frightened me," she said — inevitably.

"Well, you know I — I — " he stuttered.

But the other girl was one of these beings who are born to attend at tragedies. She had for love a reverence, an admiration that was greater the more that she contemplated the fact that she knew nothing of it. This couple, with their emotions, awed her and made her humbly wish that she might be destined to be of some service to them. She was very homely.

When the young man faltered before them, she, in her sympathy, actually over-estimated the crisis, and felt that he might fall dying at their feet. Shyly, but with courage, she marched to the rescue.

"Won't you come and walk on the beach with us?" she said.

The young woman gave her a glance of deep gratitude which was not without the patronage which a man in his condition naturally feels for one who pities it. The three walked on.

Finally, the being who was born to attend at this tragedy, said that she wished to sit down and gaze at the sea, alone.

They politely urged her to walk on with them, but she was obstinate. She wished to gaze at the sea, alone. The young man swore to himself that he would be her friend until he died.

And so the two young lovers went on without her. They turned once to look at her.

"Jennie's awful nice," said the girl.

"You bet she is," replied the young man, ardently.

They were silent for a little time.

At last the girl said —

"You were angry at me yesterday."

"No, I wasn't."

"Yes, you were, too. You wouldn't look at me once all day."

"No, I wasn't angry. I was only putting on."

Though she had, of course, known it, this confession seemed to make her very indignant. She flashed a resentful glance at him.

"Oh, were you, indeed?" she said with a great air.

For a few minutes she was so haughty with him that he loved her to madness. And directly this poem, which stuck at his lips, came forth lamely in fragments.

When they walked back toward the other girl and saw the patience of her attitude, their hearts swelled in a patronizing and secondary tenderness for her.

They were very happy. If they had been miserable they would have charged this fairy scene of the night with a criminal heartlessness; but as they were joyous, they vaguely wondered how the purple sea, the yellow stars, the changing crowds under the electric lights could be so phlegmatic and stolid.

They walked home by the lake-side way, and out upon the water those gay paper lanterns, flashing, fleeting, and careering, sang to them, sang a chorus of red and violet, and green and gold; a song of mystic bands of the future.

One day, when business paused during a dull sultry afternoon, Stimson went up town. Upon his return, he found that the popcorn man, from his stand over in a corner, was keeping an eye upon the cashier's cage, and that nobody at all was attending to the wooden arm and the iron rings. He strode forward like a sergeant of grenadiers.

"Where in thunder is Lizzie?" he demanded, a cloud of rage in his eyes.

The popcorn man, although associated long with Stimson, had never got over being dazed.

"They've — they've — gone round to th' — th' — house," he said with difficulty, as if he had just been stunned

"Whose house?" snapped Stimson.

"Your — your house, I'spose," said the popcorn man.

Stimson marched round to his home. Kingly denunciations

surged, already formulated, to the tip of his tongue, and he bided the moment when his anger could fall upon the heads of that pair of children. He found his wife convulsive and in tears.

"Where's Lizzie?"

And then she burst forth — "Oh — John — John — they've run away, I know they have. They drove by here not three minutes ago. They must have done it on purpose to bid me good-bye, for Lizzie waved her hand sad-like; and then, before I could get out to ask where they were going or what, Frank whipped up the horse."

Stimson gave vent to a dreadful roar.

"Get my revolver — get a hack — get my revolver, do you hear — what the devil —— " His voice become incoherent.

He had always ordered his wife about as if she were a battalion of infantry, and despite her misery, the training of years forced her to spring mechanically to obey; but suddenly she turned to him with a shrill appeal.

"Oh, John — not — the — revolver."

"Confound it, let go of me," he roared again, and shook her from him.

He ran hatless upon the street. There were a multitude of hacks at the summer resort, but it was ages to him before he could find one. Then he charged it like a bull.

"Uptown," he yelled, as he tumbled into the rear seat.

The hackman thought of severed arteries. His galloping horse distanced a large number of citizens who had been running to find what caused such contortions by the little hatless man.

It chanced as the bouncing hack went along near the lake, Stimson gazed across the calm grey expanse and recognized a colour in a bonnet and a pose of a head. A buggy was travelling along a highway that led to Sorington. Stimson bellowed — "There — there — there they are — in that buggy."

The hackman became inspired with the full knowledge of the situation. He struck a delirious blow with the whip. His mouth expanded in a grin of excitement and joy. It came to pass that this old vehicle, with its drowsy horse and its dusty-eyed and tranquil driver, seemed suddenly to awaken, to become animated and fleet. The horse ceased to ruminate on his state, his air of reflection vanished. He became intent upon his aged legs and spread them in quaint and ridiculous devices for speed. The driver, his eyes shining, sat critically in his seat. He watched each motion of this rattling machine down before him. He resembled an engineer. He used the whip with judgment and deliberation as the engineer would have used coal or oil. The horse clacked swiftly upon the macadam, the wheels hummed, the body of the vehicle wheezed and groaned.

Stimson, in the rear seat, was erect in that impassive attitude that comes sometimes to the furious man when he is obliged to leave the battle to others. Frequently, however, the tempest in his breast came to his face and he howled —

"Go it — go it — you're gaining; pound 'im! Thump the life out of 'im; hit 'im hard, you fool." His hand grasped the rod that supported the carriage top, and it was clenched so that the nails were faintly blue.

Ahead, that other carriage had been flying with speed, as from realization of the menace in the rear. It bowled away rapidly, drawn by the eager spirit of a young and modern horse. Stimson could see the buggy-top bobbing, bobbing. That little pane, like an eye, was a derision to him. Once he leaned forward and bawled angry sentences. He began to feel impotent; his whole expedition was a tottering of an old man upon a trail of birds. A sense of age made him choke again with wrath. That other vehicle, that was youth, with youth's pace; it was swift-flying with the hope of dreams. He began to comprehend those two children ahead of him, and he knew a sudden and strange awe, because he understood the power of their young blood, the power to fly strongly into the future and feel and hope again, even at that time when his bones must be laid in the earth. The dust rose easily from the hot road and stifled the nostrils of Stimson.

The highway vanished far away in a point with a suggestion of intolerable length. The other vehicle was becoming so small that Stimson could no longer see the derisive eye.

At last the hackman drew rein to his horse and turned to look at Stimson.

"No use, I guess," he said.

Stimson made a gesture of acquiescence, rage, despair. As the hackman turned his dripping horse about, Stimson sank back with the astonishment and grief of a man who has been defied by the universe. He had been in a great perspiration, and now his bald head felt cool and uncomfortable. He put up his hand with a sudden recollection that he had forgotten his hat.

At last he made a gesture. It meant that at any rate he was not responsible.

STEPHEN CRANE AT ASBURY PARK/THE MOST AMERICAN OF TOWNS AND ITS PIC-/TURESQUE TYRANT.*

It is a sad thing to go to town with a correspondent's determination to discover at once wherein this particular town differs from all other towns. We seek our descriptive material in the differences, perhaps, and dismay comes upon the agile mind of the newspaper man when the eternal overwhelming resemblances smite his eyes. We often find our glory in heralding the phenomena and we have a sense of oppression, perhaps, when the similarities tower too high in the sky.

The variations being subtle, and the resemblances being mountainous, we revenge ourselves by declaring the subject unworthy of a fine hand. We brand it with some opportune name, which places it beyond the fence of literary art, and depart to earn our salaries describing two-headed pigs. Asbury Park somewhat irritates the anxious writer, because it persists in being distinctly American, reflecting all our best habits and manners, when it might resemble a town in Siberia, or Jerusalem, during a siege.

A full brigade of stages and hacks paraded to meet the train, and as the passengers alighted the hackmen swarmed forward with a capacity that had been carefully chastened by the police. While their voices clashed in a mellow chorus, the passengers for the most part dodged their appeals and proceeded across the square, yellow in the sunlight, to the waiting trolley cars. The breeze that came from the hidden sea bore merely a suggestion, a prophecy of coolness, and the baggageman who toiled at the hill of trunks sweated like men condemned to New York.

From the station Asbury Park presents a front of spruce business blocks, and one could guess himself in one of the spick Western cities. Afterward there is square after square of cottages, trees and little terraces, little terraces, trees and cottages, while the wide avenues funnel toward a distant gray sky, whereon from time to

---

* *From* Kansas City *Star: 22 August 1896; reprinted from the press clipping in the Columbia University Crane Collection. The sketch was first published in New York Journal: 16 August 1896, under the head: "Asbury Park as Seen by Stephen Crane."*

time may appear ships. Later still, a breeze cool as the foam of the waves slants across the town, and above the bass rumble of the surf clamor the shrill voices of the bathing multitude.

The summer girls flaunt their flaming parasols, and young men, in weird clothes, walk with a confidence born of a knowledge of the fact that their fathers work. In the meantime, the wind snatches fragments of melody from the band pavilion and hurls this musical debris afar.

Coney Island is profane; Newport is proper; with a vehemence that is some degrees more tiresome than Coney's profanity. If a man should be goaded into defining Asbury Park he might state that the distinguishing feature of the town is its singular and elementary sanity.

Life at Asbury Park is as healthy and rational as any mode of existence which we, the people, will endure for our benefit. This is, of course, a general statement, and does not apply to the man with seven distinct thirsts in one throat. He exists here, but he is minute in proportion. He labors unseen with his seven thirsts and his manners are devious. He only appears when he has opportunity to deliver his ode to Liberty.

Besides the prohibition law, there are numerous other laws to prevent people from doing those things which philosophers and economists commonly agree work for the harm of society. It is very irksome to be confronted with an ordinance whenever one wishes for novelty or excitement to smash a cannon to smithereens. Moreover, there are a number of restrictions here which are ingeniously silly and are not sanctioned by nature's plan nor by any of the creeds of men, save those which define virtue as a physical inertia and a mental death.

But in the main it is unquestionably true that Asbury Park's magnificent prosperity, her splendid future, is due to the men who, in the beginning, believed that the people's more valuable patronage would go to the resort where opportunity was had for a rational and sober existence.

On cloudy nights there is always one star in the sky over Asbury Park. This star is James A. Bradley. The storm forces discover that he cannot be dimmed. A heavy mist can vanquish gorgeous Orion and other kings of the heavens, but James A. Bradley continues to shine with industry.

Orion and other kings of the heavens complain that this is because they do not own an ocean front. He it was who, in 1879, purchased a sand waste and speedily made it into Asbury Park, the seething summer city. He has celebrated this marvel in a beautiful bit of literature in which he does not refer to himself at all, nor to Providence. He simply admits the feat to be an evolution instead of a personal construction.

This famous feature is not obvious at once. James A. Bradley does not meet all incoming trains. He is as impalpable as Father Knickerbocker. It is well known that he invariably walks under a white cotton sun umbrella, and that red whiskers of the Icelandic lichen pattern grow fretfully upon his chin, and persons answering this description are likely to receive the salaams of the populace.

He himself writes most of the signs and directions which spangle the ocean front, and natives often account for his absence from the streets by picturing him in his library flying through tome after tome of ancient lore in chase of those beautiful expressions which add so particularly to the effect of the Atlantic.

Then suddenly he will flash a work of philanthropy of so deep and fine a kind that it could only come from a man whose bold heart raised him independent of conventional or narrow-minded people, and his grand schemes for decorating the solar system with signs will be forgotten. Withal, he never poses, but carries his sublimity with the calmness of a man out of debt.

Of course there has long been a flourishing garden of humorists here who owe their bloom solely to the fact that Founder Bradley indulges sometimes in eccentricities, which are the sun of the morning and the rain of noon to any proper garden of humorists. But he is eccentric only in detail, this remarkable man.

The people should forget that, for purposes too mystic, too exaltedly opaque for the common mind, he placed a marble bathtub in the middle of a public park and remember only that he created the greatest summer resort in America — the vacation abode of the mighty middle classes — and, better still, that he now protects it with the millions that make him powerful and with the honesty that makes his millions useful.

Of late the founder has been delivering lop-sided political orations from the tailend of a cart to stage drivers, newsboys, unclassified citizens and summer boarders who have no other amusement. "I own the pavilions and the bath houses, and the fishing pier and the beach and the pneumatic sea lion, and what I say ought to go with an audience that has any sense." The firmament has been put to considerable inconvenience, but it will simply have to adjust itself to the conditions and await his return.

In the meantime the brave sea breeze blows cool on the shore and the far little ships sink, one by one past the horizon. At bathing time the surf is a-swarm with the revelling bathers and the beach is black with watchers.

The very heart of the town's life is then at the Asbury avenue

pavilion, and the rustle and the roar of the changing throng give
the casual visitor the same deep feeling of isolation that comes to
the heart of the lone sheep herder, who watches a regiment swing
over the ridge or an express train line through the mesquite.

As the sun sinks the incoming waves are shot with copper
beams and the sea becomes a green opalescence.

4

EXCURSIONS

IN THE DEPTHS OF A COAL MINE *

The "breakers" squatted upon the hillsides and in the valley like
enormous preying monsters, eating of the sunshine, the grass, the
green leaves. The smoke from their nostrils had ravaged the air of
coolness and fragrance. All that remained of vegetation looked dark,

---

* *Reprinted from* McClure's Magazine: *August 1894. The
sketch had appeared first in the St. Louis* Republic: *22 July
1894, under the title "Down in a Coal Mine."*

S. S. McClure *sent Crane and Corwin Knapp Linson to
Scranton, Pennsylvania, Crane to write a sketch of the mine
there and Linson to illustrate it. McClure's syndicate paid no
advance, and as Crane was as usual broke he borrowed fifty
dollars from Linson for expenses. (Crane never repaid the
loan.)*

McClure's *editors thought that the ending of Crane's
sketch was too caustic of big business and expunged from his
manuscript a passage excoriating coal brokers, "men who make
neat livings by fiddling with the market." As for the coal
brokers who had recently visited these mines at the peril of
their lives, Crane concluded:*

> I confess to a dark and sinful glee at the description
> of their pangs; a delight at for once finding coal-
> brokers associated in hardship and danger with the
> coal-miner. It seemed to me a partial and obscure
> vengeance. And yet this is not to say that they were
> not all completely virtuous and immaculate coal-
> brokers! If all men who stand uselessly and for their
> own extraordinary profit between the miner and the
> consumer were annually doomed to a certain period
> of danger and darkness in the mines, they might at
> last comprehend the misery and bitterness of men
> who toil for existence at these hopelessly grim tasks.

*This passage never saw print. Linson published it for the first
time (Crane had given him the manuscript) in* My Stephen
Crane *(1958), p. 70.*

miserable, half-strangled. Along the summit line of the mountain a few unhappy trees were etched upon the clouds. Overhead stretched a sky of imperial blue, incredibly far away from the sombre land.

We approached the colliery over paths of coal dust that wound among the switches. A "breaker" loomed above us, a huge and towering frame of blackened wood. It ended in a little curious peak, and upon its sides there was a profusion of windows appearing at strange and unexpected points. Through occasional doors one could see the flash of whirring machinery. Men with wondrously blackened faces and garments came forth from it. The sole glitter upon their persons was at their hats, where the little tin lamps were carried. They went stolidly along, some swinging lunch-pails carelessly; but the marks upon them of their forbidding and mystic calling fascinated our new eyes until they passed from sight. They were symbols of a grim, strange war that was being waged in the sunless depths of the earth.

Around a huge central building clustered other and lower ones, sheds, engine-houses, machine-shops, offices. Railroad tracks extended in web-like ways. Upon them stood files of begrimed coal cars. Other huge structures similar to the one near us, upreared their uncouth heads upon the hills of the surrounding country. From each a mighty hill of culm extended. Upon these tremendous heaps of waste from the mines, mules and cars appeared like toys. Down in the valley, upon the railroads, long trains crawled painfully southward, where a low-hanging gray cloud, with a few projecting spires and chimneys, indicated a town.

Car after car came from a shed beneath which lay hidden the mouth of the shaft. They were dragged, creaking, up an inclined cable road to the top of the "breaker."

At the top of the "breaker," laborers were dumping the coal into chutes. The huge lumps slid slowly on their journey down through the building, from which they were to emerge in classified fragments. Great teeth on revolving cylinders caught them and chewed them. At places there were grates that bid each size go into its proper chute. The dust lay inches deep on every motionless thing, and clouds of it made the air dark as from a violent tempest. A mighty gnashing sound filled the ears. With terrible appetite this huge and hideous monster sat imperturbably munching coal, grinding its mammoth jaws with unearthly and monotonous uproar.

In a large room sat the little slate-pickers. The floor slanted at an angle of forty-five degrees, and the coal, having been masticated by the great teeth, was streaming sluggishly in long iron troughs. The boys sat straddling these troughs, and as the mass moved slowly, they grabbed deftly at the pieces of slate therein. There were five or six of them, one above another, over each trough. The coal is expected to be fairly pure after it passes the final boy. The howling machinery was above them. High up, dim figures moved about in the dust clouds.

These little men were a terrifically dirty band. They resembled the New York gamins in some ways, but they laughed more, and when they laughed their faces were a wonder and a terror. They had an air of supreme independence, and seemed proud of their kind of villainy. They swore long oaths with skill.

Through their ragged shirts we could get occasional glimpses of shoulders black as stoves. They looked precisely like imps as they scrambled to get a view of us. Work ceased while they tried to ascertain if we were willing to give away any tobacco. The man who perhaps believes that he controls them came and harangued the crowd. He talked to the air.

The slate-pickers all through this region are yet at the spanking period. One continually wonders about their mothers, and if there are any schoolhouses. But as for them, they are not concerned. When they get time off, they go out on the culm heap and play baseball, or fight with boys from other "breakers" or among themselves, according to the opportunities. And before them always is the hope of one day getting to be door-boys down in the mines; and, later, mule-boys; and yet later, laborers and helpers. Finally, when they have grown to be great big men, they may become miners, real miners, and go down and get "squeezed," or perhaps escape to a shattered old man's estate with a mere "miner's asthma." They are very ambitious.

Meanwhile they live in a place of infernal dins. The crash and thunder of the machinery is like the roar of an immense cataract. The room shrieks and blares and bellows. Clouds of dust blur the air until the windows shine pallidly afar off. All the structure is a-tremble from the heavy sweep and circle of the ponderous mechanism. Down in the midst of it sit these tiny urchins, where they earn fifty-five cents a day each. They breathe this atmosphere until their lungs grow heavy and sick with it. They have this clamor in their ears until it is wonderful that they have any hoodlum valor remaining. But they are uncowed; they continue to swagger. And at the top of the "breaker" laborers can always be seen dumping the roaring coal down the wide, voracious maw of the creature.

Over in front of a little tool-house a man smoking a pipe sat on a bench. "Yes," he said, "I'll take yeh down if yeh like." He led us by little cinder paths to the shed over the shaft of the mine. A gigantic fan-wheel near by was twirling swiftly. It created cool air for the miners, who on the lowest vein of this mine were some eleven hundred and fifty feet below the surface. As we stood silently waiting for the elevator we had opportunity to gaze at the mouth of the shaft. The walls were of granite blocks, slimy, moss-grown, dripping with water. Below was a curtain of ink-like blackness. It was like the opening of an old well, sinister from tales of crimes.

The black, greasy cables began to run swiftly. We stood staring at them and wondering. Then of a sudden the elevator appeared and stopped with a crash. It was a plain wooden platform. Upon two sides iron bars ran up to support a stout metal roof. The men upon it, as it came into view, were like apparitions from the center of the earth.

A moment later we marched aboard, armed with little lights, feeble and gasping in the daylight. There was an instant's creak of machinery, and then the landscape, that had been framed for us by the door-posts of the shed, disappeared in a flash. We were dropping with extaordinary swiftness straight into the earth. It was a plunge, a fall. The flames of the little lamps fluttered and flew and struggled like tied birds to release themselves from the wicks. "Hang on," bawled our guide above the tumult.

The dead black walls slid swiftly by. They were a swirling dark chaos on which the mind tried vainly to locate some coherent thing, some intelligible spot. One could only hold fast to the iron bars and listen to the roar of this implacable descent. When the faculty of balance is lost, the mind becomes a confusion. The will fought a great battle to comprehend something during this fall, but one might as well has been tumbling among the stars. The only thing was to await revelation.

It was a journey that held a threat of endlessness.

Then suddenly the dropping platform slackened its speed. It began to descend slowly and with caution. At last with a crash and a jar, it stopped. Before us stretched an inscrutable darkness, a soundless place of tangible loneliness. Into the nostrils came a subtly strong odor of powder-smoke, oil, wet earth. The alarmed lungs began to lengthen their respirations.

Our guide strode abruptly into the gloom. His lamp flared shades of yellow and orange upon the walls of a tunnel that led away from the foot of the shaft. Little points of coal caught the light and shone like diamonds. Before us there was always the curtain of an impenetrable night. We walked on with no sound save the crunch of our feet upon the coal-dust of the floor. The sense of an abiding danger in the roof was always upon our foreheads. It expressed to us all the unmeasured, deadly tons above us, as if the

roof were a superlative might that regarded with the supreme calmness of almighty power the little men at its mercy. Sometimes we
were obliged to bend low to avoid it. Always our hands rebelled
vaguely from touching it, refusing to affront this gigantic mass.

All at once, far ahead, shone a little flame, blurred and difficult
of location. It was a tiny, indefinite thing, like a wisp-light. We
seemed to be looking at it through a great fog. Presently there were
two of them. They began to move to and fro and dance before us.

After a time we came upon two men crouching where the
roof of the passage came near to meeting the floor. If the picture
could have been brought to where it would have had the opposition and the contrast of the glorious summer-time earth, it would
have been a grim and ghastly thing. The garments of the men were
no more sable than their faces, and when they turned their heads
to regard our tramping party, their eyeballs and teeth shone white
as bleached bones. It was like the grinning of two skulls there in
the shadows. The tiny lamps in their hats made a trembling light
that left weirdly shrouded the movements of their limbs and bodies.
We might have been confronting terrible spectres.

But they said, "Hello, Jim," to our conductor. Their mouths
expanded in smiles — wide and startling smiles.

In a moment they turned again to their work. When the lights
of our party reinforced their two lamps, we could see that one was
busily drilling into the coal with a long thin bar. The low roof
ominously pressed his shoulders as he bent at his toil. The other
knelt behind him on the loose lumps of coal.

He who worked at the drill engaged in conversation with our
guide. He looked back over his shoulder, continuing to poke away.
"When are yeh goin' t' measure this up, Jim?" he demanded. "Do
yeh wanta git me killed?"

"Well, I'd measure it up t'-day, on'y I ain't got me tape," replied the other.

"Well, when will yeh? Yeh wanta hurry up," said the miner.
"I don't wanta git killed."

"Oh, I'll be down on Monday."

"Humph!"

They engaged in a sort of an altercation in which they made
jests.

"You'll be carried out o' there feet first before long."

"Will I?"

Yet one had to look closely to understand that they were not
about to spring at each other's throats. The vague illumination
created all the effect of the snarling of two wolves.

We came upon other little low-roofed chambers, each containing two men, a "miner," who makes the blasts, and his "laborer," who loads the coal upon the cars and assists the miner generally. And at each place there was this same effect of strangely satanic smiles and eyeballs wild and glittering in the pale glow of the lamps.

Sometimes the scenes in their weird strength were absolutely infernal. Once, when we were traversing a silent tunnel in another mine, we came suddenly upon a wide place where some miners were lying down in a group. As they upreared to gaze at us, it resembled a resurrection. They slowly uprose with ghoul-like movements, mysterious figures robed in enormous shadows. The swift flashes of the steel-gleaming eyes were upon our faces.

At another time, when my companion, struggling against difficulties, was trying to get a sketch of the mule, "Molly Maguire," a large group of miners gathered about us intent upon the pencil of the artist. "Molly," indifferent to the demands of art, changed her position after a moment and calmly settled into a new one. The men all laughed, and this laugh created the most astonishing and supernatural effect. In an instant the gloom was filled with luminous smiles. Shining forth all about us were eyes glittering as with cold blue flame. "Whoa, Molly," the men began to shout. Five or six of them clutched "Molly" by her tail, her head, her legs. They were going to hold her motionless until the portrait was finished. "He's a good feller," they had said of the artist, and it would be a small thing to hold a mule for him. Upon the roof were vague dancing reflections of red and yellow.

From this tunnel of our first mine we went with our guide to the foot of the main shaft. Here we were in the most important passage of a mine, the main gangway. The wonder of these avenues is the noise — the crash and clatter of machinery as the elevator speeds upward with the loaded cars and drops thunderingly with the empty ones. The place resounds with the shouts of mule-boys, and there can always be heard the noise of approaching coal-cars, beginning in mild rumbles and then swelling down upon one in a tempest of sound. In the air is the slow painful throb of the pumps working at the water which collects in the depths. There is booming and banging and crashing, until one wonders why the tremendous walls are not wrenched by the force of this uproar. And up and down the tunnel there is a riot of lights, little orange points flickering and flashing. Miners stride in swift and sombre procession. But the meaning of it all is in the deep bass rattle of a blast in some hidden part of the mine. It is war. It is the most savage part of all in the endless battle between man and nature. These miners are grimly in the van. They have carried the war into places where nature has the strength of a million giants. Sometimes their enemy becomes exasperated and snuffs out ten, twenty, thirty lives. Usually she remains calm, and takes one at a time with method and precision. She need not hurry. She possesses eternity. After a blast, the smoke, faintly luminous, silvery, floats silently through the adjacent tunnels.

In our first mine we speedily lost all ideas of time, direction, distance. The whole thing was an extraordinary, black puzzle. We were impelled to admire the guide because he knew all the tangled passages. He led us through little tunnels three and four feet wide and with roofs that sometimes made us crawl. At other times we were in avenues twenty feet wide, where double rows of tracks extended. There were stretches of great darkness, majestic silences. The three hundred miners were distributed into all sorts of crevices and corners of the labyrinth, toiling in this city of endless night. At different points one could hear the roar of traffic about the foot of the main shaft, to which flowed all the commerce of the place.

We were made aware of distances later by our guide, who would occasionally stop to tell us our position by naming a point of the familiar geography of the surface. "Do you remember that rolling-mill yeh passed coming up? Well, you're right under it." "You're under th' depot now." The length of these distances struck us with amazement when we reached the surface. Near Scranton one can really proceed for miles, in the black streets of the mines.

Over in a wide and lightless room we found the mule-stables. There we discovered a number of these animals standing with an air of calmness and self-possession that was somehow amazing to find in a mine. A little dark urchin came and belabored his mule "China" until he stood broadside to us that we might admire his innumerable fine qualities. The stable was like a dungeon. The mules were arranged in solemn rows. They turned their heads toward our lamps. The glare made their eyes shine wondrously like lenses. They resembled enormous rats.

About the room stood bales of hay and straw. The commonplace air worn by the long-eared slaves made it all infinitely usual. One had to wait to see the tragedy of it. It was not until we had grown familiar with the life and the traditions of the mines that we were capable of understanding the story told by these beasts standing in calm array, with spread legs.

It is a common affair for mules to be imprisoned for years in the limitless night of the mines. Our acquaintance, "China," had been four years buried. Upon the surface there had been the march of the seasons; the white splendor of snows had changed again and again to the glories of green springs. Four times had the earth been ablaze with the decorations of brilliant autumns. But "China" and his friends had remained in these dungeons from which daylight, if one could get a view up a shaft, would appear a tiny circle, a silver star aglow in a sable sky.

Usually when brought to the surface, the mules tremble at the earth radiant in the sunshine. Later, they go almost mad with fantastic joy. The full splendor of the heavens, the grass, the trees, the breezes, breaks upon them suddenly. They caper and career with extravagant mulish glee. A miner told me of a mule that had spent some delirious months upon the surface after years of labor in the mines. Finally the time came when he was to be taken back. But the memory of a black existence was upon him; he knew that gaping mouth that threatened to swallow him. No cudgellings could induce him. The men held conventions and discussed plans to budge that mule. The celebrated quality of obstinacy in him won him liberty to gambol clumsily about on the surface.

After being long in the mines, the mules are apt to duck and dodge at the close glare of lamps, but some of them have been known to have piteous fears of being left in the dead darkness. We met a boy who said that sometimes the only way he could get his team to move was to run ahead of them with the light. Afraid of the darkness, they would follow.

To those who have known the sunlight there may come the fragrant dream of a lost paradise. Perhaps this is what they brood over as they stand solemnly flapping their ears. Perhaps they despair and thirst for this bloomland that lies in an unknown direction and at impossible distances.

In wet mines, gruesome fungi grow upon the wooden props that support the uncertain-looking ceiling. The walls are dripping and dank. Upon them, too, frequently grows a mosslike fungus, white as a druid's beard, that thrives in these deep dens, but shrivels and dies at contact with the sunlight.

Great and mystically dreadful is the earth from a mine's depth. Man is in the implacable grasp of nature. It has only to tighten slightly, and he is crushed like a bug. His loudest shriek of agony would be as impotent as his final moan to bring help from that fair land that lies, like Heaven, over his head. There is an insidious, silent enemy in the gas. If the huge fanwheel on the top of the earth should stop for a brief period, there is certain death. If a man escape the gas, the floods, the "squeezes" of falling rock, the cars shooting through little tunnels, the precarious elevators, the hundred perils, there usually comes to him an attack of "miner's asthma" that slowly racks and shakes him into the grave. Meanwhile he gets three dollars per day, and his laborer one dollar and a quarter.

In the chamber at the foot of the shaft, as we were departing, a group of the men were resting. They lay about in careless poses. When we climbed aboard the elevator, we had a moment in which to turn and regard them. Then suddenly the study in black faces and crimson and orange lights vanished. We were on our swift way to the surface. Far above us in the engine-room, the engineer sat with his hand on a lever and his eyes on the little model of the shaft wherein a miniature elevator was making the ascent even as our elevator was making it. Down one of those tremendous holes, one thinks naturally of the engineer.

Of a sudden the fleeting walls became flecked with light. It increased to a downpour of sunbeams. The high sun was afloat in a splendor of spotless blue. The distant hills were arrayed in purple and stood like monarchs. A glory of gold was upon the near-by earth. The cool fresh air was wine.

Of that sinister struggle far below there came no sound, no suggestion save the loaded cars that emerged one after another in eternal procession and went creaking up the incline that their contents might be fed into the mouth of the "breaker," imperturbably cruel and insatiate, black emblem of greed, and of the gods of this labor.

THE DEVIL'S ACRE/WRITTEN FOR THE SUNDAY
WORLD MAGAZINE/BY STEPHEN CRANE./THIS
WEIRD AND POWERFUL SKETCH WAS WRITTEN/
BY STEPHEN CRANE FOR THE SUNDAY WORLD/
MAGAZINE AFTER A VISIT TO SING SING,/WHERE,
WITH A SUNDAY WORLD/ARTIST, HE INSPECTED
THE ELEC-/TRIC CHAIR AND THE CON-/VICTS'
GRAVEYARD ON/THE HILL.*

i

The keeper unlocked a door in a low gray building within the
prison inclosure at Sing Sing. The room which he and his two
visitors then entered was certainly furnished sparsely. It contained
only one chair. Evidently this apartment was not the library of a
millionaire.

The walls and ceiling were of polished wood and the atmosphere was weighted heavily with an odor of fresh varnish. This
uncouth perfume here controlled the senses as it does in a carriage
factory. The chair, too, was formed of polished wood. It might have
been donated from the office of some generous banker.

A long, curved pipe swung from behind a partition, and at the
end of it there hung a wire almost as thick as a cigar. Some straps,
formidably broad and thick, were thrown carelessly over the arms
of the chair.

The keeper was exceedingly courteous in his explanations. He
waved his hand towards a steel door. "We bring him through
there," said he, "and we calculate that the whole business takes
about a minute from the time we go after him." His courtesy went

---

* Reprinted from New York World: 25 October 1896.

    A facsimile signature of Crane was at the end of the
sketch. Also appended was this note to the reader: "Stephen
Crane's first love story, 'The Third Violet,' will begin in the
Evening Edition of The World Nov. 4 next. It will be illustrated by Powers." However, at least two installments of "The
Third Violet" would have already appeared in Inter Ocean:
25 October and 1 November 1896.

still further. "If one of you cares to sit down in it, gentlemen, I'll strap you in and you can try to imagine how it feels." But his visitors protested that they understood perfectly that his time was very valuable and that nothing could be further from their minds than an idea of putting him to such great trouble.

It is a lonely room and silent. No sound comes to break the calm hush of this chamber. The same people who cannot know that an express train at full speed is one of the most poetic things in the world would morbidly object, in the sub-conscious way, to the smell of varnish here, and disapprove for the same reason of the comfortable and shining chair. There should be an effect a thousand times more hideous. For the room is the place for the coronation of crime and the chair is the throne of death.

We, as a new people, are likely to conclude that our mechanical perfection, our structural precision, is certain to destroy all quality of sentiment in our devices, and so we prefer to grope in the past when people are not supposed to have had any structural precision. As the terrible, the beautiful, the ghastly, pass continually before our eyes we merely remark that they do not seem to be correct in romantic detail.

But an odor of oiled woods, a keeper's tranquil, unemotional voice, a broom stood in the corner near the door, a blue sky and a bit of moving green tree at a window so small that it might have been made by a canister shot — all these ordinary things contribute with subtle meanings to the horror of this comfortable chair, this commonplace bit of furniture that waits in silence and loneliness, and waits and waits and waits.

It is patient — patient as time. Even should its next stained and sallow prince be now a baby, playing with alphabet blocks near his mother's feet, this chair will wait. It is as unknown to his eye as are the shadows of trees at night, and yet it towers over him, monstrous, implacable, infernal, his fate — this patient, comfortable chair.

ii

They summoned the "Captain," because his memory was a mine of thirty years' experience with the men in gray and black. He had conducted convict funerals until they were as ordinary to him as breakfast, dinner and lunch. It was a habit with him. The dull fall of dirt on wood probably no more concerned his nerves than would the flying, shining water of a fountain in a public park. He slowly stroked his long, gray beard and presented a demeanor of superb indifference. He was really bored. That an interest should be manifested in such matters struck him as being rather absurd.

"Did you ever see a ghost up there, Captain?" asked one visitor, with dark insinuation.

"No," said the Captain, subtly scoffing. "I did not." He looked around at the other men in the room and grinned.

"Never had a white thing gibber at you, did you?" gently murmured the visitor.

"Oh, —— no," replied the Captain.

When the visitors left, the Captain was still thoughtfully stroking his long, gray beard.

iii

On the hillside there is a place of peace. The river is spread in a silver sheet before it and the little ships move slowly with their mystic energy past it. The splendid reaches of the valley of the Hudson are here so plain to the vision that no fable prince could find a spot more suitable for his palace. In the sunshine the river is spread like a cloth.

This fair place is the convicts' graveyard. Simple white boards crop out from the soil in rows. The inscriptions are abrupt. "Here lies Wong Kee. Died June 1, 1890." The boards front the wide veranda of a cottage of modern type. If people on this veranda ever lower their eyes from the wide river and gaze at these tombstones they probably find that they can just make the inscriptions out at the distance and just can't make them out at the distance. They encounter the dividing line between coherence and a blur. It is a most comfortable house, and yet a person properly superstitious would possibly not care to offer more than $3 for it. For, after all, it is impossible for the eye to avoid these boards, these austere tributes to the memory of men who died black souled, whose glances in life fled sidewise with a kind of ferocity, a cowardice and a hatred that could perhaps embrace the entire world.

At night one could assuredly hear at this place the laugh of the devil. One could see here the clutching, demoniac fingers. It is the fiend's own acre, this hillside. The far red or green lights of the steamers swing up or down the river in serenity, distant whistles shout their little warnings, but here on this hillside, with the solemnity of the night, with the wind swishing the long grass, there surely must be gruesome action. Over this convict graveyard, where the boards show wan in the darkness, there must hover gruesome figures.

Even in the day one can weave from masses of clouds a laughing shape, with eager claws, a thing that reaches down into the earth under the simple headboards.

It takes more than this to arouse the awe of a cow. A cow cares little for superstition. A cow cares for grass. Good grass grows here. Kind, motherly old cows wander placidly among these new and old graves. Ordinarily it would be very annoying to have tombstones constantly in one's way. A solemn inscription at every turn is sufficient to vex the most gentle spirit. But these matters cannot move the deep philosophy of a cow. It is not a question of sentiment; it is a question of pasturage. A certain Roman class taught magnificent indifference as the first rule of life. These cows are disciples of the Romans. If a convict's grave is trampled by a cow, what does it matter to the Brooklyn Bridge? If the last record of a long-dead criminal is butted by a playful heifer, is the price of wheat affected? Cows understand these things as well as does a Standard Oil magnate. It is not a question of sentiment; it a question of pasturage. Somebody connected with the prison comprehends this point as completely as do the cows. The cows cannot appropriate all the wisdom. There has been another student of the Romans. Anybody can see that when long lush grass grows over graves there is a good feeding place for cows.

In Philadelphia, where everybody of historic consequence is interred, men come at certain periods and scrub the old stones with acid in order that the world may know again the best that friends could invent concerning the buried. At Sing Sing the author of the inscriptions preserves a gorgeous neutrality. When he formulated one he formulated them all. "Here lies at rest" —— After this prodigal expenditure he ceases.

This term was noble and sufficient until they cut the new road through the hill. Proper civil engineering then demanded that certain bones should not lie at rest at that particular spot, and the cow pasture was cut in half.

Time deals strokes of rain, wind and sun to all things, and a board is not strong against them.

Soon it falls. There is none here to plant it upright again. The men that lie here are of the kind that the world wishes to forget, and there is no objection raised to the assault of nature. And so it comes to pass that the dates on the boards are recent. These white boards have marched like soldiers from the southward end of the field to the northward. As they at the south became dim, rotted and fell, others sprang up at their right hand. As these in turn succumbed, still others appeared at their right. It is a steady travel towards the north. In the other end there are now no boards; only a sinister undulation of the earth under the weeds. It is a fine short road to oblivion.

In the middle of the graveyard there is a dim but still defiant board upon which there is rudely carved a cross. Some singular chance has caused this board to be split through the middle, cleaving the cross in two parts, as if it had been done by the demoniac shape weaved in the clouds, but the aged board is still upright and the cross still expresses its form as if it had merely expanded and become transparent. It is a place for the chanting of monks.